THE PROTOCOL

Victor Vendetti stood at bay in the corner of the wall beside his bed brandishing a Mason jar of wilted geraniums in one hand and a jackknife in the other. He looked as if only a monumental surge of adrenaline kept him on his feet. His shoulders were hunched over and his knees seemed ready to buckle beneath him. His breath came in ragged gasps.

'Stay away from me!' he hissed through clenched teeth. 'Don't touch my bed!'

Several other patients in the room appeared to be reasoning with Vendetti. A husky grey-haired man in a short hospital gown was shouting at him. 'Are you crazy, Vendetti? These people are trying to help you. How do you expect your doctor to treat you when you're fighting the staff?'

Vendetti aimed his knife towards the man.

'Take it easy, buddy,' he pleaded. 'Take it easy! They ain't gonna hurt you.'

Vendetti's face was ashen. 'Hell they aren't! Bastards!'

THE PROTOCOL

Sarah Allan Borisch

A STAR BOOK

published by

the Paperback Division of
W. H. ALLEN & Co. Ltd

A Star Book

Published in 1984
by the Paperback Division of
W. H. Allen & Co. Ltd
A Howard and Wyndham Company
44 Hill Street, London W1X 8LB

First published in the United States of America by
Simon and Schuster, 1982.
First published in Great Britain by
W. H. Allen & Co. Ltd, 1983

Copyright © Sarah Allan Borisch, 1981

Printed in Great Britain by
Cox & Wyman Ltd, Reading

ISBN 0 352 31478 8

This book is dedicated to my father, George White Allan, and to all healers and life-bearers.

ACKNOWLEDGEMENTS

To those who contributed their time and knowledge to this book and whose confidence and affection gave me the courage to attempt and complete a first novel, my thanks and appreciation. They are: my husband, Tom; Lorrie Gilligan; Lorrie Klukoski; Jeanne Goudy; Fr Joseph Pettit; Patti Gunn; Mark Baker; Ruth McKinley; René Pelissier; Marion Smith; Jean Spencer; Paul Fuller; Katie Eberhardt; Palmer Wright; Janet de Witt; Carol Peterson; Robert Steffel; and Jim Finlayson.

My gratitude, also, for the wisdom and guidance of my agent, Berenice Hoffman, and the editorial direction of Michael Korda, Roslyn Siegel, and Barbara Wasserman at Simon and Schuster.

Man has regions in his heart which do not yet exist, and into them enters suffering in order that they may have existence.

Léon Bloy

PART I

Chapter One

The man in Bed 3 awoke to a familiar clutch of pain beneath his shoulder blades. He opened his eyes and turned towards the grey light. One of his remaining participations in life was afforded by a view from the window beside his bed. The window looked out on a roof, and his bed was positioned so that he faced the outside brick wall of the hospital's West Wing. That wing housed the private rooms, where some fortunate patients struggled less publicly with the embarrassments of their diseases.

The last few weeks had brought a series of blizzards and snow squalls. He could gauge their temper only by the strength of the vortex whirling in the corner of the roof where the north and west wings joined. Sometimes the snow whirled like a dervish, shooting spume into the air from its centre. Sometimes, when the snow spun slowly and the narcotic was beginning to act on his mind, he whirled backward in time and the vortex took the shape of a dancer in a white tutu. He had seen her many years ago in San Francisco, and remembered her infinite grace, the curves of her spine, her arms, and her legs as she leaned, supple as a willow, into an unseen wind. Now, when she materialised, the dancer looked at him with the soft eyes of Renée, who had taken him to the ballet; Renée, who had grown up in Paris, and who had tried to polish some of his rough spots.

The morning's realities intruded into his thoughts. A pressure of urine in his bladder was building. He heard old Harold, in the next bed, moaning 'Mother' over and over. Harold always cried for his mother when he was coming out of sedation.

The wind had diminished during the night, but now it was kicking up again, rattling the window beside his bed like a prisoner beating on his bars. The heat had come on, and he could hear the metallic clanking of the ancient radiator under the window. He opened his eyes all the way and tried to shift his shoulders to lessen the pain, but for some reason he could not seem to move his upper body. He saw the face of Charlie, the young man across from him. It looked ruddy and healthy. He was sitting up in bed lighting a cigarette and grinning at him. Once a month he checked in for three days to receive chemotherapy for his cancer. He threw a good-humoured salute to Victor Vendetti.

'Better shake it up, Vic! I hear them bringing the breakfast trays.' He glanced around the five-bed ward to rally the other men.

Vic tried to return the wave and couldn't move his arm. Suddenly he remembered why. He had acted up again during the night, and they had tied him by the wrists to the metal bed rails. Now the muslin restraints cut into his thin flesh when he tried to move at all. He quit struggling, closed his eyes, and waited until he heard the voice of a nurse's aide.

'Time to wash up for breakfast!' she called in a top sergeant's voice as she walked through the door with a stack of towels and washcloths.

'Get going!' she called now, a note of cheer in her tone as she fetched basins from each man's utility cabinet and filled them with water. Charlie tugged at the back of her uniform just below her broad buttocks. She whirled around to smack him, but Charlie's face was all innocent concern.

'He can't wash, Nursie,' he told her. 'Ol' Vic can't wash himself. They got him tied down again!'

The aide walked over to Vendetti's bed and stood over him with her arms folded over her bosom.

'Well, Mr Vendetti.' She spoke in the tone of a teacher dealing with a recalcitrant child. 'What was it this time? Did you throw your pitcher at a nurse, or were you sleeping on the floor again?'

Vendetti turned his face to the window and said nothing.

4

He remembered the night now, and he dug his fingernails into his hands to disperse the pain. He was not going to answer. Too often his remarks were laced with profanity. The nurse bent over him and began to loosen the muslin restraints. He flexed his fingers and opened and closed his arms, feeling sore and stiff. He kept his gaze averted, staring out at the dark, angular patterns of roof and wall, at the curving snow. The nurse stood motionless, looking down at him.

'Do you need to void?' she asked, her scolding tone replaced by the voice of reason and professionalism. He nodded his head. He wished he could stand up and urinate on her white pant suit. His helplessness enraged him more and more. At this moment his back hurt too much for him to negotiate getting the urinal. The utility cabinet was always way behind his reach. She stooped over with her back to him, foraging around for the urinal on the cabinet's bottom shelf. Charlie smiled, gave him a broad wink, and made a quick obscene gesture. Everyone except old Harold saw it and laughed.

The nurse pulled back the covers, untied the muslin restraints, and allowed Vic to fit his own penis into the urinal. The day was beginning with an act of grace. He shuddered with relief as the tension in his bladder discharged. Then he grimaced as a spasm of pain twisted his shoulders.

The nurse removed the urinal.

'Can I have my hypo now?' he asked.

'The medications cart comes after breakfast. It hasn't been four hours since your last shot.' She gave him a glance of keen assessment. 'I'll send the orderly in to help you bathe.'

Vendetti eyed the radiator. If he could get his back up against it for the heat, it would help him through till after breakfast. The pain killed his appetite, which was small enough anyway. The floor was the best place. On the floor he could curl up like a cat. He had padded the floor with his own overcoat and bathrobe and Charlie's, as well as his pillow. But they went wild when they found him on the floor.

'There are organisms down there!' the head nurse had

shouted. Shit. He was crawling with worse than organisms. He had the plague of plagues. He wondered what they were saving him from—or for. He closed his eyes against the string of tears, raging against the failure of his body and his growing helplessness.

'Ready for a washup?' It was the voice of Hugh, the black orderly who bathed him when the pain was bad. He lay back and let the strong hands of the orderly turn him. He closed his eyes against the sight of the wasted muscles of his arms and legs. For all his strength, Hugh was very gentle. Some of Victor Vendetti's rage receded as Hugh sponged his body with warm water. He gave him an expert back rub with lotion and then put clean sheets on the bed, rolling him from side to side and pulling the bottom sheet under him.

'You ask your doctor to write an order for a sheepskin for you. It'll help cushion your back from that hard mattress and the plastic cover,' Hugh told him. He patted him on the shoulder as he helped him get into a clean hospital gown.

'Can't you get me a sheepskin?' Victor asked.

'No, I have to have an order from your doctor.'

'Well, I lay on the floor by the radiator last night because no order ever went through for a heating pad. I asked Dr Prince for that.'

Hugh thought for a moment. 'I'll see if the resident will order the pad and the sheepskin,' he said. 'Now you try to stay out of trouble, Victor, okay?' He moved across the room to the old man.

Victor lay back in the clean linen and watched the snow. Someone delivered a breakfast tray and cranked up his bed. He poured milk on his hot oatmeal and ate a few bites. He sugared it, but it was still tasteless. He sipped some of the coffee. It was not very hot. He thought about the coffee shop in a small town near Phoenix where he and Renée had some-times had breakfast. The coffee was always delicious and piping hot. It was made from well water, which gave it a special flavour. They would have eggs over easy, and he would have country sausage and hash-browns. Renée ate as daintily as a cat, cutting each bite of her egg separately.

6

Afterwards, they would climb into the Packard convertible and kiss, tasting each other's coffee-flavoured breath.

He shuddered at the bitterness of what he sipped from his cup now. He put it down on his tray and lay back on the pillow trying to summon the silky feel of Renée's auburn hair. The other men were talking back and forth and eating their breakfasts. An aide was spooning oatmeal into old Harold's mouth, and he could hear the sucking noises Harold made whenever he ate or drank. He never wore his dentures.

He hoped the nurse would come with his hypo soon. The pain beneath his shoulder blades was mounting. Whenever it reached its peak, he felt as if he were impaled on a spike that was hidden in his body. He tried to hypnotise himself by concentrating on the hum of the men's conversation. He set his jaw and gritted his teeth to wait.

Chapter Two

Down the hall from the five-bed ward, the morning's activities had begun in the nurse's station. The medications cart was being loaded. The residents were checking out the charts of patients they were assigned to. Some of the physicians had arrived on the floor and were preparing to make rounds. Since Seven Main was a cancer unit, it chiefly accommodated the services of the hospital's oncology specialists. Sometimes surgeons and other specialists came to Seven Main on consultations. Very few internists or general practitioners followed the treatment of their patients once they had a cancer diagnosis.

This morning Dr Virgil Prince, oncologist, and his entourage occupied centre stage in the station. Two new residents were standing at attention on either side of his chair. His office nurse was pulling the metal-covered patient charts from their slots in a hivelike storage unit.

Christie Wilson was seated on a stool at the counter making entries in a chart when she saw one of the new nurses on the floor collide with an important member of the Prince team. The nurse backed away and excused herself, but the other woman threw back her head and raked her with flashing eyes.

'Who are *you*?' she demanded, her voice husky and imperious.

'Mary Hogan, LPN,' the girl answered, riveted by the intense green eyes of her questioner.

'You're new.' There was a second pause. 'Watch where you're going from now on. People are handling medications in breakable vials around here.' She had a firm jaw and flaring nostrils. Something about her evoked the image of a temperamental filly in a lightning storm. She tossed back her mane of streaky tawny hair and tilted her jaw. Then she swung into Prince's circle with an air of confident authority.

Mary eased into a corner near the entrance to the utility room. She had come to read the night shift's charting on the patients in her corridor. Christie reached out and touched her lightly on the arm. 'I'm Christie Wilson, a medical social worker,' she said, pointing to the plastic badge on her lab coat. She smiled at Mary and whispered, 'Don't worry. She can't bite.'

No one else could hear her. The interest of everyone in the station was glued to Dr Virgil Prince.

From their protected corner Christie and Mary took time to study him as he luxuriated in the fixed attention of his audience. He looked as though he must be in his early forties, with a medium build and well-developed muscles under a finely cut suit. He was leaning back in a swivel chair, his face turned to the resident who stood on his right. Christie and Mary watched his face in profile. It was handsome, sensitively masculine. His voice was his most distinguishing feature – or rather, his manner of speaking was. It was almost deliberately slow and indolent. He had an inflection in his voice that could make the most mundane remark seem arch and filled with innuendo. Had his voice been loud, he would have seemed more arrogant. His bearing, the set of his head on his shoulders, was arrogant.

Suddenly he turned from the profile position. Christie saw Mary register a quick surge of shock. The skin on the entire right side of Prince's face was a deep reddish purple. It looked as if he were wearing a half-mask. His eye, nose, and mouth on that side were perfect in form, but marred by the birthmark.

Turning again, he resumed the profile position, the perfect side of his face towards the room. The woman with the streaked hair handed him a manila folder. Prince smiled lazily and narrowed his eyes as he spoke to her.

'Thanks, Brenda. Is this the new input on our prize patient?' he asked softly, running his fingers delicately over the portfolio.

'It's all there,' Brenda answered. She put her portfolios down on the counter and slid her slim hips onto the seat of one of the high stools that lined the counter. She reached across the taller of the two residents and pulled a metal chart out of the hands of Prince's office nurse.

'He lives in a slum neighbourhood over on the West Side,' she said in a low, casual voice. 'The woman he listed as next of kin lives with him. They aren't married. The nurses say she is slovenly and stupid. He has recently signed himself out of two other hospitals – without physician's orders; once in the middle of the night. He's never had a personal physician. Two staff doctors in the other hospitals diagnosed the cancer.'

Brenda crossed her legs and leaned back against the counter on her elbows. 'He was brought in through Emergency, picked up from a gutter on Front Street. The police paramedics thought he'd been hit by a car or was ill, since he wasn't drunk.'

'Are we talking about Vendetti?' Lindsay, the taller resident, asked. He had a blond beard and steel-rimmed glasses.

9

'Yes,' Prince answered. 'I read him the riot act yesterday. He threw his bedpan and two water pitchers and uttered some obscenities to one of the nurses. This is the end of the line for him. Either he submits to authority around here or he's out on his can. If he stops acting like an animal, we will treat him. If he doesn't, he will end up in a jail infirmary, or die in the street.'

'Let me see the chart,' Dr Lindsay said. Brenda passed it over to him.

'CA of both lungs,' she told him crisply. 'The hospitals he checked out of won't take him back.'

Christie turned around to address Prince.

'Where is he?' she asked.

Prince glanced at her and smiled a slow smile. Then he stood up. 'Let's go,' he said to his team. 'I want to see if our little conversation yesterday subdued him any.' They walked out of the station: Brenda in the lead, carrying her portfolios, Prince just behind her, then the residents and his office nurse.

After they were out in the corridor, Prince turned around and spoke over his shoulder to Christie. 'He's on the five-bed ward. You're welcome to the referral. So far all his communications have been violent and obscene.'

He went on down the hallway, discussing a pancreatic cancer located in one of the private rooms.

Chapter Three

Down the corridor, a cluster of nurses stood transfixed in the doorway of the five-bed men's ward. They seemed to be watching some kind of show going on inside. Dr Prince and his team were coming from the other end of the corridor, moving at a fast pace just short of a run. One of the nurses' aides was in the lead. She was highly agitated.

10

'He's in the corner!' she panted over her shoulder. 'He threw a urinal at the LPN when she tried to dismantle a make-shift bed he built out of chairs!'

Brenda's eyes were wilder than usual, but her confidence had not been jangled.

'Get an orderly!' she snapped at the aide. 'We'll see what's going on.'

The aide turned to go, then stopped. 'Hugh's in there now.'

Prince's team pushed its way through the group in the doorway, Brenda still in the lead. Prince turned to the aide.

'Go get some leather restraints – two pairs!'

The aide nodded, looking bewildered, and headed for the utility room. Prince followed his team into the room. In the middle of the room stood the head nurse and the black orderly with their hands stretched out, apparently cajoling.

Victor Vendetti stood at bay in the corner of the wall beside his bed brandishing a Mason jar of wilted geraniums in one hand and a jackknife in the other. He looked as if only a monumental surge of adrenaline kept him on his feet. His shoulders were hunched over and his knees seemed ready to buckle beneath him. His breath came in ragged gasps.

'Stay away from me!' he hissed through clenched teeth. 'Don't touch my bed!'

Several other patients in the room appeared to be reasoning with Vendetti. A husky grey-haired man in a short hospital gown was standing between his bed and Charlie's and shouting at him.

'Are you crazy, Vendetti? These people are trying to help you. How do you expect your doctor to treat you when you're fighting the staff?' He stepped forward cautiously. He had been watching Victor Vendetti's unorthodox behaviour for two days now.

Vendetti aimed his knife towards the man.

'Watch out, Martin!' Charlie yelled. Martin Kiley moved back against the wall. Charlie leaned forward in his bed.

'Take it easy, buddy,' he pleaded. 'Take it easy! They ain't gonna hurt you.'

Vendetti's face was ashen. 'Hell they aren't! Bastards!' He

11

spat in the direction of Prince's group. 'Bitches!' He sagged against his bed of chairs and pointed the knife at the group filling the room.

'Take it easy, pal!' Charlie called out again. 'Here comes your doctor. He'll take care of the pain.'

Prince had come to a halt about five feet inside the doorway. He remained motionless, assessing the situation. His face was empty of expression, but his eyes were burning. Brenda squared her shoulders, pushed her forelock out of her face with a quick gesture, and took three steps towards Vendetti.

'The knife is dull, Vendetti. Drop it,' she said.

Vendetti's lips curled as he formed some soundless curse. His eyes riveted on Brenda and he lunged forward. At the same moment, Hugh and the two residents rushed to grab him. Before they could touch him, his knees buckled. He sprawled across the floor between the hospital bed and the three padded chairs he had pushed against the radiator. The Mason jar crashed and splintered. The knife hit the floor and slid across the room.

Dr Lindsay and another resident picked their way around the broken glass and lifted Vendetti onto the bed. Blood was running from a gash in his cheek where he had hit the side of the metal bed. Hugh came to Vendetti, touching his head, rubbing his arms.

'You'll be okay, Vic ... you'll be okay,' he murmured. Lindsay examined the gash and instructed the head nurse to sterilize and bandage it.

Hugh held a towel to Vendetti's head. At last the RN came through the door wheeling the cart with hypos and medications.

'Hey, Vic,' Charlie called, 'your hypo's here. They're gonna give you your hypo now.'

Victor Vendetti didn't seem to hear. He lay utterly still on the bed. Only his chest moved, heaving up and down, sucking in the air. Prince turned to his office nurse.

'Add Valium to the morphine injection for the next four hypos. We need him quiet while we decide what to do with him.' He strode over to the bed and stood looking down at Vendetti. Brenda had moved to the other side of the bed. They flanked Vendetti now. The aide arrived with some leather harnesses with metal buckles. Brenda began to apply one set to Vendetti's wrists. She handed the other one to Hugh.

'Strap his ankles to the bottom corners of the bed,' she ordered.

Hugh paused. His face flinched as if someone had flicked a whip over it. Brenda threw him a sharp glance.

'Do it *now*. It'll take a while for the injection to work.'

Hugh bent over Vendetti and slowly strapped on the restraints. He fitted the metal thongs through the holes and slipped the straps through the buckles.

The group in the doorway slowly dispersed. An aide arrived with the antibiotic and bandages. Hugh took them from her. He began washing the cut gently and applying gauze and tape.

Prince cleared his throat and shook the bed slightly with his hand.

'Vendetti,' he said carefully in a dispassionate tone, 'I want you to know that you have committed assault and battery in this hospital. If I wish, I can swear out a warrant. I feel sure a prison infirmary will constrict your freedom far more than a health-care delivery system.' He paused and waited. Vendetti made no sound. Prince cleared his throat and continued.

'If you create no further scenes, I will keep you here for tests to determine whether radiation therapy is indicated for your disease. If it is not, I will plan to put you on chemotherapy, probably a combination of drugs.'

Vendetti remained silent.

Prince's office nurse walked up to the bed with the hypodermic syringe, sponged Vendetti's bony arm, and injected the morphine and Valium. Hugh had finished dressing his face wound. A woman from Housekeeping swept up the glass, and Hugh retrieved the jackknife.

'Confiscate the knife,' Prince directed. Hugh closed the

knife and stood looking down at it in the palm of his hand. He walked over to the window and raised his palm to the light. The knife was quite beautiful. It was about six inches long, and the case was made of mother-of-pearl. He turned it over. There was a silver plate on it with an engraved inscription. The message had been worn thin. It said:

> To Victor
> For conquering the wall of death
> Always – Renée

'Dr Prince will write some orders,' Brenda announced to the staff. 'Meanwhile, see that anyone bringing Vendetti flowers puts them in a plastic container.'

Everyone began to leave the room. The men settled down to watch the morning game shows on the television set.

Martin Kiley mopped some sweat off his forehead with a Handi-Wipe and climbed back into bed. Thank God his tests were all done. Dr Prince had told him that he could go home in a couple of days. If he ever had to be admitted again, he would accept only a private room. He'd had it with the ward. Not only was this nut Vendetti up all night building beds and dragging chairs around, but the old guy, Harold, was calling his mother or gasping as if he were about to die. The worst of it was there was nothing he could do about it all.

'Feisty little guy, ain't he?' Charlie called to him, and indicated Vendetti. 'Hope I'm that gutsy when I get old.'

Martin forced a smile. Vendetti made him angry. His refusal to cooperate seemed to Martin stupid and self-defeating. He himself had done well putting himself into the hands of Prince, who had been recommended to him as one of the few local doctors who knew how to treat cancer. Prince had got him into remission and kept him in it for a year. He had recently developed some odd symptoms, but he trusted Prince to take care of those too.

He looked over at Charlie, and a familiar despair overwhelmed him. Charlie was a little older than his oldest son, but he somehow reminded him of Josh. He had the same eagerness and freshness about him. It had been a long time since Josh had appeared eager and happy around him. Now he rarely saw him, and he'd accepted the notion that his son no longer loved him.

Martin closed his eyes. He was afraid of weakness and had learned to disguise tears.

'Yeah. He's feisty, all right,' he replied to Charlie. 'If you'll turn down your TV speaker, I'm going to take a nap before lunch comes.'

'Sure,' Charlie answered. He cut down the sound and shut his own eyes. He felt a little tired himself.

Virgil Prince proceeded down the corridor next to Dr Lindsay and Dr Burns.

'We're about to examine a very interesting cancer of the colon in seven-fourteen,' he advised the residents. 'I want you to notice this woman's attitude. She is quite typical of my patients. She knows her life is in my hands and would stand on her head on Main Street if I said it was part of the therapy.' He smiled slightly at Lindsay, who was the more verbal of the two new residents. 'She has an advanced disease.'

Lindsay frowned. 'Advanced disease? What can you offer her? What is her hope?'

'Her *hope*?' He paused in his gait, and the entourage halted with him. 'Her hope is that she is one of ten cancer patients in this country who are receiving intravenous injections of a new experimental drug. A month ago it wasn't available here.' He pulled a gold case out of his pocket and lit one of the cigarettes with a matching lighter, inhaled deeply, and resumed his pace down the corridor.

'How many suicides have you seen on the Unit?' Lindsay asked.

Prince emitted a dry laugh. 'None. What kind of ass would try to commit suicide in an acute-care hospital – unless he wants a fractured sternum?'

'Have any of your patients who go home in advanced stages tried to take the easy way out?' the resident persisted.

'Lindsay.' Prince paused and looked directly at his

questioner. When he continued, his voice was laced with an exquisite patience. 'When you have finished your tour of duty on the Unit you will realise that almost all cancer patients react passively. They want to turn their fate over to an authority. Whether life is bitter or sweet, they want to be saved. They will accept any new treatment, any experimental drug. It is through this assurance that we have developed the protocols. They will complain of side effects. They will be terrified of the risks. But they are *more* terrified of death.'

'No suicides . . .' Lindsay pondered Prince's words as they walked on down the corridor. 'Amazing,' he muttered to himself, 'amazing.'

'We are moving into the big time.' Prince's voice wrapped around the words like velvet. 'You will be watching Broadcliff emerge as a cancer research centre over the next year or so. I have some large government grants pending.'

The group was silent as its members processed the weight of this statement. Prince's eyes followed with satisfaction the swing of Brenda's hair and the twitch of her white-clad haunches just ahead of them.

'Who the hell would bring Vendetti flowers?' he asked Lindsay in a lazy, quizzical voice as they walked through the glass-panelled doors towards the private rooms in the West Wing.

Chapter Four

Victor Vendetti was conscious, but in a state of complete exhaustion. All his rage had been expended. He lay and experienced the slow return of normal breathing. He heard the rise and fall of voices and applause on the television set. He felt the stiff presence of leather straps around his wrists and ankles but was, for the moment, too empty to care. He opened his eyes carefully and turned to the window. The snow was blowing into the corner of the roof in slow downward spirals. He lay watching it and waited for the appearance of the dancer. He felt the heat of the hypo effect beginning to flow into his flesh, into his muscles. It was akin to the soft rush of desire, the warmth of blood rushing through his body when Renée touched him.

He watched the snow. It was not lashed by the wind now; not harsh and cruel with frenzy. Its circles were soft, as slow and meditative as a Debussy poem. He gazed into its white rhythms until the warmth of his body made him drowsy. Sometimes, before the hypo knocked him out, he saw the eyes of Renée, soft and vague with fear, trusting him, full of love – and dread.

'Vic, I can't do it,' she would say, firmly closing her eyes against some image in her mind.

'Yes, you can. I'm going to teach you. I'll hold you in front of me. You'll feel every motion and tension of my arms and legs. You'll learn what to do with your body – from mine.'

He had taught her that fear was good. 'Only idiots feel no fear,' he told her. 'You must hold on to the fear and use it. You must ride the fear onto the wall.' The tension of fear gave force to their imagination. He had pumped his own confidence into her. He had taken her onto the wall for the first time, fitted against the curve of his own body. He had watched her become more courageous. He had watched her eyes flash and her pride grow. She was quick and lithe. She rode the wall alone even sooner than he had predicted. But as he watched the snow now, he saw only her eyes, muted with fear. They became obscured in snowflakes and gradually disappeared.

He did not fall into a deep sleep, but lay in limbo between the rise and fall of the television laughter and applause and the snow-spiral of his private view. Sometimes the surge of voices became the roar of the crowd in the bleachers above the wall.

After a while, the wind picked up and the spiral of snow again became a vortex; became his own body and Renée's spinning around the arena, going higher and higher up the wall. He could hear the screams of the women and the groans of the men as they gained speed, and he felt the rush of the wind in his face, the tension of Renée's torso against him and then her strong thighs on his shoulders. At the end she had ridden on his shoulders and, finally, on her own cycle.

They commanded big money after he took her into the act. There was the drawing card of her beauty – but more than that, the added drama of building up from their solo rides to the acrobatics they did at the climax, both of them hurtling around the wall, their bodies joined in a conspiracy against death. When they became expert at one trick, he would devise a more dangerous and spectacular one.

The vortex blurred, and he heard only the hiss of snow against the windowpane. He half-slept.

Images came and went, out of nothingness, out of blackness. He thought that night had come, like a black curtain surrounding him. Then something like the snow swirled slowly, like a white kaleidoscope, into its centre. He heard a voice saying 'Victor.' He settled into a new dream of Renée, but felt a warm hand bringing him back, touching his arm; then the precise searching of a slim finger under the leather straps at his wrists. The finger began to stroke the skin where he had pulled against the restraints. His eyes felt too heavy to open. He lifted the lids with an effort of will and stared into the eyes of a woman. She was leaning over him, searching his face. Something in her eyes startled him into almost full consciousness. They were grey, alert and probing, but softened with the unmistakable shadow of fear.

'Victor? Mr Vendetti . . .?' the voice was saying. 'Try not to pull until they take these off.' She slid her finger out from under the restraints and slipped her hand into his.

Vendetti closed his hand over hers and sighed. He saw her blurring in the haze of the vortex. It spun out slowly and lazily from a black nucleus, darkening her face until it consumed the sphere of vision within his brain. He sank into a drugged sleep.

Chapter Five

Father Stefan Franciscus had left California knowing he
faced the attrition of a post beneath the rank of his training.
On his arrival in Brandenburg he had been billeted at St
Thomas', one of its most ancient churches. His assignment
was to function, on round-the-clock call, as Catholic
Chaplain in the city's largest acute-care hospitals. He was
also to be second-string priest at the parish. He had been
received and given his orders by a senile and inebriated
senior priest. He was glad the Bishop had termed the
assignment 'temporary'.

He drove in a day of blizzards to make his first hospital
rounds. It was night by the time he got to Broadcliff. Leaving
his car on the lowest level of the parking ramp, he put his
head down and marched in the direction of a doorway nearly
obscured by blowing snow. He found the lobby and walked
up to a middle-aged clerk to announce himself.

'Father Franciscus, Hospital Chaplain. May I look over
the Roman Catholic file?' Several warring shades of pink
makeup decorated her face. She inspected him with interest
and handed him a metal Cardex file from under the counter.
There was a fair-sized list of Catholic patients. A perverse
corner of his mind chose to address the list from the end. The
last name was Zalenski. The second-last name was Vendetti.
They were both on Seven Main.

'I guess Seven Main is what I want.' He smiled at the clerk
and glanced around him.

'That's the Cancer Unit,' the lady told him. Her face took
on an expression of pious commiseration. 'Take one of the
elevators at the end of the hall to your right.' She pointed out
the direction with a chubby finger.

He tucked the black leather case containing his missal and the holy oil under his arm and headed for the elevator. Evening silence had settled in. The corridors of the hospital were almost empty. The section he was in was the oldest wing of Broadcliff. The ceilings were high, and the dim night lighting made the effect cavernous and foreboding.

He found Mrs Zalenski's semiprivate room in the North Wing and walked in. The room was very small – barely large enough for two beds, two utility tables and chairs, and two metal clothes lockers. A half-open curtain separated the two beds, and a small sink hung from a wall by the door.

A young woman was reading by her night light in the bed next to the window. She was wearing a pale pink paper cap. The cover of her book said *Learning Through Suffering*.

'Mrs Zalenski ...?' Franciscus began.

The young woman looked up from her book and nodded in the direction of the other bed. A woman with greying hair lay in the shadows in the bed by the door. Some kind of pump motor was pulsing near the bed. A plastic tube was inserted in her nose. Her head was thrown back on the pillow. Her eyes were partly open, but apparently sightless. Her mouth was open wide, and her chest heaved as she breathed in regular, rasping gasps.

Franciscus looked down at her and felt a mixture of horror and kinship. Death was no stranger to him. In the earlier part of his life it had been his constant companion. But the outrage of its more grotesque outlines still shocked him. He turned to the young woman with a questioning look.

'She's been in a coma for three days,' the woman told him. 'It's a mercy. She had too much suffering before that.' She looked at him for a few seconds. 'You're not her parish priest. Are you a friend?'

'I don't know her. I'm a hospital chaplain. It's my assignment to call on Catholic patients. Have you seen her parish priest?'

The woman pursed her lips and was silent for a few moments. Then she began to speak in a confidential tone.

'It's very sad, Father. Thelma Zalenski threw her parish priest out of the room three weeks ago. She said he treated her like an object, not a person – as if he was a mechanic who'd been sent to deal with a broken motor and that little bag he carried was a toolkit.'

Franciscus felt a constriction in his chest. He knew the feeling. Sometimes he suffered from it himself.

'Does she have a family?'

'Her husband comes up. Her two sons live away. They were here a week ago. Her husband just stands and looks at her now. He doesn't know what to do. They say she's been sick a long time.'

Franciscus touched her hand.

'Thank you,' he said, 'I understand.' He moved around the foot of the bed to Thelma Zalenski's cubicle and pulled the flimsy privacy curtain between the two beds. He jimmied the plastic visitor's chair out from between the table and the metal locker and pulled it up to the bedside. Then, suppressing a small wave of guilt, he chucked his black leather chaplain's kit on the floor beneath the chair and sat down beside Thelma.

His eyes were drawn to her face. Robbed of flesh, it was reduced to the eloquent bones of spirit. Though marred by the plastic tube, the curves of her nostrils, the firm line of her jaw and chin spoke of pride and integrity. The ugly lineaments of death had distorted her mouth, but he could still detect the sweet curve of her lips. Deep frown lines interrupted the high slope of her brow.

He needed to touch Thelma Zalenski's life. His glance moved around the cubicle to the metal locker. A pale blue dressing gown spilled its silky volume through the open door. In a corner by the locker was a pair of small, high-heeled slippers – grey suede. He looked around for pictures. The table space was too small for anything but medical necessities. He wondered what she had loved.

His experiences in a prison camp during the war had caused him to believe that persons in a coma could still feel and hear. At any rate, he believed in the protection of

21

thought and presence. He was haunted by the parish priest and his commitment to the dispensing of sacramental salvation. He had always wondered if anyone could know God who had not suffered human love.

A conviction had grown in him that hostile circumstances could somehow abort a vital process in the transition from life to death. He sensed that the experience of dying was a crucial one. He wondered if the stranger on the bed before him had fallen into a coma with no healing transition from her rage at the priest.

In the arena of death, he felt the old doubts assail him, like a choppy sea. His mind groped for an anchor he had used before. On the occasions when he had been most engulfed by loss – others' and his own – he had tried to recall rare moments when unexpected grace had struck into the darkness. He took Thelma Zalenski's hand between both of his and shut his eyes. He set his will to conjure whatever experience of love and meaning came to him in memory, and to let it flow into her; to hold it as a path between them. She must be given good passage from this world to the next. He sat this way for a long time, bent over the bed, holding her hand. He was no longer aware of her laboured breathing. He was attentive to a silence in his own centre.

After a while he felt a kind of peace settle about them. It filled the darkness around the bed. First it was gentle, like a benediction. Then it became stronger, and indeed as intense and personal as love. He wondered, briefly, if he only imagined it; but its reality flowed through his hands and into his arms and chest, into his head, discharging doubts. Its strength finally brought the release of tears. He drew one hand away from hers and fumbled for his handkerchief. The physical problem of tears gradually changed his focus. He was aware, now, of the room. He heard the clanking of a radiator as the heat came on. The light on the other side of the curtain had gone out. He heard gentle snoring coming from the darkness.

Thelma Zalenski's eyes stared sightlessly into the dim circle of light around her bed, but it seemed to Franciscus

22

that her breathing was slower. The gasping had stopped. He felt that his visit was completed. He gently withdrew his other hand. But something like an afterthought, or the pull of a Jesuit conscience, compelled him. He retrieved the holy oil from his kit beneath the chair, moistened his finger with it, and made the sign of the cross on Thelma's forehead. He murmured the anointing prayer under his breath. Then he left the room to find the patient named Vendetti.

Chapter Six

Some time in the early night Victor Vendetti awoke in the darkness. His awareness unfolded slowly from the depths of morphine dreams. He had dreamed of, or seen, a woman with grey eyes. She had rubbed his wrists. She had called him by his name.

A streak of light fell across the foot of his bed from the light in the hallway. The door to the ward was slightly ajar. His mind wound between realities and dreams and finally into awareness of the creeping onslaught of pain. He reached for his button to put on the call light, but the straps brought him quick recognition that he could not move again. He would have to call out and hope one of the other men would hear him and put on his light to signal the nurse.

'Charlie!' he called. Someone was snoring so loudly it drowned out his voice, which had grown weaker during his illness. 'Charlie!' he rasped again. He heard only snoring, then the word 'Mother ... Mother ...' over and over. Now he had roused Harold.

His arms and legs were cramped and restless from being so long in the same position. He tried to relax his muscles, to lie utterly still. He wondered if they would remove the restraints in the morning. He wondered if anyone would give him a

23

heating pad. If only he weren't so damn weak, he'd get his clothes and walk out, the way he had before. At least, if he were home, Stella would bring him a heating pad, whiskey, and aspirin when he needed it. Although lately the whiskey hadn't helped the pain the way it used to.

He tried to remember the warm flush of the whiskey going to his head and his groin and his legs, and to make himself feel it. His mind began to spin tiredly between images of Dr Prince and drug injections, and the comforts of his past life. He wondered if the cancer drug stopped pain. The doctor had said they would treat him if he stopped acting up. His head was throbbing now. He wished the damned nurse would wander in. Night was always the worst. Now he had to urinate. The doctor had mentioned swearing out a warrant.

The throbbing in his head, the pressure in his bladder, and the spike of pain in his shoulders began to confuse his mind. The bed seemed to turn, or the room did. He wished he could go round, round, round, and disappear into the vortex; spin around on this wall of death and enter the void at its centre. Just as he had dared death, taunted death, and defeated death on the wall, he now seduced it in his mind. He spoke to death and urged it to take him; asked for it to deliver him – into freedom or even nothingness.

He had shut his eyes to blunt the heat and the pounding in his head, but a new noise in the room alerted him. He looked up and saw a figure, a figure that seemed to be clothed not in hospital white, but in black. It moved alone, quietly, along the shaft of light from the doorway and approached his bed. He watched it come towards him and wondered if he had conjured it, if it was, indeed, the shape of death. A painful sob caught in his throat. He had wanted to meet death head on – in a rush of power; not chained to a bed by his own weakness, and the authority of strangers.

He shut his eyes again. He lay in the darkness behind his closed eyelids and waited; for release, for cessation, for oblivion. He felt a hand touch his, and hold it. It was a human hand. At first he wondered if it was the hand of the girl who had materialised out of the white vortex of snow.

But this hand was rougher and stronger. The fingers were thick. Tears stung his eyes and trickled down his cheeks. He opened his eyes and saw a man's face looking down at him. The face came closer. He felt the bed move. The man had taken a seat near him, on the side of his bed.

'Mr Vendetti ... ? Victor ... ?' he asked.

'Yes.'

He felt the man's hand try to lift his, then fingers discovering the leather straps and the metal buckles.

'How long have you been in these?' the man asked. The light from the door caught his face and his shoulders as he moved. Victor saw his white collar and knew he was a priest.

'Since before lunch.'

'You ate? You could ...'

'They took them off while I ate.'

'Why are they on?'

There was a silence.

'Never mind. What can I do?'

'I have to urinate. I can't press the call bell.' There was a pause. 'I hurt bad, all over.'

Franciscus saw that Vendetti's face was wet. His features were a mask of suffering, rage, and frustration.

'Where is the urinal?' he asked.

'On the bottom shelf of that table.' Victor turned his head to indicate the cabinet next to the bed.

Franciscus reached down and opened the door, retrieving the urinal. He explored the metal bars on the side rails of the bed and located the buckles on both wrist straps.

'I'm opening these buckles,' he said. 'Can you handle the urinal?'

'If you crank up my bed a little.'

They were both whispering. Victor Vendetti watched as Franciscus' hands moved swiftly into and out of the beam of light, undoing the straps. He began to massage the numb wrists and forearms. He felt the absence of flesh. As thin as the man was, he was amazed at the hard muscles still remaining in his bony arms. He handed him the urinal and started to pull the curtain around the bed.

'My ankles,' Vendetti whispered. 'I need the straps on my ankles loosened.'

Franciscus felt tension like a chain around his chest. The patient had been spread-eagled into a flat crucifixion. All that was missing was the cross and the nails. He slipped the sheet back and undid the buckles that held the ankle straps. Beneath the straps the skin was red and raw.

'I'll wait on the other side of the curtain,' he told Vendetti.

He walked out of the cubicle and stood at the end of the room flexing his hands and looking out the window into the snow. The glow of the parking-ramp lights illumined the snowflakes. They fell as slowly and lazily as down. The blizzard had worn itself out. The motion of the snow cushioned the force of his rage. He heard no sound from the cubicle, so he parted the curtain and stepped over to the bed.

Victor Vendetti was lying limply against the pillows with an expression of relief on his face. The lines etched by pain and grief were there, but some of the tension was gone.

'Have you got any salve or lotion in your cabinet?' Franciscus asked.

Vendetti leaned over and opened the drawer. He handed a plastic bottle of skin lotion to Franciscus.

'We all got one of these,' he told him.

Franciscus took the bottle and poured some in his hand.

'Let's see what this will do for the abrasions,' he told Vendetti. He began to rub it into his wrists and up his arms, massaging one arm at a time, pressing the muscles and releasing them where the skin was not raw.

'Can you turn over?' he asked.

Victor nodded his head and turned slowly, wincing with pain as he moved.

Franciscus poured lotion on his back and massaged that – gently at first, then gradually with some pressure.

Victor could feel the tension begin to drain out of him, and with it some of the pain. His head felt clearer and less hot. By the time Franciscus' hands had moved up and down the taut muscles of his legs and applied the lotion gently to his sore ankles, he felt he had been released from a vice. The priest helped him turn on his back again.

'Can I do anything else?' he asked. 'Can I give you water?'

'Please,' Vendetti said. He watched Franciscus as he poured water from the Styrofoam pitcher.

His hair was iron grey, and his eyes were very blue. Vendetti guessed him to be in his fifties. He had seen high-speed drivers, like himself, who had similar faces. This priest looked like a proud hawk who had seen human tragedy and comprehended it. Vendetti sipped the water. The hawk's eyes watched him. They were at once fierce and – something else. Vendetti searched for it in his mind. They were the eyes of a man who had been broken. Vendetti wondered if strength could emerge from brokenness. These were new thoughts to him, and very strange.

'Can I do anything else?' Franciscus asked.

Victor Vendetti had quit going to Mass thirty years before. He had tired of the meaningless flow of verbiage intoned in Latin, a language he didn't know. The homilies bored him. The music was fine, sometimes. But he did not believe in the ritual – that men could receive grace by eating bread and drinking wine because it was God's body and blood. The wall and the cycle were his ritual, and Renée had been all the blood and body he could ever need or want. Suddenly he thought of something else.

'You have to secure the straps – buckle them again,' he told Franciscus. 'If my doctor thinks I got out of them he can swear out a warrant. I'm not strong enough to leave – yet.'

'Swear out a warrant?' Franciscus asked.

'For me assaulting the staff.'

A look of incredulity spread over the priest's face. 'Some time I'll have to hear about that. I have to leave now, but I'll be back. If you have any friends around here, ask them to bandage the raw skin on your ankles and wrists.' Franciscus sat on the bed and buckled the four straps. He inserted the thongs several holes looser than they had been before.

'Father . . . ?' Vendetti began.

The priest had stood up to leave. He had tucked his black kit under his arm.

27

'Yes?'

'How come you don't read the Bible? Do you give the sacraments? ... the last rites?'

The priest looked at him closely. He was silent for a few moments, staring at Vendetti in his restraints. Finally he said, 'Is it important to you to prepare for death?'

Now Vendetti was silent. He looked out at the snow.

The priest laid a hand on his shoulder.

'Good night. Try to get some sleep.' He stepped to the foot of the bed and cranked it down until Vendetti was lying almost flat. He pulled up the sheets and the thin blankets and smoothed them over his body.

'I'll tell the nurse to look in on you in case you need anything.'

'Thanks, Father.'

Vendetti watched him move back along the shaft of light and disappear out the door.

Franciscus walked down the hall to the nurses' station. The ward clerk was sitting on a stool, knitting a sweater.

'Where is the head nurse?' he asked her.

'The head nurse isn't here at night.'

'Who is in charge, then?'

'The charge nurse.'

'May I speak with her?'

'She's out on a break.' The clerk eyed him a bit defensively.

'I'd like to leave a message for them. Tell them the Chaplain would like them to check his friend Vendetti. He needs some attention and some pain medication. You might mention that Victor Vendetti's welfare is of interest to the Pope.'

He turned and left the Cancer Unit through the stairwell, on his way to find the Orthopaedic Unit and the next Catholic on his list.

Chapter Seven

At 7 a.m. Mary Hogan approached the five-bed men's ward to begin her morning duties. She entered the room with apprehension. Noisy breathing came out of the darkness. She aimed her flashlight at the floor so as not to startle the men. They were all sleeping. Charlie and the men on either side of him were snoring gently. She guided the beam of light to the floor area between Harold and Victor and moved her slim body into the space. Harold appeared to have slipped into a coma. His eyes were partly open, and glazed. His breathing was heavy and rasping. Victor lay on his back and did not stir. She knew he had received a pain injection within the last couple of hours.

One of her deepest conflicts, since coming on the Unit, was between her private knowledge and her assigned duties. There was the constant problem of having to awaken patients who had fallen into merciful unconsciousness after long bouts with pain and anxiety. They were subjected not only to her own required schedule of routine physical checks, but to the taking of blood in order to measure damage done by chemotherapy and radiation therapy. On the Surgical and Medical Units her conflict had not been so severe. Most of those patients recovered, or died quickly. To interrupt their rest did not seem so cruel. But these patients, in spite of all the treatments, did not have long to live, or would live for months in varying degrees of pain and discomfort. She was convinced they should be cared for in a place where their own internal timing counted for more. But acute-care hospitals like Broadcliff had to function around the order of their own routines, and they were always understaffed. When the doctors made rounds in the morning, they wanted to see the most recent vital signs recorded. She must rouse the men, one at a time, and take their temperatures and blood pressures, then, with Hugh's help, do bedpans and baths.

Vendetti's leather restraints had bothered her mind throughout a restless night in her own bed. She walked over to him now and gently lifted the covers. She played the beam of the flashlight over his wrists and ankles. One leg was slightly bent, and his arms moved as she lifted the sheets. He was not spread-eagled tautly as before. She did not see Hugh come into the room and was aware of him only when she felt his presence beside her.

'Morning,' he whispered.

'Hi.' She looked up and saw him smiling at her. She gestured with the flashlight towards the leather straps.

'Someone loosened them,' he said, in a barely audible whisper close to Mary's ear.

'Looks that way,' she answered. 'He could almost get out.'

'He didn't try.'

Mary shut off the light. They stood, quiet and motionless, looking uncertainly into the darkness where Vendetti lay. Finally Mary drew a deep breath.

'I hate to wake him up. I always hate to wake them up.'

'We have to,' Hugh stated. 'I'll turn on the night light next to Harold. He won't see it.'

Mary watched Hugh walk around Harold's bed and snap on the light. Harold did not call out 'Mother' as usual. He did not respond to the light.

One of the men next to Charlie, Mr Danvers, cleared his throat. He was an older man, very dignified and mannerly.

'Miss Mary . . .? Is that you?' he asked. Hugh walked over to his bed, Mary following.

'Morning, Mr Danvers. Anything I can do for you before Mary takes your temp?'

'Yes . . . yes,' Mr Danvers' voice dropped to a low, modest murmur. 'I need some physical necessities . . . attended to. Could you help me down the hall to the bathroom?'

'Do you feel strong enough?' Hugh asked. 'I can pull the curtain . . .'

30

Mary walked over to Charlie's other neighbour, Martin Kiley. He sat up and hung his legs over the edge of the bed.

'Would you like your bathrobe?' she asked. Kiley nodded.

'Damn early hours,' he grumbled.

'Just let me get your temp. Then you can go down to the bathroom,' Mary told him. She popped the thermometer into his mouth. Hugh was walking slowly towards the door with Mr Danvers, his arm around his waist. Danvers hated the bedpan and the urinal. As long as someone would support him, he chose to walk down the hall to the toilet. He shaved himself every morning, even though his hand sometimes shook badly.

Mary put her fingers on Martin's wrist to take his pulse. She was thinking how much harder it was for men to accept the physical indignities of illness. Women had lived with it for years. It was in their bones; all the distortions of gestation and childbirth, the physical struggles with babies and children. Their destinies had forced them to develop ameliorating graces against the bondage of their bodies.

Mary removed the thermometer from Martin's mouth and recorded his temperature and pulse rate on her pad.

'You can go to the bathroom as soon as Hugh gets back with Mr Danvers,' she told him. Charlie had awakened and turned on his bedside light. He was rubbing his eyes and coughing up phlegm. Mary looked over at Victor. He was still sleeping. He must have been given an elevated dose of medication – or his pain had remitted. She would take care of all the others first and let him sleep as long as possible.

When Mary went out to the supply room for fresh towels and linens, Hugh followed her. They stood between the shelves loading sheets and towels on a metal cart.

'How are you doing so far?' he asked. 'How do you feel about working on this Unit?'

Mary was slapping towels on the cart with more force than necessary. It was a few moments before she spoke.

'I'm angry a lot. I feel like crying a lot. I carry it home with me.' She was talking a lot too, suddenly, she thought, and glad for a chance to say it. She felt safe with Hugh.

'Think you'll stay?' he asked.

31

At the end of her first day after she had been transferred from a General Surgery floor, Mary had seen Victor Vendetti lying beside the window, tied down with muslin restraints. His rawboned, emaciated face was turned to the snowy window and wet with tears. The sight had haunted her ever since.

'Get off that Cancer Unit,' her husband had told her, with some sharpness in his voice, when she tossed around at night unable to sleep. 'Ask them to transfer you to Obstetrics. Everybody there has a future.'

Maybe he was right. But the need on the Cancer Unit stunned her, and somehow called to her.

'I'm going to give it another week,' she said to Hugh, in answer to his question. 'Maybe two,' she added, aware the first week was coming to an end.

Hugh leaned back against the linen shelves and watched her. 'You ought to come to the conferences we have every week. They're like rap sessions. Everybody's under pressure here. Some of them handle it one way, some another, some not so well. These rap groups help. You get things off your chest. You get support from each other. You can share things. You don't take so much home then.' He waited. Mary had stopped stacking the towels.

'Christie Wilson leads the discussion,' he added.

'Christie? I saw her in the nurses' station yesterday, before Victor pulled the knife.'

'That's her.' Hugh smiled. He had the gift of being able to go quickly from serious concern to enjoyment. 'You ought to talk to her. You ought to have lunch with her someday,' he said.

Mary had noticed that Hugh never sat with his group in the cafeteria at lunch. She guessed he didn't have a group. There were few orderlies at Broadcliff, and he was the only one on the Unit. There were a couple of male LPNs and one black female RN. The nurses from each unit always sat together. The social workers sat together. The office personnel sat together. The Housekeeping employees sat together. She had noticed the intense, almost worried expression on the faces of people carrying their trays into the cafeteria, as their eyes combed the dining room to locate members of their own strata. If none were present, they had to eat alone.

Everyone huddled with his own group for security – except Hugh. She had seen him sitting with the women from Housekeeping; with Christie, a social worker, and another girl from Social Services. She had seen him sitting with a chaplain once and had even watched him break into a group of nurses from the Operating Room. He was a free soul. She touched his hand and squeezed it.

'Thanks, Hugh. I'll come to the conference. I'll try to talk to Christie,' she told him.

'Hang in with us awhile,' Hugh said. He flashed his white smile, then suddenly became serious. He frowned down at her. 'You got a gift to be a fine nurse. You got instincts for what's important and what isn't. And you got love. I saw it the first day you came on the Unit. Don't you be afraid.' He looked intently into her eyes to underline the words. Then he turned to the linens again. 'You start Charlie on his bed bath. He's still got the chemo I.V. I'll wake up Vic Vendetti and see what needs to be done for him. Okay?'

They finished loading their cart and headed back to their tasks on the ward.

Chapter Eight

Virgil Prince had been in Brandenburg for two years. He had done his residency in an Eastern hospital and been invited to join a group of internists whose senior member was Dr Stanford Bracebridge. Not many months had passed before Bracebridge was forced to conclude that he had grasped a medical tiger by the tail. As an internist, he had been faced

33

with many of his long-term patients' developing cancer. For years he had looked forward to adding a bright young doctor to his staff whose speciality would be the relatively new field of oncology. Now the overflow of patients who flocked to the office, referred by their physicians to Virgil Prince, forced Bracebridge to consider adding yet another oncologist to the service.

In the beginning, Bracebridge had been relieved to have someone in his own office to whom he could refer the patients who were stricken with malignant tumours. But the character of Prince's practice had begun to change since his decision to enter into a national research programme. Each patient was now treated according to protocols demanding expensive tests and the amassing and recording of precise data. When they died, autopsies were required in order to determine the extent to which the chemicals had killed the cancer cells. The information gained from the dead was as vital as that gained from those who continued to live.

More nurses and technicians had been added to their staff. Most of the chemical injections were given by the nurses. Prince examined patients and talked to them at the outset of their admission to his service. After that, he saw them only when a crisis occurred – if it became necessary to abandon a chemical that was no longer effective, or that had destroyed so many white cells as to be life-threatening. The research programme often made it necessary for him to make trips out of town to special conferences.

Stanford Bracebridge was Chief of Internal Medicine at Broadcliff Hospital. This position gave him considerable prestige in the structure of the institution. He was in his early sixties, solidly married, and had some grown children. He had a deeply philosophical nature hidden behind a somewhat whimsical, and sometimes comic, facade. His friends remarked that he was humanistic, that he had practised holistic medicine before it had a title. Now he was becoming more and more disturbed by the sense that his group practice had evolved – or deteriorated – into a factory with an assembly line; or worse, into a single, sterile machine. Somehow, the life and content of Virgil Prince's research consumed the value of the patients' identities and needs.

Occasionally Bracebridge interrupted his own rounds to go down and chat with the doctors in Radiotherapy, who treated some of Prince's patients with X-rays. He had great empathy with Edward Nippert. Nippert was much younger than he, but they understood each other.

On the day following Victor Vendetti's insurrection and defeat, Bracebridge descended the cement stairs and threaded his way through the queue of patients and technicians to Nippert's office. He found him leaning back in his swivel chair, his feet on his desk, leafing through a chart.

Nippert looked up and saw Bracebridge's tall, dishevelled form standing in the doorway.

'Come in, come in!' he said. He swept some papers from the deskside chair. 'How's it going?'

Bracebridge pulled a handkerchief out of his trouser pocket and wiped his forehead. He settled his long, rumpled frame into the chair and sighed.

'We had a standoff up on the ward yesterday. An old man pulled a knife on the Prince entourage.'

Nippert's eyebrows lifted for several seconds; then he laughed. 'He didn't want any more chemo?'

'Hell no,' Bracebridge intoned. 'He hadn't even been treated yet. Prince was called for a consult because this bum had a history of lung cancer.'

'Why the knife?' Nippert's eyes were bright and intense. He leaned forward in his chair.

'The nurses said he was sore because they tore up a bed he made for himself on the floor beside the radiator.' Bracebridge settled back in the chair and grinned broadly. 'Goddamn. Wish I'd seen it. Some orderly said Brenda was the one who faced the old guy down.'

'Is Prince taking the case?'

'Yeah. Vendetti – that's his name – has no doctor. You know Virg. Insurrections put him on his mettle.'

The two men sat silently. Finally Nippert spoke. He was

sitting with his elbows on the desk, his chin on his fists. He had very fine dark hair which occasionally fell onto his forehead. This, and the intensity of his eyes, sometimes gave him a combative appearance.

'I hear the grant has gone through,' he said.

'You heard right. Now the hospital administrators blush and genuflect whenever Virgil enters the room. They flutter around him like brides in a harem.'

Nippert considered this for a few moments. 'Got any other new patients?' he enquired.

'Ten were put on the protocols in the last week. I'm looking for another oncology man to take up the slack.'

There was a silence. Bracebridge withdrew his eyes from Nippert's steady gaze and drummed on the chair arm with his fingers. Nippert spoke again.

'You told me a week ago you were thinking of retiring. I gather you still think the chemo is a high-wire act.'

'It's the *variables*.' Intensity coloured Bracebridge's voice. 'The *human* variables.' He leaned across the desk until his face was close to Nippert's. 'I've seen some of my old friends die because they were wiped out. Prince had beaten the cancer – at least, it was remitted – but there was nothing left of *them*.'

Bracebridge slumped in the chair; his shock of white hair shadowed his face. Nippert watched him, his own mind charged with the dilemma.

'Don't refer anyone else until you feel better about it. Meanwhile, you might just decide to retire.'

'No ... *no* ... I have to know *more*.' Bracebridge spoke through the baffle of his folded hands. 'I keep hoping there'll be a breakthrough, an honest *cure*. My other partners refer patients to Virg too. I brought him into the group. I'd like to go out to pasture with some peace of mind about those patients and their treatment.'

'A treatment that inflicts no more harm than the disease?'

Bracebridge sighed deeply. 'Sometimes I argue with myself that it's better for a person to feel he's doing something – *anything* – other than just waiting.'

36

Nippert picked up a brass paperweight and tapped it rhythmically on the patient's chart in front of him. Finally he spoke.

'We're walking on a high wire down here too.' His voice was low and tinged with fatigue.

Bracebridge stood up and stretched his long body. His suits were always ill-chosen, rumpled, and his ties and lapels spotted.

'Somehow I never lie awake at night worrying over your motives,' he drawled. He walked towards the door, then turned back. 'I understand Virgil is going to send Vendetti down to you for an opinion – wants to rule out radiotherapy before he puts him on chemo. The man's dirt-poor. Of course, he's eligible for Medicaid.'

Nippert stood up and walked with Bracebridge into the corridor. He placed a hand on his arm. 'I'll watch out for Vendetti's knife,' he told him, grinning. 'Meanwhile, concentrate on the rewards. You're pretty close to the seat of power when you're in research.'

Bracebridge did not reply. He walked on down the corridor waving one long arm in the air and disappeared among the stretchers and the uniformed technicians.

Chapter Nine

Christie arrived on the Unit that morning with some apprehension. Her intended visit with Victor Vendetti had been aborted by the standoff with the knife, and its aftermath. She wondered if he would be too angry to speak with her, in too much pain, or simply too drugged with pain medications to know she was there. When she had come in the day before, he had just been locked into the leather restraints and had seemed barely aware of her presence.

Today she hoped to reach him in some way. If she succeeded, no restraints would be necessary.

She went into the nurses' station, found Vendetti's chart, and paged through the medical reports to the Progress and Consultation section where the physicians made their sometimes illegible entries. She saw that Prince had already been in and had written that Victor was being referred to Dr Edward Nippert for possible radiation therapy. He had also written an ironic aside:

'Leather restraints have dramatically reduced patient's assaults on staff.'

She went on to the section labelled Nurse's Notes. The nurse on the night shift had written some cursory statements:

'Patient voided dark, cloudy urine. Complained of back pain. Asked for heating pad. Meds given. Patient coughed up thick, blood-stained sputum.'

She looked up from the page and saw the new LPN, Mary Hogan, standing beside her.

'Excuse me,' Mary said. 'I didn't mean to interrupt.'

'It's okay.' She shut the metal chart. 'I wasn't getting much information, except that Mr Vendetti still hasn't got a heating pad.' She looked at Mary and saw an urgent questioning on her face. Mary had none of the opaque, masklike expressions some of the nurses cultivated as professional objectivity.

'Did you ... did you talk with Victor Vendetti yesterday?' Mary began. 'I saw you go into his room after the ... after they put him in leather restraints ... and I wondered, are you going to try to see him today?' Mary asked.

'Yes,' Christie told her. 'Are you assigned to that ward? I mean, does he know you? I didn't meet him the other day; he was under medication. If someone he knows could go in and introduce me, it would help.' Christie seemed glad of the chance to talk with someone who was interested in Victor Vendetti. Mary leaned towards her.

'I've been doing his vitals and routine care since he was admitted. I just started on the Unit this week. He seems like an unusual man.' Mary suddenly stopped and looked around her. A couple of nurses were watching them with interest. Christie got up from her seat on the stool. She slid the chart into the slot.

'Do you have time to stop in his room with me now?' she asked.

'Sure.' Mary walked around the counter. She was relieved to get out of earshot of the station. One of the interested listeners was a nurse by the name of Roberta Smith who had been described to her as an informer.

Christie and Mary left the station and walked down the corridor to a corner where they could safely talk.

'How was Victor this morning?' Christie asked. 'Can you tell me anything about him?'

Mary thought for a moment, searching for the right words.

'Well,' she began, 'he's really been terrible; you know – wild. But . . . he has a reason to be. He's in a lot of pain and he knows everything's out of his control. He's . . . well, he's different from the others. He doesn't conform. Maybe he can't.' She looked directly into Christie's eyes. 'I've noticed that when people are very sick and get put into hospitals they really become submissive. They almost lose their own identities and *wills* . . . They depend on us for – everything.' The expression on Mary's face told Christie that she found these facts not an endorsement of medical power, but a human tragedy. They looked at each other intently for a few minutes, feeling a sense of comradeship and recognition. Then Christie spoke:

'. . . And Victor just kept battling. He didn't know the war had a built-in ending.'

They arrived at the ward. Everything was fairly settled now. The bustle of the men's morning care routine was over. Charlie was watching a show on TV. Mr Danvers was reading a book on Greek civilization. Harold stared blindly at the ceiling, his ragged breathing a grotesque accompaniment to the laughter and applause from the tube.

Mary and Christie said hello to Martin Kiley and crossed over to Victor's bed. He was lying with his face turned to the window, and he was awake. Christie stepped into the space between his bed and Harold's. She stood looking down at Harold for a few minutes; then she ran her fingers through his thin hair and let her hand rest on his forehead. Victor Vendetti had turned from the window now and was looking at Christie. He watched her as she touched Harold.

'I hope he's found his mother,' Vendetti said in a thin voice. 'He kept everyone awake calling for her.'

'Let's hope so,' Mary answered. 'Victor, I brought a friend of mine in to meet you. She works here at the hospital and has time to talk with the patients.' Christie turned to Victor and held out her hand. Then she remembered the restraints and slipped her hand under the blanket to grasp his. He was studying her face. Something in it was familiar.

'I'm Christie Wilson. I came in to talk to you yesterday, but you were pretty tired. You'd just had an injection,' she told him.

Victor remembered now: the girl with the grey eyes.

'I have to leave,' Mary said. She smiled at Victor and Christie. 'Put your call light on if you need anything, Victor, or Christie can come and get me.'

Victor nodded his head. 'Thanks,' he said; 'for everything. My ankles don't hurt since you bandaged them.'

'Hugh asked Dr Lindsay to order you a sheepskin pad. Maybe you'll get one today,' Mary told him. Then she hurried out of the room.

Christie pushed the footstool close to his bedside and sat down. They were now on the same eye level. They sat quietly for a few moments, neither of them speaking, but each studying the other rather openly and without self-consciousness. Christie found him intensely interesting. His face was emaciated, its craggy structure painfully etched against the caverns of his cheeks and the hollows of his temples. He had bushy grey eyebrows and hair. His eyes were a light hazel colour, and very alert. His hands were rough and gnarled, with dark nicotine stains on his fingers. He indicated the window with a movement of his head.

'Was it bad driving out there? What is it like in the streets?' Victor asked.

'The snow stopped for a while this morning,' Christie told him, 'but it's supposed to storm again tonight. If you have to be grounded, this is a good time for it.'

'You aren't a nurse,' Victor observed. He thought a moment, and felt a brief anxiety. 'Are you a doctor?'

Christie laughed. 'No, hardly. I'm a social worker. Social workers talk with patients. Some arrange for transfers to other hospitals, or help people find nursing care at home.'

Victor watched her speaking and wondered about her. She didn't have a bossy, authoritative manner, like most of the staff. She seemed thoughtful, and very personal. Her grey eyes studied him with a probing interest.

'I saw the bed you fixed for yourself out of chairs. It made me curious about you. Why did you want to lie on the chairs?'

It was the first time anyone here had asked him why he did anything. All the things he had done to get near the radiator they had merely reacted to with shock, outrage, and swift punishment.

'I got a lot of pain, especially my back and shoulders,' he explained. 'At home I had a heating pad, and when it wore out I got my bed close to the space heater. The heat relaxes me, even if it can't make the pain go away. Charlie gave me his bathrobe and his pile-lined coat, and I used my own bathrobe and coat, and I made a bed right up against the radiator on three chairs. Before that, I fixed one on the floor.'

'I saw it,' Christie said. 'It was like a nest; like the places cats find to be warm in.' She leaned forward on the stool. 'Victor, you are really good at improvising. What's your profession?'

Victor Vendetti dropped his glance and seemed to be studying the white cotton coverlet. His mouth turned down at the corners and his jaw twitched slightly.

'I haven't got a profession ... anymore. I've been sick for the last year.'

'What did you do before you were sick?' Christie persisted. There was something remarkable about Victor Vendetti. She sensed an indestructible core of strength; even more, an

41

indestructible identity – a rough grace. He looked at her as if he were measuring her approximate depth. Then he said:

'I was an attendant in a parking lot. I parked cars down on Front Street.' He raised his eyes and looked closely at Christie. Her voice appealed to him. It was many-shaded, with a slight huskiness. It seemed warm and familiar. He wasn't put off by her personal questions. It only pained him to answer them. Her face was quite close as she leaned forward to hear him. She was resting her arms on the bed and twisting her interlocked fingers together. Her eyes probed his as if she expected to uncover buried treasure. They were alert and lively.

Christie suddenly smiled and looked at him as if she thought he was teasing her.

'And what did you do before that?' she demanded.

He saw that she accepted nothing at face value, and liked that.

'I worked in a carnival.'

'A carnival!' Her eyes widened. She had thought of him as different, as special, and now she saw the connection. 'Carny' people were a breed apart. They were freewheeling vagabonds; misfits in all the hierarchies of polite society.

'What did you do in the carnival?' she asked.

'Set up the rides. Took care of the machinery. Put up the tents and booths, and took them down again.'

'Where was the carnival?'

'The one I was with travelled around the Southwest ... warm country.' He caressed the word 'warm' with a sudden soft timbre in his voice. He watched her responding. She reminded him of a child listening to a fairy tale, her face brightening at some image of gay, colourful existence. Balloons and costumes filled the sterile space around them. He wondered about her life and whether she had always lived in the cruel, grey winters of Brandenburg. His eyes travelled to the snow-covered rooftop and back to her face.

'The Southwest is a different world,' he told her. 'You never freeze. You lie by pools in the winter. You never have to shovel your car out to go somewhere.'

42

'I know. Once I went to visit my uncle in California. It was in January, and there were orange and pink roses, and hibiscus.' Her mind too wandered out to the snow, seeing beyond it.

'Have you ever been to Phoenix?' he asked her.

'No. I guess I flew over it once, the time I went to California.' She paused and smiled at him, her face merry, amused at the thought. 'Maybe your carnival was down there then. Maybe I flew right over where you were and I didn't know I would meet you someday.'

Victor wished he could move – lean forward and touch her hand. 'We lived in different worlds,' he said gently. He thought a moment and then asked, 'Did you always live in the north country?'

Christie nodded her head. She had leaned her elbow on the bed. Her chin rested in her hand. 'Even farther north, and snowier than this,' she said.

'Where?'

'In Canada.' A remoteness began to veil her face. He felt a sudden withdrawal.

'You should go to Phoenix,' he told her, trying to bring her back. 'You'd love it there. And you'd love it in Vegas. Vegas is even more full of lights and excitement, like a carnival, like ... Christmas, all the time.' He watched her face light up again as he spoke, then drift away and become shadowed. His instincts told him that she was one of the lonely people. He had known too many of them in his life. Some were drifters. Some had never left their hometowns or their families. They all lived in the centre of a silence, even in the midst of carnivals. He forgot his own pain and his restraints. He summoned his hearty voice again realizing how rusty it was, how long it had been since he had used it.

'If I didn't have this cancer ... I'd ... I'd take you to Phoenix, and to Vegas too. You ask your husband to take you.' He paused a moment. 'Are you married?'

'No.'

'A pretty girl like you, and not married?'

'Well, I was once, but ...' her voice trailed off. She had

43

suddenly become aware of an audience. Roberta Smith was standing in the centre of the room. Christie wondered how long she had been listening. She was looking from Christie to Vendetti, her eyes grim and her mouth in a thin line.

'If you're through with your *counselling*, Mrs Wilson, we will take over with Mr Vendetti. Dr Prince has left orders for him to be seen by Dr Nippert in Radiotherapy.'

Christie stood up and looked at Victor.

'We have visited long enough for today,' she said.

Vendetti reached towards her with his eyes. 'Can you come right back later, when they're through with me in Radiotherapy?'

Christie looked at Roberta Smith's closed face, then turned to Victor. 'I'll try. But if I can't get back today, I'll come tomorrow, same time as today. Okay?' She reached down and took his hand. 'Maybe they'll decide they can remove these' – she indicated the restraints. 'At least you'll be out of them for the trip to Dr Nippert's office.' She squeezed his hand. 'I'll see you soon, Victor. I'll check with Hugh and Dr Lindsay about the sheepskin and the pad.'

Victor watched her out the door.

'Don't forget to come back!' he called after her. He looked up at Roberta Smith, who was standing stiffly by his bedside looking down at him. Behind her a woman in a pink uniform had walked up with a stretcher. Roberta folded her arms over her chest and began to speak in a measured, toneless voice.

'Dr Prince has left orders that these restraints may be removed provided you do not cause trouble either here or in Radiotherapy. I would advise you to watch your tongue and to do as you are instructed.'

Roberta opened the buckles of the restraints and released the straps around Victor's wrists and ankles. She was trying not to look at Vendetti. Not only did he have metastasized cancer, but he had said obscene things and run amok on the Unit. Victor Vendetti was a distasteful assignment. She was comfortable and proud when she took care of young wives and mothers, husbands and fathers, young people, or even

44

dignified elderly patients, who had cancer. Those patients gave something to society and had a reason to be living. But Vendetti was a dirty, obstreperous old man. Dr Prince had said he was picked up in a gutter on Front Street, a low-class neighbourhood near 'skid row', and Brenda Stone had told them he lived with some stupid old woman who wasn't his wife. She looked down at Vendetti's bony arms and legs, his wasted body and gaunt face, and felt a wave of revulsion.

'Can you roll over onto the cart?' she asked, glancing away from the exposed parts of his body. Vendetti was rubbing his wrists and attempting to rub his ankles. They were numb. His legs felt weak and awkward.

'I can roll over,' he said. The pink-clad escort reached out and supported some of his frail weight by lifting him under the arms. Roberta snatched a thin blanket from the bed and covered him with it. Thank God, she thought, she was an RN and didn't have to handle his basic physical care.

She walked beside the stretcher until they arrived at the elevators. Then she spoke to the attendant.

'Tell Dr Nippert to call Seven Main extension if Vendetti gives him any trouble. Let me know as soon as he is returned to the ward.' She turned on her heel and walked briskly back towards the nurses' station.

Chapter Ten

Stefan Franciscus rose early enough each day to carry out a morning ritual he had engaged in since the beginning of his priesthood. He always worked out with his weights for fifteen minutes, then knelt to say his morning prayers. While he prayed, another part of his mind was processing the position he found himself in on this new assignment. When his thoughts interfered with the prescribed prayers of morning or evening, he sent towards God one message: 'Use me!' If indeed God was using him, the strange pattern was clear. He had been forced in middle age to forfeit all his holdings and return to the beginning.

On a winter morning two days after his arrival in Brandenburg he knelt beside his bed, half in prayer and half attentive to the scenes in his past that had begun to illuminate the present.

Franciscus' new post had cast him back into a strange wedding with his youth. His role of hospital chaplain had been a demotion in status within the Church. But even more crucial to his inner life was the equation which the cancer unit formed with the most desperate experiences of his life. As he struggled through the punishing winds and heavy snows of Brandenburg, his mind made pilgrimages backward to the steamy plains of Luzon. As he waded through the snow to his car in the rectory lot, he could feel himself trudging again along a dusty road to the north in a ragged company of defeated and weary men, away from the battleground and towards an unknown prison.

The series of flashbacks to his youth had begun the night he found Victor Vendetti aching and thirsty in his hospital bed, and discovered the leather straps that held him motionless.

Since then, other patients had stared up at him through hollow eyes recalling the faces and voices of old comrades. 'I can't make it. I can't go any farther,' they had said over and over, and there was a silent plea for forgiveness of that failure. The soldiers he had marched with on the death-stenched road to San Fernando mingled in his mind with the patients on Seven Main.

After he returned to the States and during his seminary years he would awaken at night in a cold sweat seeing again the fallen men, the bursts of orange fire as shots rang out, and the flocks of circling buzzards who followed their progress to feed upon the dead. But the memories of the march and the prison had gradually faded from his mind, replaced by the activities and concerns of his teaching responsibilities.

The long journey that had brought Franciscus to Broadcliff had begun with his decision to become a priest. It was a decision that had evolved slowly and steadily since his boyhood. Its seed had been planted in his heart earlier than in his mind, for the Church had been his refuge for as long as he could remember. In all the chaos and disconnectedness of his childhood it had preserved an island of meaning. It had offered both structure and mystery. In it he had first found patterns of order, beauty, and symmetry.

His mother had died when he was five and his sister was ten. He had vague recollections of her face smiling at him and of a gentle touch which had suddenly been lost to him. After a brief attempt to work and keep house and care for his children, his father had placed them in the home of a favourite cousin. The woman was a good person and meant to be kind, but was overburdened by five children of her own and a bullish husband who turned cruel on drink. When he came home in a black mood, he would thrash whichever child crossed his path. His own children had become sullen and stoic, but Stefan, who had never known violence, crouched with enormous eyes in corners. His timidity and silence had the effect of unspoken accusation, adding guilt to the drunken rages of his protector. After he received several severe whippings, his sister, Jeanette, had taken to hiding him in an upstairs bedroom and reading to him whenever Uncle Fred came home upset. There were not many books in the house, but she had found an illustrated children's version of the stories of the Gospels and an illustrated version of Longfellow's poems on a bookshelf. Stefan's life in his new home had been one of violent contrasts. The sounds of oaths, crashing furniture, and shouts of pain mingled in his mind with the cadences of Evangeline and Gabriel and images of Jesus in the Temple or walking the dusty roads of Judea.

Aunt Emma and Uncle Fred were good Catholics. They sent all the children to parochial school. The school and the Church had gradually become Stefan's true home. They, and a corner between his bed and a window where he and Jeanette huddled cross-legged over the precious books,

47

formed his pattern of security. Jeanette had read them over and over. He had never grown tired of the stories.

The safety and protection of their reading corner had given him a disposition towards books and learning. He was a bright and eager student. During his school years he was taken under the wing of various Sisters and Fathers. All his mentors had vocations in the Church. By the time he was an altar boy he could imagine himself in no other vocation than the priesthood.

He was guided into a fine Jesuit college and graduated with honours at the beginning of World War II. His plan to enter the priesthood was suspended because of a debate with his conscience he could resolve only by joining the service; if he had gone immediately to the seminary he would never have been certain whether priesthood had been an escape made necessary by his terror of violence, a vocation entered into through cowardice.

He was inducted into the Army, and after finishing basic training was commissioned a second lieutenant with the Thirty-first Infantry and shipped to the Philippines. After some months of fighting in the jungles of Luzon there was a humiliating surrender. He and thousands of other prisoners were herded into Mariveles Air Field at daylight on April 10, 1942. Then began the eighty-seven-mile forced march north to San Fernando. The men who survived the torture and exhaustion of the march were loaded into cattle cars and transported to a prison camp in the Central Luzon plain.

The tortures of the prison camp combined illness, beatings, and starvation. There were few medical supplies to treat the sick. The men who had survived the march were weak, if not diseased. Those who were considered hopeless were laid on the ground beneath the raised floors of the prison dormitories. They lay beside the dead, waiting to be buried.

The camp had been converted from Army quarters into a prison, so the conditions were makeshift. One day he and another prisoner were sent out beyond the barbed wire to fill some cans of water. Franciscus and his companion dumped the cans and took off into the jungle. They were befriended and hidden in Philippine villages and remote farmers' huts until the Americans made their landing on Luzon three years later.

A search for meaning in the suffering he had seen and experienced further confirmed his old commitment to the priesthood. After a period of recuperation in a Stateside Army hospital he enrolled in a California seminary. The questions he had carried with him from the rigours of his childhood and the horrors of Bataan led him to organize his studies around history and philosophy as well as the prescribed theological programme. He finished his work at the seminary with high honours. When he offered his first Mass, he was thirty-two, somewhat older than his classmates. His ministry was to be on the faculty of a nearby Jesuit college.

His service experience added to the weight and reality of his achievements as a scholar. In a few years he earned a considerable reputation as an authority in existentialism – Christian, atheist, and agnostic. He was held in high esteem by the hierarchy of Catholic academic circles. But his experiences in the war had effected profound changes in him. The dogma, the fabric of institutionalized Catholic theology, stretched at its seams like an outgrown overcoat as he struggled to move within it. Only the prestige and power of his position sweetened the incongruities he wrestled with.

His life among many deaths had left him as responsive as a child to both pain and love. After a prolonged internal battle he broke his vow of celibacy with a beautiful young woman student. She lingered with him for a year in a tortured idyll until the problems of their concealed union and the appearance of a more freewheeling suitor persuaded her to end it. She had been his first deep love and his first sexual experience. He felt for a while like a demented man.

As the scars began to heal, he became relentless in his commitment to bury himself in the achievements of scholarship. He succeeded so well that his position in the academic world put him in the company of scholars from many religious and nonreligious backgrounds. His rank in the university and in the community gave him what he recognized too late as a dangerous sense of freedom. It brought him to his first real experience with one of the perils inherent in power – its high visibility.

Two years before his banishment to Brandenburg, a friendship had developed between himself and David Scott, a young student. They were drawn together by the boy's brilliance in philosophy and his musical talent. Franciscus had always been a devoted listener, but had never learned to play an instrument. The boy, David, was a fine pianist. As their friendship deepened, Franciscus spent hours each weekend on long walks with his pupil, debating theories. They would wind up at David's apartment, and Franciscus would meditate and dream through the twilight while David filled the room with sounds he had almost forgotten.

Gossip had been going the rounds for some time before Franciscus heard it. Rumours reached David's ear first in the form of snide remarks made by classmates. Franciscus, protected by his position of power and secure in the esteem of his colleagues, ignored the rumours as being beneath contempt or response, believing they would die a natural death.

But several months later his superior at the university called him into his office and broke the news that he was terminating his assignment. When Franciscus protested and mentioned appeal, the superior assured him that because of the high esteem he had earned through past achievements, a board had already debated the decision and reached a conclusion. It had taken into consideration factors beyond the awkward situation of his relationship with David Scott. The discussions he led in his classrooms had for a long time verged on heresy. His personal philosophy was of dangerously open character, and therefore the committee had decided to recommend a month's vacation rest, then a quiet transfer to an entirely different ministry. His superior told him that he was to serve for at least a year as hospital chaplain in a small Midwestern city. At the end of that time, it was felt, the welfare of his spirit would have been served sufficiently to permit the superior there to find him a position as a parish priest.

As Stefan Franciscus' morning prayer mingled with the memories of the past, he was struck with a new truth. His fall from power had presented him with a new, less obvious freedom. He was not connected with any of the hospital hierarchies, and therefore he could not be directed and controlled by them. In the highly technological power structure of an acute-care hospital, his function was looked upon as outside the pale of critical consideration. He had no road map and no superior here, but he knew he walked on holy ground. The devastation was not unlike the waste of battle. Each person he saw presented a unique and crucial question. All he could do was meet them where they were, via the bridge of his constant prayer, 'Use me!'

He got up from his knees and glanced out the window. The grey brick walls of the rectory courtyard reflected pale beams of sunlight from the east. A weight had been removed from his spirit.

He had lifted the dumbbells to replace them on the rack in the closet when he heard a knock on the door. He opened it and saw Fr Hollihan, the parish priest at St Thomas', standing unsteadily in the hallway. His customarily red and puffy face seemed more ravaged than usual. He coughed for a moment and deposited some phlegm in his handkerchief.

'I hope you can say the five o'clock Mass, Father,' he said in a muffled voice. 'I'm not well today, not well at all. I think it's a touch of flu. Don't want to spread it.' His shoulder bumped against the wall as he turned away.

'I understand,' Franciscus said quietly.

This happened about twice a week. Sometimes the old man claimed it was arthritis. He drank before dinner and late into the night, alone in his room. The housekeeper had informed Franciscus of the problem before he had his bags unpacked on the day of his arrival. He watched the ageing priest weave slowly down the hall.

'Take care,' he called after him. 'Get some rest.'

He retrieved his weights and replaced them in the closet.

51

He had purchased them when he received his appointment to the university. The Bataan march had taught him that his body must always be ready for the existential moment when its ability to endure would determine whether he would live or die.

Chapter Eleven

Mildred Schultz, supervisor of the Seven Main Cancer Unit, was captain of a ship which moved through tricky cross-currents and dangerous shoals – and whose passengers were doomed to drown. Her chief problem was managing the crew. The mood on the Unit was volatile. In spite of their shield of authority and their training in the stance of objectivity, some of the nursing crew became emotionally involved with patients.

Mildred had long ago defined the type of nurse who functioned most smoothly on the Unit, caused the fewest waves, and melded her own will most thoroughly, and productively, with the ultimate authority of the doctors. This type was low-key in her personality and opaque in her emotional structure. She never related to patients as equals, and received a pleasant gratification through wielding her power over them. Most important of all, the ideal nurse on the Unit was group-oriented, subservient to the authority above her, and never inventive.

Today she had called a meeting with the two women she trusted most in maintaining the status quo. For some time she had observed small pockets of inventiveness appearing on the Unit – unobtrusive at first, but now multiplying dangerously, spawned by the eternal enemy of good nursing practice: personal response to the patients. Mildred had also heard the disturbing news that some of the nurses were seeking out Christie Wilson to discuss matters involving the needs of the patients. An independent spirit was suddenly appearing on the Unit. It had grown after the nurses' conferences began, with Christie as leader of the discussions. Mildred saw, for the first time, a real danger to her own authority and power over the nurses. Christie had proved very effective with depressed and angry patients. Mildred had thought, in the beginning, that her presence on the Unit might have the effect of deflecting the inordinate emotional needs of the cancer patients away from the nursing staff. But something more had happened. Some nurses were drawn to Christie's way of relating to patients and families. If it continued, Mildred's control of the Unit would be dangerously undermined. A few nurses had even been heard questioning the decisions of the oncologists.

Today Mildred had called a meeting with RN Roberta Smith, her most trusted deputy, and Brenda Stone. Brenda too was a nurse, but beyond that, she was Dr Virgil Prince's new assistant. Mildred tidied up her desk and plugged in the percolator on a small table beside her chair. She had called this conference none too soon. The arrival of Victor Vendetti on the Unit might prove to be a catalyst that would explode the issues at stake. It was essential to devise a counterattack.

Roberta Smith was the first to arrive. She greeted Mildred with an enigmatic smile. She had a quiet, cool manner and perfect grooming without makeup. Her whole effect was low-key, but nothing on the Unit missed her scrutiny. She was the ideal informer, and totally loyal to Mildred.

'Mmm, smells good,' Roberta purred, indicating the percolator. She sat down in one of the straight-backed office chairs, her spine erect, hands folded in her lap. Mildred always thought of her as a *Mona Lisa* type. Moreover, she reeked of purity. Any doctor moved to profanity on the Unit immediately censored his mouth if he saw Roberta approaching. Mildred wished she had ten like her.

She inhaled the aroma of the coffee and began to relax. Brenda would be late. She was always late. Mildred believed it was one of her contrived gimmicks. She decided to begin

53

the exchange the conference had been called for.

'How's the morning been going? Anything new?'

'Oh, fine. Everything's under control. Vendetti is down in Radiotherapy. Dr Nippert is supposed to decide if he should be treated.' Roberta's smooth face was touched by a shadow of concern. Mildred saw that she had something more to divulge.

'I understand Vendetti has calmed down considerably,' Mildred offered.

'Oh, the restraints have done wonders. He lay absolutely still on the cart when we wheeled him to the elevator.'

'No profanity? No refusal to go?'

'No.' Roberta looked straight into Mildred's eyes. Mildred was the older of the two women. Together they were a study in monochromatic understatement. Roberta was consistently the pale, scrubbed, colourless blonde. Mildred was an allover dun colour, and slightly dumpy. In the corridors, Roberta carried her tall, slender body with rigid erectness. Mildred was slightly round-shouldered and had very little presence.

The coffee had stopped perking. Mildred leaned forward and poured. She looked over at Roberta.

'Anything in it?'

'The usual.'

Mildred dropped a cube of sugar into each cup. She leaned back and smiled.

'It looks like the problem with Vendetti is pretty well solved. He has a "stage four". The metastasis is extensive. He'll lose his fight fairly quickly.'

'Well' – Roberta dropped her eyes – 'there's just one thing . . .' There was a long pause while she took small sips of coffee from her cup. She seemed to be reflecting.

Mildred leaned forward, her yellow eyes narrowed. '. . . And that is? . . .'

Roberta's face took on an expression of pained puzzlement. 'Christie Wilson was with Vendetti when I came to take him to Radiotherapy.'

'Well,' Mildred responded, guardedly, 'we hoped she

would absorb some of the burden we carry with difficult patients.'

'That's just it.' Roberta's smooth brow became furrowed. 'When I walked onto the ward, Vendetti was ... well, it appeared that he was rather in command, and ... questioning *her* about *her* life.' Roberta stared levelly into Mildred's eyes. Neither of them spoke for a few moments. Mildred sensed that the statement contained a key to solving her dilemma over Christie.

There was a sharp knock on the door and Brenda entered, carrying, as always, her stack of yellow portfolios. This morning her usually dramatic manner was tinged with an edge of boredom. Mildred had noticed that she had a distinct tendency to conserve her lustre when no doctors or residents were around. Brenda was a type Mildred congenitally disapproved of, but having found herself in the same political bed with her, she had determined to make full use of Brenda's considerable guts and her intimate position with the seat of power.

Brenda looked about, a bit impatiently, for a place to perch. She tucked her bottom over the corner of Mildred's desk.

'I have to be at another meeting fairly soon. What's up, Mildred?'

Mildred bridled a little at being deprived of the preliminaries, but decided she had better come to the point.

'I asked you to come to this meeting because I realize it is in your interest, and certainly Dr Prince's, to be aware of any divisive influences on the Unit. I do not think I am being premature to warn you that such an influence has been noted.'

There was a small diminishing of Brenda's air of haste, and of her boredom. She put her portfolios down on the desk and looked at Mildred closely.

'Oh, yes?' She glanced over at Roberta, whose face was bland and expressionless. Mildred continued.

'Some of the nursing staff have been overheard asking to speak with Christie Wilson about dealing with the patients' emotional problems, and about their own feelings relating to problems here.' Mildred watched Brenda and waited. Brenda looked thoughtful. She bit the cuticle of her index finger daintily.

'Doesn't she lead discussions with the nurses? Who set that up?'

'Her supervisor in Social Services,' Mildred answered. 'She persuaded me that a social worker/counsellor could defuse some of the tension the nurses build up by working full time with patients who are ... uh, not all recovering. It seemed logical. But now it appears that Mrs Wilson was trained in a far different modality than what is workable in a medical institution. If nurses step down from their role of authority to discuss and explain every medical decision the patients disagree with, this Unit is headed for trouble.'

Brenda's eyes narrowed. 'Be specific.'

Mildred turned to Roberta and gave her a meaningful glance. Roberta's pale face took on the expression of a teacher's pet reciting her lesson.

'I told Mildred the other day that I really needed to discuss some things I had overheard on the Unit. Two of the nurses said they'd heard Christie agreeing with a patient who didn't want to continue her chemotherapy. They said they felt they too should be more honest with patients in the future; that half the time they felt the oncologists caused patients to suffer unduly by treating them too long, and it hurt them more than it helped.'

Brenda slid off the corner of the desk and poured herself a cup of coffee. She lit a cigarette and inhaled slowly. Mildred grabbed the ball again.

'It is dangerous form for our nurses to make value judgements about treatments. Those decisions belong in the hands of the doctors.'

'It will be very difficult to maintain control over patients, to get them to follow their medical orders, when someone else is encouraging them to think for themselves and even go against medical decisions.' Roberta's voice was tense.

Mildred decided it was time to pull the ace out of her

sleeve. 'I realize that Dr Prince has in the past thought very highly of Mrs Wilson and been impressed with her handling of problem patients. You realize it may be difficult for us to limit or control her operations on the Unit if he continues to ... support or sponsor her.' She spoke carefully and slowly in a voice tinged with regret at being forced to succumb to the inevitable.

Brenda took a deep drag from her cigarette and stubbed it out in her saucer. 'Dr Prince will not be a factor in whatever decisions you make regarding Mrs Wilson. He has his hands full with other things. He is going to be delegating to me many of his time-consuming tasks with patients. I will be screening all his phone calls and handling most referrals. If you want to diminish Wilson's influence with the nurses, it can be done cleanly and unobtrusively by a gradual change in her assignments.'

Mildred was listening attentively. She liked what she heard. However, there was a catch.

'But I can't change her assignments. Her supervisor is Margot Edwards, Director of the Social Services Department.'

Brenda smiled sweetly. 'Yes, I know. I also know that with the removal of Dr Prince's interest and protection from Christie Wilson, Margot Edwards will be only too glad to see that her time is increasingly consumed by arranging nursing-home deployments.' Brenda poured some coffee and drank it down, black. She glanced at Roberta and Mildred. Roberta's eyes contained a veiled triumph. Mildred leaned forward. Her voice was coolly dispassionate.

'You are suggesting we deal with the problem through her supervisor and that she be retracted from the Unit, slowly,' Mildred paraphrased.

Brenda had taken out her lipstick and was carefully applying it. She took her time, then replaced the lipstick and a small mirror in her pocket.

'To get rid of her suddenly might cause a reaction from some of the nurses, even some of the patients. Let her continue to see the ones she's had, and any who reenter. As

57

you know, cancer patients who come onto the Unit are temporary clients. If she gets no referrals and her disappearance is slow, it shouldn't cause a ripple. They will be too busy to notice. Their minds will turn to something else. Just don't go for the big bang.'

Brenda flashed a brilliant smile at Mildred.

'Keep in touch. Let me know what you arrange.'

Mildred stood up and smoothed the front of her uniform.

'I'll contact Margot Edwards today.

They shook hands.

Brenda picked up her portfolios and started through the door. She looked down at Roberta and emitted a throaty laugh. She touched her on the shoulder.

'Just don't get caught up in any big romances, babe,' she quipped. 'Mildred would have to find three British spies and an Auschwitz graduate to replace you on this Unit.'

She flounced out of the small office, Virgil Prince's 'beeper' emitting its pulsing alarm on her right thigh and the scent of Cabochard trailing in her wake, mingling with the odour of antiseptic in the stuffy corridor.

Chapter Twelve

Francine Lindemueller sat fidgeting in a secluded booth in the Pirate's Cave. She and Brenda were meeting for one of their bimonthly lunches, and after making certain that no one from Broadcliff was in the vicinity, she had carefully chosen a corner booth.

Francine was a nurse in the Intensive Care Unit and thought of herself as Brenda's confidante. She was a short, chunky girl with heavy bone structure. Her own gracelessness had spawned the fascination she felt with Brenda. She was convinced that Brenda had missed her true calling. She should have been a movie star, she was that glamorous. Francine unzipped her huge canvas handbag and pulled out a pack of cigarettes and a plastic lighter. It went out before she could ignite the cigarette, but after two more tries she was able to draw in a mouthful of smoke. It got in her eyes and made them water. She coughed and put the cigarette in the ashtray. She wished she could smoke like Brenda, with her nonchalance. A cigarette was always a charming prop for Brenda. Sometimes she would gaze enigmatically at her companion through the mists of exhaled smoke. Sometimes she would put the cigarette into her mouth very slowly, punctuating the conversation with narrowed eyes and a pout. Brenda never choked. One night Francine had seen her in a restaurant with Dr Prince. She had waved a cigarette in a long, slim gold holder, making a little gesture between them as she spoke.

She saw Brenda come through the door now. As she made her way between the tables, she held her head high and her shoulders back. Her hips undulated beneath her belted coat, and the men at the tables she passed all turned to look at her. She smiled at Francine, slipped out of the fur-lined leather coat, slung it over the seat of the booth, and curled her body in beside it. She tossed her head, shaking droplets of melted snow from her hair.

Her hair was the most striking thing about her, Francine thought. She must recently have had it streaked. It was thick and hung below her shoulders. Its tawny colour was accented with pale, almost silvery streaks that lifted from her temples and followed randomly down its long, silky length. This mane plus her glittering green eyes gave her the look of an exotic feline.

'It's nasty out there.' Brenda shuddered and smiled, making her dimples show. 'What are you drinking?'

'Coca-Cola and whiskey,' Francine told her, reaching over to touch the lining of the leather coat. 'What is it? Is it new?'

'It's ranch mink,' Brenda answered dully, making a little *moue* – 'an old thing Frank gave me. It's warm.'

Francine stroked the fur and wondered why Brenda's

husband was still buying her goodies. She wondered, also, if he suspected anything about her liaison with Virgil Prince. Brandenburg was small enough for hospital gossip to get around. Frank Stone was an important attorney who was being groomed for action in his political party. He was also a close friend of Stanford Bracebridge, who moved in political and academic circles as well as medical. She had often seen Stone in his company at the hospital. Beyond that, Frank was an athlete, although he was much shorter than Brenda, who was as tall as a high-fashion model. He was on the local polo team. Francine had seen his picture in the Sunday *News Herald*. He was seated on a black horse, a white helmet on his head. The caption said: 'Upcoming socialite-lawyer is no slouch at polo.'

The waitress appeared at Brenda's elbow.

'Bring me a Margarita,' Brenda told her, 'and give us a while to relax before we order.' She turned a bit on her seat and crossed her legs; then she pulled out her cigarette case and lit one with her lighter. She gazed past Francine as she drew a deep drag and exhaled slowly.

'So what's new on the ICU?' she asked.

'Oh, nothing much,' Francine replied, an edge of boredom in her voice. She took a long sip of her drink.

'Anything new on the gossip circuit?' Brenda focused her eyes now, and grinned. 'You know, following Virg doesn't give me much time for girl-talk.' Her drink had arrived, and she took a small sip. 'Half the time I don't even hear the scuttlebutt on the Cancer Unit.' She leaned back and fastened Francine with a fond, expectant gaze.

Francine settled back in the soft seat cushions and gingerly puffed on her cigarette. Brenda saw a familiar look of self-importance settle over her plump face. Her large eyes took on an expression of serious confidentiality.

'Well, you must have heard about the social worker who is into massage,' she said, doing a fair imitation of Brenda's voice when it slid into a cool purr. She pretended to be busy stirring a lemon around in her glass as she waited for Brenda's response. An expectant silence hung between them.

Francine tried a long drag on her cigarette and coughed, watching Brenda from behind her napkin. She saw that she had scored. The green eyes had widened suddenly, then blinked. Brenda sipped her drink and picked up the menu. After she had studied it, she responded to the question.

'No. I really don't hear too much, Francine.' She put down the menu and leaned forward, her voice very gentle. '*What* social worker? What *kind* of massage?'

Francine forced herself to take a pregnant pause. Her brow wrinkled. 'I don't know her last name, but I think her first name is Crissy. Yes – that's it. Crissy *something*. In the cafeteria the other day one of the nurses from ICU was talking to a friend from Seven Main. She told her this Crissy is really good at massage and has been studying about new ways to control pain.'

'A *social worker*? What can she know about analgesics?'

'It isn't about *medication*. This nurse says this Crissy got rid of somebody's headache with massage when they asked for an aspirin.'

'A *patient's* headache?'

'No. Some girl on the floor. One of the aides.'

'So?'

Francine sighed deeply and affected an elaborate patience. She took another sip of her whiskey and Coke.

'Well, the point is that some of the nurses asked her to show them how to do it, and ...' Francine paused again.

'... And what?' Brenda was leaning forward now, her eyes alert, focused on whatever Francine would say next.

'This friend of mine said that this Crissy told them she'd be glad to teach them what she did. She said Crissy had once helped one of the cancer patients to make it through to the next scheduled medication by massaging him and that it really helped *his* pain.'

'My God!' Brenda leaned back on the cushions, a funny smile on her face.

'Isn't that illegal?' Francine asked primly. 'I mean, isn't it unethical? Don't you have to be a physical *therapist* or a nurse, to give physical treatments to patients? I mean, I

61

always heard that . . .' Her voice trailed off, and she frowned.

Brenda ground out her cigarette in the ashtray. 'She has no credentials, no licence, as a social worker to touch bodies therapeutically.'

Francine watched Brenda's face. Her features always became sharper when she was computing something. The information had not only scored, but scored heavily. That always made Francine feel unique and important. Rumours were circulating that Virgil Prince was becoming a big research person. It was possible that even she, as Brenda's informant, might become an indispensable cog in the executive wheel.

The waitress came up to the table to take their order.

'When we finish our drinks,' Brenda told her. 'In fifteen minutes.'

Francine relaxed, basking in the response her revelation had produced, and kept still. She had learned from experience not to ask Brenda questions. Brenda usually asked *her* questions. The first few times she had exhibited overt curiosity about Brenda's life she had been met with a cold silence. Brenda had confided all she had confided of her own accord. Francine had been in on the progress of her affair with Virgil Prince from the beginning, and she had become privy to the confidences by knowing enough not to pry. She had the odd feeling that Brenda had no friends she could confide in and no one she trusted. It warmed her to think she might, in fact, be Brenda's one and only friend.

Francine sat back now and listened to Brenda chat. The news had affirmed something for her, Francine suspected. She was telling about an upcoming junket Virgil was making to Iowa. He was taking her with him, and she had to convince Frank Stone that a whole group from Oncology was going also. Francine watched Brenda sip her drink, smoke her cigarette, and laugh and whisper. Occasionally she laughed and whispered back. She wasn't worried about whether Brenda would convince her husband. She knew Brenda could pull off anything she set her mind to. Sooner or later, Brenda would tell her the news of their Iowa trip. It would be almost as if she had been able to fly out of Brandenburg on a plane herself.

Chapter Thirteen

The department of Radiation Therapy was located below the lobby level of Broadcliff, and partially below ground. Its nucleus was a large, lead-lined windowless room containing the linear accelerator. This machine was a monster version of an ordinary X-ray machine. The lead-shielded metal casing which housed the huge gantry head of the accelerator arched up from the floor on a steel axle, its ominous weight suspended above the steel treatment table. Around the walls of the room a pastoral mural had been painted to alleviate the mood established by the powerful machine and distract attention from its function. The accelerator brought the span of exposure time from delivering lethal doses down to one to two minutes. One of its great advantages was that it concentrated its energy on the smallest area of living cells, to hone in precisely on the site of the cancer itself.

Some of the patients who were referred for radiotherapy were well enough to come on foot, or in wheelchairs, as outpatients. They waited their turn for treatment in a small waiting room where they could talk with each other or page through magazines. The very ill, brought on carts by the hospital escorts, were pushed into a corridor and left to wait their turn. The corridor where they waited, sometimes in dreary queues, was long, narrow, gloomy, and windowless. Small offices lined it, mostly inhabited by the staff radiologists. Some housed the calculators and computers the doctors used to determine the precise number of rads that would be used to bombard each cancer site. Between the long passageway and the lead-lined room of the linear accelerator was the anteroom, also a monitoring room, containing desks and a closed-circuit television monitor, on which the doctors and technicians could view the patient as he lay beneath the accelerator. No one could remain with the patients. The technicians positioned them on the table so that the cancer site was in precise conjunction with the path of the X-rays. Then they left, closing the lead-lined doors, and observed the treatment on the screen, out of the range of its energy.

Many of the patients referred to the treatment as 'the vault', a site of predeath entombment. For them it was a taste of the grave's isolation, proffered to them while they still lived.

While the oncologists' war on cancer was waged with chemicals, Edward Nippert and his partner, Gunnar Bjord, fought it with the power of high-energy X-rays. Their side effects were similar to the poison of the chemicals, with the addition of burns that resulted from the X-rays. It was a burning that gave no warning until the skin reddened, became painful, and sloughed off. The rays had no warmth. Their power was silent and secret. They broke molecular linkage, and this diminished cancer masses in human bodies. Minds that had become deranged by brain tumours sometimes became lucid again. Patients who were limping, or could not walk, from bone cancer sometimes began to walk easily and without pain. The cancers were controlled, diminished – but not cured. Nippert and Bjord had irradiated certain cancers that were excisable by surgery, thus causing a safe atrophy which made surgical removal possible. Many of these patients were cured.

Nippert and Bjord had vastly disparate backgrounds and religious philosophies. But on some matters their minds and spirits were in accord. They maintained a great respect and an intelligent apprehension concerning the lethal force which they controlled and used. They did not confuse its power with their own.

Determining when treatment was in the best interest of the patient and when it was not required a delicate balance of knowledge of the tools at hand, the physical and psychic condition of the patient, and time to explore his perceptions and needs. Both physicians made these decisions with the utmost care. But more and more they found themselves embattled, even besieged, in a struggle with power masquerading as a commitment to the preservation of life.

Victor Vendetti's trip to the Radiotherapy Department was without dramatic incident. He lay quietly on the stretcher going down in the elevator, but had difficulty keeping still while he awaited his turn to be examined. He lay among many other patients who were stacked along a narrow hallway on stretchers or in wheelchairs, isolated from each other in the separate prisons of their diseases. Some looked closer to death than he. Some had intravenous tubes in them, with bottles and poles attached to their stretchers. He lay there for what seemed a long time before he was rolled into an examining room. Five minutes later, the doctor came in. He was a tall, soft-spoken man who examined him carefully and questioned him about the location and extent of his pain. He introduced himself as Dr Nippert and told Victor that what he learned in this examination, plus what he read in the chart about his history, would determine whether he could advise radiotherapy treatments.

'What can they do to help?' Victor asked.

'Radiotherapy kills cancer cells. The patient is placed beneath a linear accelerator which delivers lethal doses of extremely high-powered X-rays to the cancer.'

Victor considered this. It appealed to him. He could understand it. The linear accelerator murdered death.

'What else does it do? Does it hurt?' he asked.

'It damages everything – all cells within its path. We get around this by trying to shield it from all areas but the cancer site. ... "Does it hurt?"' Nippert paused and took the giant risk he always took; had decided to take. He spoke slowly and looked directly into Vendetti's eyes.

'It doesn't hurt while the treatment is being delivered. But sometimes later. There are always side effects. All treatments

– all drugs – have side effects. Sometimes there are skin burns. Sometimes nausea and extreme fatigue.'

Victor considered this for a few moments. Both men silently explored each other's eyes. Then Victor looked away. He looked down at his right knee. It was small and bony, sticking through the gap in his hospital gown. A congestion was growing in his chest. He coughed until his throat cleared and he could summon his voice.

'Dr Nippert, I appreciate your ... honesty.'

Nippert saw Vendetti's pale eyes growing watery under the grizzled eyebrows. He felt a surge of that familiar, damnable provocation to lie. Victor's rounded shoulders and his caved-in chest lifted a little. He leaned towards Nippert.

'Dr Nippert, I'm tired and weak already. I don't know if I have enough strength to meet a treatment that would make me weaker and more tired.' He watched the doctor closely.

Nippert didn't answer right away. He appeared to be taking invisible measurements. He smiled slightly, but his eyes remained serious. They were grey-blue and contained depths and shadows born of much inner struggle. He commanded the most powerful source of energy yet known to destroy cancer cells. His profession was to control and use it. He had spent the last twelve years of his life picking his way through a moral jungle of greater and lesser evils. Only a few of the cases he treated could be called 'cures.' But he knew already that Victor Vendetti was not one of these fortunate cases. He watched Vendetti closely as he spoke.

'We have difficult judgements to make when we are dealing with cancer. We try to base our decisions on whether to radiate by determining if the treatment will do less harm than the disease. Perhaps the treatment could slow the cancer's progress, but would be too difficult for your body to tolerate. In your case we cannot hope to cure,' he said, gently, 'but in some instances radiation can be palliative.'

'Palliative?'

'Lessen the pain you're experiencing.'

'That would be a help.' A slight glint of hope played over Victor's face.

Edward Nippert laid a hand on his shoulder. He felt the network of thin bones and hollows under the hospital gown.

'I want to go over your chart and discuss it with my partner, Dr Bjord. I will get back to you and your doctor by tomorrow.'

'My doctor ...? Dr Prince?' Victor asked.

'Yes. He referred you to me for this consultation.'

Victor felt a quick diminishing of comfort. Prince's manner was cold and arrogant. It smelled also of contempt. It added to his own sense of helplessness. Men who projected Prince's qualities had always inflamed his fighting instincts, or had aroused an animal need to form barricades of silence and protection. He wished his fortunes could be put into the hands of the doctor he faced now, instead of Prince. He knew his body had betrayed him, had slipped out of his own control. All he had left to himself was his mind. He wondered how long he could control that.

Chapter Fourteen

Victor Vendetti knew that regardless of what Dr Prince and the new doctor in Radiotherapy recommended, he had to make the final decision in his treatment. Dr Nippert had given him a good idea of the power in the linear accelerator. It could at least be directed to one area. But he was unsure of the way the chemicals worked. They too were meant to kill cancer, but they would be absorbed into his whole body. He wondered how far the cancer had carried its invasion. All he knew was that it had begun in his lung.

It had been evident to him from the first day on the ward that next to Harold, he was the sickest man in the room. Mr Danvers was older than he, but did not seem to be in as much pain. He was sure his own cancer had progressed beyond the lung. He turned and looked at Harold. His face was a ghastly yellow. His mouth gaped wide open. A bloody saliva seeped from the corners of his lips. He wondered how long a man could linger in this sightless, noisy disarray; this long struggle with death.

Charlie's voice interrupted his reverie.

'Hey, Vic! Your priest friend came in while you were gone. Said to tell you he'd come back tomorrow.'

The priest had returned! Victor felt a warm swell of energy in his chest, then a quick slump of disappointment at missing him. He would have liked to talk to him today, *now*. He was different from the priests he had known before; a man who might be able to share with him some of the uneasiness he felt in facing decisions. Well, he would see him tomorrow – unless someone decided to wheel him somewhere for more tests or consultations.

'Hey, Vic!' Charlie was in a big mood to talk. He slapped himself on the leg and laughed loudly. 'Now that you got them shackles off, you're free for some action, eh?' He waited a moment and then continued in a conspiratorial tone, 'Maybe your girlfriend'll call on you today.'

'What girlfriend?' Vic asked, with minor annoyance.

'The good-looker,' Charlie teased. 'Not yer old lady, buddy. I mean the one that's *built*.' Charlie cupped his hands just beneath his chest and jiggled them. 'Man, has she got knockers!'

Victor said nothing. He had been thinking about Christie Wilson as he lay in the corridor lineup awaiting his turn to see Dr Nippert. The long, bilious-green walls; the grey, thin-lipped creatures on the carts; the bottles and tubes and poles; the anonymous, drab hospital gowns; all had pushed his mind, in self-defence, to evoke Christie as he had told her of Phoenix and the carnival. He wondered if she would be back. He felt, now, that he was poised between two poles of understanding. They had suddenly emerged at either end of the void over which he hovered: the face of Christie and the face of the priest, the touch of Christie and the touch of the priest. They intruded into his reveries, mitigating chaos.

Either his pain had lessened, or the fact that for some reason they weren't making him wait so long for his medication had decreased its intensity. The removal of the restraints let him change his postion. Just after he had returned from Radiotherapy Department, Hugh had come in, proudly bearing a heating pad and a thick white sheepskin. It was actually fuzzy acrylic, but it cushioned his back from the hard mattress and its plastic cover. Some spirit of softness seemed to have entered his situation, which before had been hostile and punitive.

He spent the afternoon dozing against the warmth of the heating pad. When he felt pain returning, a nurse came and gave him the injection before he pushed his call light. When he woke between naps, he heard nothing but Harold's rough, dragging breaths. The other men slept. The eternal snow let up for a while, only a few desultory flakes drifting between the outside walls.

Victor was lying on his side watching the hypnotic drift of the snowflakes when he felt a hand on his shoulder. He turned to see Christie Wilson standing by his bed. She was smiling as she had been when he told her about Phoenix.

'You're free!' she said in a low voice.

Victor turned onto his back and crunched the pillow up under his head.

'Want me to wind up your bed?' she asked.

He nodded and smiled. She had come back too, like the priest. She leaned over and cranked up the head of his bed.

'What time do you get off work?' he asked.

'Oh, this is my last call.'

'It's bad out,' he said, glancing out at the snow. 'You hadn't ought to start out from here too late.'

Christie didn't look at the window, but the shadow of the snow crossed her eyes and her cheeks. He looked at her clearly and closely for the first time. She had a jaunty nose, he thought, just large enough to convey a certain pride. He had seen Indian squaws in Arizona with cheekbones less prominent than hers. Her hair was an uncertain style, full of stray wisps. It hung to her shoulders and was an unremarkable brown. She had a high colour in her cheeks, and he noticed that she moved swiftly and gracefully. The sense of motion and purpose in her body was mitigated by her eyes. They filled with lights only when she smiled.

He realized he was staring at her. She made a quick little motion with her hand, brushing away a strand of hair, and fumbled with her pad and pencil. She stashed them in a pocket of her lab coat and sat down on the large footstool. He picked up the conversation in a casual tone.

'I'm glad you came back. I was talking so much about myself, I ... well, I didn't get to know much about you.'

She took a deep breath and seemed to relax. 'Well, we were interrupted, and I was really interested in hearing more about ... the carnival, and your life ... and what you did in Phoenix when you weren't putting up the carnival and taking it down.' She was looking at him as if she were waiting for the next instalment of a television series. 'Tell me,' she asked, 'who was the most interesting person you ever met while you worked in the carnival?'

Victor felt a slow rush of pressure, like surf, rising in his chest. The invisible fingers of her mind touched what was still alive in him, immutable and undiseased.

'The most ... interesting person was the girl ... the girl I rode the Wall of Death with.'

There was a silence, electric and gentle, like sparks on a bed of fur when it is stroked.

'The Wall ... of Death?'

'The Wall of Death,' he repeated, 'is a feature of the carnival. I used to ride the Wall of Death.'

'How do you ride the Wall of Death?' Her voice was low, almost a whisper.

Vendetti was not an educated man. He had learned all he knew in the alleys of life and in the dark, mystical caverns of the church; a church that enacted magic rituals in a language he could not understand. He had extracted all he knew of beauty and subtlety from the church, and all he knew of power from the alleys. Now it became very important for him to explain to Christie the Wall of Death.

70

'Can I borrow your pencil?'

She gave him a felt-tipped pen. He looked around for paper. Her pad was too little.

'Open the door of the utility cabinet,' he told her. She crouched down next to the bed and opened the cabinet.

'There's some paper bed pads there. Give me one and I'll draw on it.'

She found the pads, larger than desk blotters. He put several in his lap and began to draw, being careful not to puncture the paper with the pen.

'This is the wall,' he explained, 'like a deep barrel.' Their heads bent over the pads together. It was becoming hard to see. Darkness gathered outside the window. Christie stood up and snapped on the light. Victor felt an urgency to finish his explanation. The privacy afforded by the other men's sleep was temporary.

He sketched swiftly, defining a large circle, the aerial view of the arena, and then a profile view, showing the angle the wall followed.

He held it out to Christie and traced circles with his finger, spinning out from the centre into widening loops, up and up and up the wall, then contracting back again, like a vortex into the nucleus of the circle.

'But you ... *rode* this' – she looked up at him, her eyes confused – 'you rode this ... on what?'

'We rode it on motorcycles.'

'The girl ... and you? I can't imagine it! It sounds impossible.' She looked at him, her eyes alive again, measuring his authenticity against her own imagination. She looked baffled; then, suddenly, sad. 'How brave you were. How brave she must have been!'

She looked out the window into what was now night, and the ghostly swirls of the snow.

'How fast did you go? What kept you up on the wall?'

He pointed to the diagram with a thin finger. 'You can see we began at the bottom, in tight circles. The wall had a gradual slope there. But then we climbed, making three-hundred-and-sixty-degree turns. We were at a ninety-degree

71

angle to the wall. People said we went faster and faster, until we were almost too fast to watch. The power lay in not going over the top.'

Christie's eyes were riveted on his face, moving, searching, as if there were a secret that he alone could tell.

'How did you come down?' she said.

'Bottoming out. It was the steering. We deaccelerated, until we came to the bottom again.'

Christie curled her arms around herself as if the night and the snow had penetrated the window sash.

'Where is she now? What ...? Why ...? Did she ...?

Suddenly Victor was aware of the other men. Charlie was moving about, looking up at his I.V. and checking the tube, careful not to jerk the arm it entered. Kiley had put on his call light, and Mr Danvers was trying to get out of bed, an anxious look on his face. Harold was still breathing.

Christie leaned forward, oblivious to the men around them. She touched his hand.

'Renée died,' Victor said, in a husky whisper. 'Everything depended on steering, your grip on the bars, tooling up precisely, and your control at the moment when you turned the cycle down. She overcontrolled and flipped it over.'

Christie's eyes held his, unwavering.

'She ... her back was broken. She died on the way to the hospital.'

Victor's voice had been eloquent. Now he faltered and could not continue. He leaned back on his pillows and turned away. There was no view. Only the night.

Christie reached out and grasped his hand.

'You were with her?'

Her touch forced him back.

'I rode in the ambulance. I held her when she died.'

He looked at Christie. Her face was not devastated. She looked at him as if she had just witnessed a miracle of triumph.

'How lucky ... how *fortunate* she was ... you loved her,' she said.

Victor watched her in amazement and confusion. 'Lucky?

72

I *killed* her. She was thirty-three years old . . . beautiful, and dead.'

'How did you kill her?'

He couldn't mistake it. Christie was puzzled. Confounded.

'You see, she was always afraid. But I persuaded her. I *taught* her. I rehearsed her. I gave her confidence – to ride the Wall of Death.'

A loud clatter of wheels and metal kitchenware broke between them. The dinner carts were being wheeled into the room. Victor was relieved that the men's interest had been deflected from himself and Christie.

Christie stood up. 'I'd better go. Your dinner is here.'

'And it's dark. Be careful. It's still snowing and blowing,' he warned her.

Christie nodded. Hot trays were delivered to Charlie, Mike, and Mr Danvers. Victor's food was still on the cart.

'I'll be back,' she said.

He wondered from where. He wondered where she had come from, what men had loved her. He did not know yet, buried in the intrusion of the hospital, what had happened between them.

Chapter Fifteen

Christie had to write in the charts of the patients she saw, under Progress and Consultation, brief appraisals of the patients' attitudes; their states of mind. She walked into the nurses' station after she left Vendetti and pulled out his chart. All the other entries were medical. The last bore Dr Nippert's signature: '*Metastasis to bone and probably elsewhere. Radiotherapy might be palliative for bone pain, but advise against it. Patient in weakened condition.*' She picked up her pen and wrote beneath it, '*Patient seems more*

73

comfortable in mind and body. Will continue to visit with him.'

She replaced the chart and walked towards the elevator. Then her need to remain, for a while, with all that Victor had said turned her in the direction of the stairway exit. It was silent, empty, and cool. On some of the landings there were windows. She stopped on all the window landings to watch the changing aspect of city lights. They glittered and guttered like candles behind veils of snow.

From the safe bastion of the building she could pause to drink in the eerie beauty of the snow. But she was afraid to drive at night in storms. In the city streets, the neon lights were her guideposts. She did not live very far from Broadcliff. But if she had to drive outside the protection of the lights, an engulfing vortex whirled before her headlights, creating vertigo and a sense of suffocation. She was aware, after years of experience, of the symbolism of the snow. For a long time snow had been her own Wall of Death, unconquered and triumphant.

She descended the stairwell, remote now from the snow. The secret of Victor Vendetti opened inside her mind slowly, like a flower. She would try to hold it as a talisman against the dangerous enmity of death within herself.

When she reached the bottom of the stairwell and made her way to her office, the institution enveloped her again: the official smell of wood-panelled corridors, the purposeful gait of a few doctors and nurses moving along them. It was one of the quiet hours at Broadcliff. No patients were being transported for tests or surgery. No visitors surged through the doors. She pulled on her boots and her coat, slung her bag over her shoulder, and wrapped a muffler around her neck. The parking ramp was a dismal, echoing vault, frozen and full of shadows. She found her car and wound downward in the narrow space between the huge concrete floors.

When she emerged at the exit, the snow was moving horizontally, whipped by a vicious northwest wind. Even the flashing neon signs on bars and stores along her route blurred and faltered in the thick onslaught of the storm. She felt the old panic falling like an icy blanket over her face, making her feel blind and breathless. She grasped the wheel more tightly and tried to focus on whatever coloured lights beamed through the blizzard. There was not too much farther to go. But when she turned off the main street, the neon signs ended. Her own neighbourhood offered only the guidance of widely spaced streetlights. The funnel of snow in her headlight beams whirled dizzily. Suddenly, she was back in Canada.

She tried to pray to discard the panic. She tried her litany: 'I'm not in the wilderness. I'm two blocks from home, two blocks from shelter'; but her mind was in the grip of the snow. For a moment the gusts of wind abated. She came under the beam of a streetlamp, and saw the front of her apartment building. She turned into the driveway and stopped in the carport. Her body was shaking. She wound her muffler loosely around her face, the antidote to overbreathing. She sat in the car for a few moments, looking at the lights from the apartments. When her heart had quit pounding, she left the car and ran, against the wind, into the entrance hall. She fumbled with cold hands for her key and let herself in the door. Her apartment was on the ground floor. She flicked on the wall switch, which lit a small lamp by the window, and leaned back against the closed door. After a while, she discarded her wet coat and boots. She lit the gas log in the fireplace and a group of candles on the coffee table. She thought of Victor Vendetti and the carnival. The room gradually lent her its warmth.

She went into the bedroom and took off her clothes. She pulled a long coral robe out of the closet and wrapped herself in it. Then she went to the mirror and brushed her hair. Static electricity made it snap and stand out around her face like a haze of cobwebs. She leaned forward and gazed at her own face in the mirror. It looked empty and haunted. She had learned, with difficulty, not to be aware of her body. She felt that she had no existence – except in those moments when she looked at someone, or something, with love.

75

Today, as she had talked with Victor Vendetti, she had felt so alive. But the snow could obliterate her.

Snow. A thing in nature so fragile it disappeared in the palm of her hand, destroyed by the heat of her body.

She walked away from the planes and hollows of her face and poured a drink. Then she went in to sit by the fire. She wondered if Victor had ever sat by a fire. In Phoenix you would never need one. She sipped her drink and drifted into the terrain of the past.

Canada and its cruel winters pursued her with memories of her marriage, memories of alienation. She had imagined when she first knew Joe that the sensations she felt when he touched her body were the signs of love. In her early teens she had sat in dark movie houses with her girlfriends and watched love born between two people when they touched. Having first experienced the power of these feelings with Joe, she could not endure the touch of other men. They lived in the lush Ohio Valley and spent the summer of their meeting hiking along the river and in its surrounding hills and forests. A mystical connection she had always felt between herself and nature expanded to include Joe. Once, in her imagination, this tie had composed a holy trinity. Joe was not a talker. He was darkly handsome and very strong. His silence produced the effect of depth. The power of unconsummated sexual need held them together until their marriage over a year later. Both of them had been raised in strict religious families. Her parents had died in an auto accident when she was thirteen, but her father's sister, with whom she lived, kept a benign Calvinist eye on her. She was able to control her passion with her fear of pregnancy.

The honeymoon was spent in their first home in northern Canada, a log house at the edge of the forest preserve where Joe had found the job he had always wanted. He was in charge of all the facilities at the preserve. In summer he was busy overseeing the campers and tourist facilities. In the winter he went cross-country skiing with his buddies. In the spring he fished with them, and in the fall he hunted.

They were married in the fall. The honeymoon was a nightmare.

The ultimate union of minds and bodies Christie had envisioned was obliterated by an ugly reality she could never have foreseen. Joe told her with a lascivious glint in his eyes that his sexual initiation had taken place with a group of seasoned whores and a few of his more precocious buddies. Christie stood alone and naked, listening as he spoke, and was taken to bed by a stranger. He handled her body as if he were acting out the ritual of a massive dirty joke.

She lay awake in the night weeping silently and listening to him breathe. In the morning he left on a tour of the preserve. She was empty and ravaged. That autumn she walked through the forest in the rain. She watched rain drip from the last leaves of the trees and knew that the unity she had felt with Joe and the earth had been an illusion inside her head.

Eight miles from the forest was a small town. Christie combed the libraries and bookstores for minds that might explain the nature of illusion. When Joe left on his excursions, she read for hours. What made people believe that love existed? What was the source of the mystical bond between her and the trees, between her and the hills and the sand beach? She sensed that for Joe, nature was something to be conquered. For her, it was the home of a guardian presence which might reveal secrets and wisdom.

Through October and November she watched the leaves dry and fall. When the snow came, it was the shroud for a death within her. The insects petrified, and the gulls departed. Ice choked the lake. Finally, sky, meadow, forest, and water became a monochromatic grey-and-white. The earth was a sepulchre over which veils of snow moved hypnotically, a white smoke which suffocated by chill.

When Joe came home he crawled into bed beside her, groping for her breasts. She reached for him and pressed herself against him. His hot presence mitigated the terrible death within the snow. Although he made noises like a rutting animal, his eyes, in the light of their bedside lamp, squinted at her with amusement and a touch of contempt. An invisible company of whores writhed together within Christie's flesh as he savaged her.

Summer came and melted the walls of snow. The meadow

77

and shore creatures returned, and their voices called to her. She spent part of each day walking through the woods and fields or along the shoreline. One day while walking through the field she met a woman who lived in the nearest town and drove out to the country often to explore Christie's favourite haunts. They began to meet for coffee and discovered they had much in common. She understood Christie's sense of isolation. They shared the summer and the fall, and they shared their favourite books. Knowing Pam helped her to endure the knowledge that another winter was approaching. She had found a temporary escape from the alienation and hostility in her marriage. When winter came, it was gentled by the new relationship.

One day towards the end of November, after several weeks of anxiety, she learned from her doctor that she was pregnant. It was not a happy discovery. Only her body had been possessed by Joe. But a child must have a spirit. Could something alien to her be taking form within her body? Or could it be someone she would recognize as her own? She drove home from the doctor's office more aware of the dread within her than of the growing child. The answer, she knew, could come only from the response of her husband. Only he could confirm the pregnancy as a blessing, or label it a curse.

Joe had been gone on a deer-hunting trip. The news of the baby had to wait for his return. For three days her mind explored the possibilities. Would the knowledge that she was bearing his child change him somehow? She had read stories of men who seemed to develop new tenderness and sensitivity when they were about to become fathers. She waited, with fear and with hope, for Joe's return.

He arrived back from his trip late at night. She knew he was drunk when she heard him stumbling around the house. Once a chair crashed to the floor. He muttered a few curses as he climbed into bed, then slept heavily until morning. He offered no conversation at breakfast, answering her questions about his trip grudgingly. He had not got a buck. He rose from the table and went to put on his coat. She followed him and put her hand on his arm.

'Joe,' she began. She felt shy and frightened and awkward. 'I was in town ... Tuesday. The doctor said ... he says ... I'm pregnant ... about two months. ... We ...'

Joe wheeled around and stood facing her. His eyes raked her body slowly. His face broke into a crooked grin.

'Yeah?' he replied. 'Well, Mike tells me getting knocked up makes some women hot as pistols. Maybe I'll luck out with you for a change.'

She watched him, and a new emotion filled her, crowding out the old paralysis of misery and futility. For the first time in her life she felt hate; more than hate – rage, and she knew she was capable of murder. She stared at him with the new strength her hatred had bestowed; then she turned and went into the bathroom, locking the door behind her. She could hear him stamping around the house, mumbling to himself. Finally, the door slammed and there was silence. By evening she had packed everything that mattered to her – her books, her shells, and her rocks – and had moved temporarily to Pam's house. Pam had told her about an old doctor who was known to perform abortions in the nearest small city. She would go with her to make sure that there were no complications.

Christie made the appointment and endured the procedure with grim resolution. After it was finished, she felt relieved and cleansed. The abortion was not only the excision of a foetus. It was a brutal sacrament, the price she must pay to purge her body of any residue of Joe's possession of it.

The next day she phoned her aunt in Brandenburg and made arrangements to visit her. She wanted to put Canada and everything that could remind her of her marriage and its bitter termination behind her.

She departed from Pam's house in a light snowfall, which grew heavier as the day wore on. The road led into hilly country. At the summits of the hills the snow was driven by wind and obscured her vision. The farther she travelled from the scene of her marriage, the more vivid the lost possibilities of the child became. In the wild whiteness of the landscape, images of its face began to form. It looked at her with her father's eyes, with his smile. Her mother's long, fair hair blew about its face. It turned and gestured to her with her grandmother's incredible grace. It might have been ... *My God, it might have been* – gay and brave. It might have been kind.

Now she could not see the edges of the road. The snow swirled in circles against the window. The snow smothered, like a blanket stretching to infinity. The car was no longer moving. There was nowhere to go. The world was a white shroud covering the child. She put her head down on the steering wheel and waited to drift soundlessly into the shroud the snow had offered.

Now she shuddered and moved towards the warmth of the fire. The old horrors of Canada and her marriage were over. Only the snow could revive their ghosts. She walked over to the table. The candle flames played on her collection of shells and driftwood. They evoked the blessed days of summer when she had been in the sand, drunk with air and sunshine, her legs tired with long climbing. She picked up the shells and stared at the pale rainbow streakings in their contours. Then she looked at the driftwood. She had found a piece shaped like a gull, another like a porpoise. She loved their pale grey colour and the grooves the water and the sun had carved in their surface. The gull was her favourite. Once she had been lying on the sand, half asleep, and had opened her eyes to see a gull standing near her feet, looking at her, grave and beautiful and unafraid.

She picked up the driftwood gull and stroked it. On one of her walks along the shore she had seen a dead gull. Its decomposing body lay directly in her path, its soft white feathers, the dark wing tips, and the proud head intact. She had stopped to look at it, and tears had filled her eyes; not tears of pity, but of wonder. She looked at the ravaged, open flesh and saw the gull in flight, lifting its wings in an arc against the sky. When she had come to work at the hospital, she had seen in the most wasted bodies the history of their strength. Their secret and hidden grace, their true beginning,

80

all that had been consumed by cancer or by age, still hovered like a glow against the ruin.

One of the disciplines she had learned told her she must eat. She was not hungry, but she put two eggs in to boil, and dropped some bread into the toaster. She lit a gas jet under the teakettle.

She walked into the bedroom and turned down the bed. It was a bed she had purchased at the end of her marriage; not so wide as to remind her she was alone, not so narrow as to be uncomfortable.

She thought of Victor in his narrow hospital bed, alone. He had held Renée in his arms when she died. Renée had not been alone. She too had been afraid, and he had taught her courage.

Suddenly, without knowing why, she dropped to her knees beside the bed, put her head on her arms, and wept.

Chapter Sixteen

The morning after the blizzard, Victor awoke and saw a patch of sunlight on the bottom of his blanket. Since the beginning of the last February storms he had been too involved in his own pain and struggle to think of Stella. Now the comparative peace that had settled over his body was giving him time to reflect. He knew it was only a respite and that he would have to use its clarity well.

Yesterday a volunteer who delivered the mail had brought him a note from Stella. She had written: *Can't get to hospital till the snow lets up. Hope you liked the geraniums. They're still blooming. Hope the doctors get you better so's you can go home.'*

Poor Stella. She had got him in the middle of his downward spiral, just before he bottomed out. He did not know who had rescued whom. He was a has-been, but her whole existence had been misery. It was even possible that joining forces with a washed-up stunt man had been the high point of her life. Now his bouts with hospitals had made even the security of his comedown look good. The ramshackle house they'd lived in, part rotting wood, part tar paper, seemed like a haven of peace. Stella's soup and chili, the potatoes and hamburgers, his cheap whiskey glowing amber in the lamplight were homely and imperfect blessings. He looked back on them with an appreciation lent by distance. He knew he had been tougher on Stella as he grew more ill. He wondered if she would try to make it to the hospital now that the storms had stopped. If she did, he would make a real attempt to be nice to her. He should never have joined up with her in the first place. He had not cared much about his life by then. It was a relationship formed in emptiness.

Victor washed up when the aide brought his basin, and ate breakfast slowly, downing most of his cereal and milk. His mind drifted between his days of power in the carnival and his impotent life with Stella. The cancer now hung like a large, programmed finale over the incongruities of time. His life appeared lopsided to him. He believed that most lives were a mixed bag: up and down, a little success, a little failure. His had been sliced down the middle: the first half a Technicolor, wide-screen epic, the second a drab black-and-white, B-grade filler.

The girl came and took his tray. Charlie's I.V. had been removed earlier and he was down in X-Ray. Kiley was sleeping. Mr Danvers was reading again, and Harold breathed on like a lopsided metronome.

He wondered if Christie Wilson had made it home safely. She had left the hospital last night in the worst of all the storms. The priest had not appeared again. He might have been trapped in the snow. Washing and eating breakfast had tired him. His back pain was creeping up again. The cancer behaved like an animal at bay, like the tiger in the carnival acts he'd seen. It lurked quietly in a corner when cowed by the morphine. But tigers remained inwardly coiled and ready to spring the moment the trainer relaxed his vigil.

Suddenly, there were voices and footsteps. He recognized the predominant voice as Virgil Prince's. The doctor and his group entered the ward. He saw some of the faces that had surrounded him the day his chair-bed was dismantled. The two younger doctors followed behind Prince with the same blonde nurse. Preceding Prince was the green-eyed bitch dressed in white who had told him his knife was dull. His eyes explored her face. She was the kind of woman he had vigorously avoided all his life: an artist in treachery concealed behind a facade of reason. The facade did not confuse him. Her mouth recalled a few whores he had encountered who had a genius for delivering the secret pleasures of pain.

The sound of footsteps roused Martin Kiley from his nap. Prince led the group to his bed. Victor observed the look of eagerness on Kiley's face as he awoke and saw his doctor.

'Hi, Doc!' He rubbed his eyes and raised himself on one elbow. 'Got any news yet? Have you seen the results of the tests?' Kiley's eyes searched Prince's face. Victor wondered what the doctor's expression might reveal. His own bed faced Kiley's at an angle. All he could see was a rear view of Prince and a small portion of the bad side of his face. When Prince answered, his voice was warm and confident with the slight hint of a chuckle. He turned the pages of Kiley's chart and scanned them.

'Well, I can see why you've developed some troublesome new symptoms. The blood studies have turned up some evidences of metastasis. We also discovered a new lesion on the X-rays.'

Kiley's face clouded over. His voice became thin. 'What's a metas ... a metas ...?'

'Well, Kiley ...' Prince's voice became even more easy and relaxed. 'It means your disease has spread a little; but there's no cause for alarm.' The chuckle was audible now. 'We see this a lot with your type of disease. Fortunately, we don't have to depend on any one drug. We use combinations. They are very effective with metastasis of this kind.'

Victor was fascinated by the rich implications in Prince's voice. Confidence and humour glowed through its modulations. It was almost as if Prince had caught a few elves making minor mischief at the bottom of Kiley's garden and were wise to their ways. He looked forward to tricking them out of their silly projects. He had outwitted them an infinite number of times before.

There was a pause in the conversation. Kiley's face had passed from alarm into guarded relief. Prince handed his chart to the blonde nurse.

'You let *me* worry about it, Kiley. Meanwhile, you can leave here this afternoon if you want to. I'll have all your new medications ready. Brenda will drop them off to you later this morning.'

Kiley heaved a sigh of relief. 'Great! Okay!' He reached his hand out to shake Prince's, but Prince had already turned away and had taken another chart from a stack in the nurse's hands.

'Vic-tor Ven-det-ti,' Prince read aloud in a little singsong as he strolled across the room with the open chart. He glanced briefly at Harold; then he and his entourage grouped themselves around the foot of Victor's bed. The faces of the young doctors were bland and unremarkable. The face of the little blonde nurse was composed into the lines of professional distance, but there was a gentleness about her. His glance moved reluctantly to Dr Prince. The first time he had seen him, Victor had been consumed with pain and enraged to find himself helpless again, trapped in another hospital. He vaguely remembered the initial shock of seeing Prince's face. At first he had thought the deep discoloration was from burning, that the man had been in some terrible accident. Later he decided it was a birthmark, larger and more unusual than all the others he had seen. As he looked up at him now, he thought how curious it was that the marking covered almost exactly half of Prince's face, dividing it in a vertical line from his neck to his hairline. When he had first seen it, he had reacted with pity and a puzzling sense of kinship. Then Prince's dictatorial approach, his barely disguised contempt had cancelled out all sense of trust or empathy. The mask had now become, for Victor, part of the general aura of dread and distaste which permeated all of his encounters with Prince. The manner of this doctor's visits resembled more accurately a general flanked by his military aides than a doctor accompanied by colleagues.

Victor raised himself as far up on his pillows as he could. He lifted his sunken chest and his chin, summoning as much dignity as the anonymous hospital gown and his own weakness allowed.

Prince stood looking down at him. He looked at the metal-covered notebook in his hands and paged through it, appearing to study it, his face expressionless. Finally he spoke, in a lazy and negligent tone.

'I am pleased to see that you have settled into the structure of hospital routine. It is essential that you understand that we are calling the shots around here if you expect treatment for your disease.'

Vendetti watched Prince closely and listened carefully. He said nothing.

'The consultation I arranged for you with our radio-therapist has resulted in his advising against treatment. Nippert is a good doctor, but leans to conservatism. He feels you are too debilitated to be subjected to treatment. Fortunately, I am more aggressive in my approach to cancer – whatever the stage of its discovery. I specialize in chemotherapy, which can be adapted to treat a broad range of disease. We can use the chemicals in combinations tailored to your exact needs.'

Prince waited again. Vendetti still gave him his undivided attention but said nothing.

Prince snapped the metal chart shut with a sharp clank. 'We are studying the results of some blood work we did on you, Vendetti, and I want to get a scan to determine whether your weakness may indicate some bone involvement. Depending on what we learn in the next week, I am pre-pared to start you on a course of chemotherapy. We will hope it puts you into remission. The terms are these: You put yourself into my hands. No more theatrics. I run the show. You have not done well under your own steam. If you recall, before you were brought here, you were sick enough to collapse in a gutter.'

Prince turned away and pulled a handkerchief from his pocket. He raised one leather-booted foot and placed it on the plastic chair, carefully buffing some salt stains from the toe. Vendetti watched him for a moment, then glanced at the residents. The bearded one was looking over at Harold, whose breaths were becoming more laboured and dragging. Prince had finished with his shoe and returned his glance to Victor. Victor studied the faces looking down at him, feeling like a lone soldier facing the opposing army with an empty gun. He fixed Prince with a steady gaze.

'The chemotherapy is poison?' he asked. There were a few seconds of silence; then Prince shrugged his shoulders.

'All drugs are toxic,' he drawled. 'The purpose of the treatment is to destroy the cancer. The toxicity produces side effects, but normal body cells resist toxicity more than cancer cells.'

Victor listened to Prince and did not feel impressed. He wondered if a man with Prince's attitude could dispense anything but a further distortion of his person; poison not only his body, but his mind.

'I'll think about it,' he said, looking directly into Prince's eyes.

Brenda and Prince exchanged a swift glance.

'We will get test results in a week,' Prince answered. 'However, this hospital will not give bed space to patients who have refused treatment. It is an acute-care hospital. My speciality is chemotherapy. If you decide against it, you have no doctor.'

Vendetti's eyes turned steely. He felt an unnatural strength surging into his body. It rose in his loins and flowed into his arms and legs. He wondered if hate could heal cancer.

Virgil Prince turned and walked towards the door. Vendetti noticed, for the first time, that he moved with extraordinary grace. He could have been a good aerialist. The blonde nurse moved out of the room first. The tawny-haired one brushed past Prince, covertly grazing his arm with one of her breasts. It was not a gross act. She was modestly endowed. Prince's entourage was almost out the door, except for the bearded resident, who had not moved from the foot of Victor's bed. Suddenly he turned towards the door and called out, 'Dr Prince!'

Prince halted in the doorway and turned his head. The resident walked swiftly towards him, lowering his voice.

'The old man – he appears to be dead.'

Prince paused and glanced swiftly at Harold, then continued through the door.

'Check it out,' he called over his shoulder. 'We'll be down in the West Wing.' He walked out into the corridor. Dr Lindsay stepped over to Harold and felt his pulse. He put his stethoscope on his chest. The metronome had stopped. He hesitated a moment, then pulled the green privacy curtain around Harold's bed. .

Victor lay back on his pillows and waited for the resentment in him to recede. The last time he had felt this dangerous upsurge of anger and strength, he had tried to take on the whole staff. He felt more secure now, and a little stronger, but he knew better than to indulge his urge to retaliate. Also, before he was kicked out of the hospital, he wanted to see the priest and Christie Wilson again.

Two feet away from him, Harold lay dead. The silence behind the curtains attested to a toilsome achievement. Harold had earned whatever blessings an improbable Heaven could offer. The only other dead body he had lain this close to had been Renée's.

He shuddered and turned his mind away from the memory. He felt more comfortable in the room with Harold's corpse than with Prince and his medical team. He had forgotten how to pray, but he closed his eyes and sent some good wishes into the alien country of death.

There was some kind of chant a Catholic was supposed to say, a prescribed prayer for the dead, but he had forgotten it.

He lay thinking of the church of his boyhood; the deep, mysterious shadows in the high, vaulted ceilings above him and in the niches where the painted saints stood. He remembered the smell of incense and wine, perfume and sweat. He had shifted his knees around on the hard prayer bench and watched the hands around him as they fingered their rosaries. He had thought of the darkness and hardness as a repository for sin. People came to church bearing their woes, the sins they had already confessed and some they could never utter, and the woes and the sins were absorbed into the hard wooden benches and into the holiness of the shadows. When he was a child in church, he thought he had felt the presence of God when he looked into the faces of the devout who prayed and into the flames of the votive candles.

He heard the rumbling of wheels coming through the door and saw two attendants with a stretcher. They disappeared behind Harold's privacy curtains. There were the sounds of sheets and blankets being moved, some muffled bumping and whispering, and the cart emerged with its neatly wrapped burden and was pushed away. He heard the sounds of the bed being stripped. He rolled over and turned his face to the window. The brick wall of the West Wing was bathed in sunlight. He realized how long it had been since he had seen the sun. He heard light footsteps behind him, beside his bed.

'Good morning,' a voice said.

He turned and saw Christie standing by his bed with a wheelchair.

'How are you feeling today?' She touched his hand. Victor drank in her presence and smiled. She was wearing a tan sweater and pants under her white lab coat. 'I thought we could celebrate the sun by getting out of this room for a while. If I help you, can you climb into the wheelchair?'

Victor nodded. 'You're looking pretty this morning,' he said. It would be good to get out of the room, to be in a chair for a change. Maybe they could find a private place to visit, where Charlie, Kiley, and Mr Danvers couldn't witness every word they said. He pointed to the small clothes locker.

'Would you hand me my bathrobe out of there . . . and my slippers?'

Christie lifted out a rumpled and faded maroon bathrobe and dusted it off with her hand. It was a mess from his attempt to use it as a pad for his first bed on the floor. She pulled out some ratty felt slippers and helped him get his arms into the robe. Victor slid his legs over the edge, and she fitted the slippers over his thin, calloused feet.

'I'll wrap the blanket around your legs when you get in the wheelchair,' she told him. She moved the chair as close as it would fit. Victor slid off the bed and put his feet on the floor. He felt light-headed and wobbly.

'Lean on my shoulder . . . there. . . . Ease into the chair. . . . Good. You're all set now.' She lifted the blanket from the bed and crouched down to tuck it around his legs and ankles. Her hands were deft and swift. He caught a scent of some light cologne, like wet flowers. She stood up and rested her hand on his shoulder, squeezing it. The pressure of her touch warmed him. Her hand was very strong.

It had been days since Victor had moved farther than the space around his bed in an upright position. He felt as if he were barrelling down the hall on a bike. He gripped the arms of the chair with his hands and watched the walls of the corridor and the people in it pass at a dizzy pace. Actually, Christie was pushing him slowly.

Christie guided the wheelchair to a small alcove in the West Wing corridor. It was deserted. Sunlight poured through a floor-length window onto a sofa. Some large green plants lifted their leaves to the light.

Christie turned the wheelchair around so the sun would fall on Victor's back and legs. He leaned against the chair and closed his eyes for a moment, letting the warmth seep into his bones. The sun melted the tension in his nerves and muscles. It relaxed him almost as much as whiskey.

Christie took a seat on the sofa. She stretched her arms, took a deep breath, and sighed.

'It's heaven, isn't it? Once, when I had the flu, I moved out of a dark bedroom and lay on the floor in the dinette – like

89

you! – where there was a south window. The sunlight made me better.'

Victor watched a tautness in her face relaxing. Her eyes closed. She smiled and lifted her face to the sun.

'Did you have any problem getting home last night?' he asked.

She opened her eyes and looked at him. 'Well . . . not really trouble. I made it okay. There was a lot of wind.' Her face looked suddenly diminished, as if the sun had passed behind a cloud. It lasted only a moment. She looked up at him quickly and smiled, as if she had pulled a blind on the storm.

'After I got home, I turned on the gas log in my fireplace and fixed a drink. I felt very cosy.'

She leaned forward and put her chin on her folded hands. 'I watched the fire and thought about you and Renée,' she said. 'You had really just begun to tell me about her when I had to leave. What kind of a girl was she? What was she like?' Her eyes were very bright and seemed to reach for something she had never had.

Victor shut his eyes and summoned Renée's image. After all these years, more than three decades, he still saw her with a clarity presented by no other memory. He was old now; the proof confronted him in the sight of his body. But Renée never grew old. She had been arrested in time. Her body was still graceful and supple. Sometimes she stood with her booted feet planted wide apart, sleek knickers showing the curves of her hips and thighs.

She stood that way now, as he had seen her a thousand times. Her gloved hands were on her hips. Her dark auburn hair blew around her face, glinting in the sun. She grinned at him with a secret smile, her eyes full of messages she sent only to him. They had been rehearsing, drilling for the act. They had just wound down from the top of the wall. She had made a perfect stop just ahead of him and leaped off the cycle.

'Smooth?' she would ask, when he walked over and took her in his arms.

'The smoothest.' He pressed her against him, fitting their

90

thighs together. She was a creature of extremes. She could move with the grace and assurance of an angel, or freeze into silent withdrawal and fear. She was like a high-strung thoroughbred. Everything in her bloomed and flourished with the hand of a good trainer. At least he had caught up with her before she was ruined by a bad one. In the years since her death he had relived their time together endlessly, replaying every detail of their private and public lives. Those retained a colour and clarity which made the present pale and spectral.

Christie entered his reverie. 'Do you mind talking about it?' Her voice was soft and careful.

'No,' Victor answered. He told the truth. There was no one around anymore who remembered Renée, or who knew about the days when they rode the wall. He had lived with his memories the way the restless spirit of a dead man might reenter and inhabit the living places he had loved. His true life resided in the sepulchre of the past. He had unlocked that sepulchre when, for the first time, he spoke Renée's name aloud to Christie.

'No,' he repeated, 'to talk about it to you makes me feel more alive.' He waited a moment, looking into her eyes for signs that she understood. He was learning that her eyes had what must sometimes be an unfortunate transparency. Now they reflected the history of isolation in his statement. With Christie he was no longer a ghost.

'Please tell me about her,' she said.

He rested his head on the back of the chair, watching Renée's image come into focus again.

'I met her in the carnival, like I said. But when I met her she was an acrobatic dancer. She was more of a dancer than an acrobat.' He smiled, and laughed a little hoarsely. It was the first time Christie had heard him laugh.

'She was trained in ballet,' he said. 'She grew up in Paris and then moved to Frisco.' He paused again, and his expression hardened slightly. 'She met some guy who was a gymnast and had got into acrobatics. He persuaded her to leave her dancing and go with him. They joined up with a group of aerialists: you know – the guys on the trapeze and the high wires. They play in circuses, mostly.'

He watched Christie. She was absorbed in the story. He could tell. She wasn't just listening to be polite. When he paused, she waited eagerly for him to continue.

'Well, this guy she had taken up with and the gang of aerialists joined the carnival. The first time I saw her, he was putting her through her paces, and the head aerialist was with them. They were breaking her in to the wire. They had her on a wire about two feet off the ground.' He thought for a minute. 'Did you ever spend any time around horses?'

Christie shook her head. 'No.'

'Well, horses have sensitive mouths. That's why you guide them with a bit – a thing attached to the reins that fits in their mouths. A bad trainer will jerk a horse around. He'll try to mould it by intimidation and insult. I stood back and watched this guy – his name was Gustav – training Renée. She was graceful and strong, and she was sensitive, a thoroughbred if I ever saw one. He was handling her the way a bad trainer handles a horse. I watched them from a seat in the bleachers for a long while. Finally, she slipped. She fell and turned her ankle. "You don't listen!" he yelled. "You're moving like you had a stage under you. There's no stage, baby, only air!" She was embarrassed. I think she'd seen me in the bleachers, and the head honcho aerialist was laughing. But she was too proud to cry. I made a point of watching them from then on. I knew if he kept it up he would break her spirit. I watched him, too. Everywhere. He was a muscleman, one of those handsome macho types, and crazy about himself. His way was to find something beautiful and rare and own it by getting it off balance.

'One day Gustav was off bumming around with some of the guys in the troupe, and I saw Renée come and sit in the bleachers. I was getting my cycle warmed up for a practice. I waved to her so she'd know it was okay with me for her to watch. I did some fancy moves that day, knowing that I had her attention. From that point on, she was mine. It began slowly, but I knew she belonged with me the minute I set eyes on her. I only wish I'd been a big impresario in San Francisco instead of a death driver in a carnival.'

As Victor spoke, a ruddy glow invaded the paper grey of his face. His eyes, usually remote and staring, glinted and threw off sparks.

'How did you take her away from Gustav?' she asked, almost in a whisper.

'It didn't need much doing. I think she only got involved with Gustav in the beginning because he came on like a big man; then, after that, from lostness.'

'Did she have a hard time getting away from him?'

'After she left him, he came after her. But he only did it once. I wasn't afraid of him. Bullies can be handled once you have them tagged. I came back to the trailer one day and he had Renée cornered against the bed. It was too small to fight in there. Every time he went after me, I ducked and he went crashing into the walls. He cut his head against a metal cupboard. When he saw the blood, he went ape. I shoved him out the door on his back and grabbed a kitchen knife. The air was knocked out of him, and by the time he could focus I was on top of him, with the knife pricking his gullet.'

Victor stopped for breath. He hadn't done this much talking since before his lungs were shot. Christie was on the edge of her chair, her eyes wide and blinking.

'You stabbed him – with the knife?'

Victor leaned back and smiled. He was getting his wind back. He shook his head.

'The big ox was terrified of blood. When he felt the tip of the knife against his neck, he bawled like a baby. When I let him loose, he got up quivering like a tower of Jell-O and crawled back to his gang. He outweighed me by a third. Next day he packed up and left the carnival. He never would have made a good aerialist. He had no grace and no class.'

They sat back and looked at each other. Vic shut his eyes and turned his face to the sun.

'Feels good,' he said. 'You know what to do for people.'

'How long were you together?' she asked.

Victor didn't answer for a moment. He seemed lost in the

93

warmth of the sun and his own thoughts. Finally, he opened his eyes and looked at Christie.

'Two years.'

'When did she start riding the wall with you?'

'Not for about six months. She just luxuriated for a while. She did some work around the carnival – sold tickets once in a while, for something to do when I was working out. She was offered a job dancing. The manager wanted to replace his old "Little Sheba." I wouldn't let her dance in any carnival. Her style was opera house.' His mouth curved with a smile.

'What made her begin? How did she come to ride the wall at all?'

'After she got over her long hassle with Gustav, she began to feel a little restless. One day she asked me if I would teach her how to ride the cycle. "Maybe we could do the act together, Vic – a *pas de deux*!" She laughed. She used to love to throw French at me. She was really afraid in the beginning, but I encouraged her. I taught her how to handle fear. Before long, I knew it was an act that could go over big. She loved the speed and the audience excitement.'

Christie looked at Vic as if he were a magician. Vic felt some affirmation grow inside him.

'You really fitted together,' she said. 'You matched each other. I can see how it was.'

'She loved me,' Victor said. 'We had a fine life. We made forays into Vegas and Frisco. The carnival moved around, and we even travelled on our own. I was making plenty of money. I won even more in Vegas. Everything I touched turned to money, or love. Renée gave me luck. Some people carry grace like others carry poison. She showed me the high life, too – culture; fine restaurants, art galleries . . . and the ballet.'

He saved his breath for a few minutes. Christie's eyes looked wistful.

'Did you ever see the *Swan Lake* ballet?' he asked.

Her face became animated again. 'Once, when I visited in California. Did you ever see *Giselle*?'

94

'No. It must have been after my time,' he answered. He waited a moment, resting again. He had one more thing to tell her. He took as long a breath as he could manage.

'Renée danced the Swan Queen when she was a ballet apprentice, before Gustav. But I never saw her do it on a stage. One night in Phoenix we wandered onto the floor of the arena after the show was over. The place was deserted. It was only lit by the moon. I said, "Dance the *Swan Lake*." Well, she did it – more beautiful than in an opera house. There was no music. Only her body moving out there alone in the moonlight. The music was in her head. She knew it by heart.'

He bowed his head and closed his eyes, to dim the sunlight. Tears rolled down his face and fell on the maroon bathrobe.

'I never saw anything like it before or since,' he said. He wiped his eyes with the back of a gnarled hand. The old curse always crept into his finest memories. It was bad enough to kill, but to kill something rare, something wondrous . . .

Christie reached out, sensing the encroachment of some darkness in his mind.

'You really saw her. You *knew* her. She must have been able to know, to really know, what kind of woman she was . . . because of you.' She sat silently for a time, filled with the images of this rare, reciprocated tenderness. Then she leaned forward and touched his hand. She forced him to look at her and searched his eyes.

'How many women ever really know what they are like, even if they are beautiful and graceful . . . or brilliant? Someone who loves you can give you . . . give you your *self*.' She emphasized the last word, but her voice faltered. She said it in a whisper.

Victor absorbed her words carefully. He sat very quietly, looking at Christie with sharp attention. She had said something like that before. She had said Renée was 'lucky'. He had the strange sensation that his own history was shifting around inside him, as if the pattern of its meaning were being rearranged.

'Christie,' he said, 'I'm out of breath. I haven't talked this much for a long while. Tell me about you. Let me rest.'

'There isn't a whole lot to tell. I haven't had an exciting life, or anything.'

'You work here, with all these sick people. They die.' He looked at her with a question. She gazed back, waiting for him to say more. He picked up a different thread. 'Do you have a boyfriend?'

She shook her head. 'No. Once in a while I go out with somebody. There's no one special.'

'Does it make you – afraid – being with all these sick people, who die?'

'No. Sometimes – if I can't help them, if they want to get home and we can't get them home . . .'

He watched her for a moment and decided to go back to her private life. 'You were married. What was your husband like?'

Christie smiled. Then she laughed briefly, without mirth. 'He was big, athletic – a jock; the strong, silent type. When you were telling me about Gustav, I thought of him. Only he didn't try to train me for anything.'

'Did you fall out of love with him? Who left who?' Victor's eyes teased a bit.

'I left him,' she said in a toneless voice. 'I was very young when I married him.'

'Why did you stop loving him?'

There was a long silence. Christie looked down at her fingers and twisted them in her lap.

'He was a bowsman – an archer and a javelin thrower, among other sports. We were on our honeymoon, taking a walk on the edge of town. He had found a long, thin stick and sharpened it. He was throwing it at targets: bushes, pieces of paper, and things. He'd say, "See that yellow leaf?" and he would pierce it with the javelin.

'A grey cat stepped out of some bushes and trotted into the path about fifty feet ahead of us. He aimed and threw his javelin. He pierced the cat. She took a long time to die.' Her face looked suddenly older and empty.

96

'How soon did you leave him?'

'I stayed with him too long. It was over a year before I left. I was brought up with strict ideas about marriage. Leaving him never occurred to me as an option. When I finally left, it was a simple instinct for survival.'

'Did he throw his weight around with you?'

'He had a bad temper. But that was only part of it. We lived up in Canada, in a remote country town.'

'Were you afraid of him?'

'No. In the end, all I was afraid of was the snow.'

'The snow?'

'It filled the air. It surrounded me. It erased me. It was more real than I was.'

Victor thought of all the snowstorms since he had been at Broadcliff. Now the snow lay shining on the roof outside the window like a blinding platinum blanket.

There were footsteps on the asphalt flooring behind them. They turned around and saw Hugh.

'Hi there, man! You're up and around. That's good to see!' He smiled broadly at both of them.

Christie stood up and smoothed her hair. 'Maybe you can help me, Hugh. I have to get Victor to bed now. This is his first ride out of the ward that wasn't on a stretcher.' She put her hand on Vic's shoulder.

'Bed will feel good for a change,' he said.

Chapter Seventeen

Chemotherapy had always seemed to Christie to be a two-edged sword. During her time at Broadcliff she had seen many patients who had received the treatments in an early stage of cancer and had responded well. Some had bought precious years of time. On the other hand, she saw patients being treated when their bodies could no longer tolerate the chemicals. Side effects added to the trauma of their disease. The lives of these patients ground miserably on in a tangle of machines and plastic tubing. Many patients lapsed into coma with chemicals still running into their veins. Among other body-chemistry changes, the chemicals destroyed vital white blood cells. In order to determine the extent of the treatment's effect, blood samples had to be taken daily. After months of this, patients had few veins left that were usable for blood sampling. Their arms were a mass of bruises. The taking of blood became a dreaded daily torment. The complex artillery of medical technology aimed at preserving life managed only to prolong it. When remissions faltered and the terminal stage began, the artillery became a monstrous irony.

The morning after the blizzard, Christie was called to the room of a patient she had been visiting for several weeks. The lady had been treated for three years with various combinations of chemotherapy. Mrs Warsoski was a middle-aged Catholic lady with a devoted husband and a large group of children and grandchildren. She was very devout, keeping a votive candle burning constantly on her bedside table.

Father Franciscus had popped in one day, having seen the candle as he passed by on his rounds, and he and Mrs Warsoski formed a friendship. She had become more attached to him than to her parish priest, who still continued to visit her.

The day of her dying, Christie went into and out of the room checking to see if the family needed anything. Mr Warsoski had remained in his wife's room all of the night before. Her sons and daughters had come in relays throughout the preceding week, as her condition worsened. Now she was mostly unconscious, almost in a coma. Mr Warsoski called Christie into a quiet corner of the hall.

'She can't talk,' he said. 'She drifts in and out; sometimes awake, sometimes not. She wants to die now.' He was speaking slowly, with weight and emphasis on every word. But his face was puzzled. He placed a heavy hand on Christie's shoulder. 'She needs something yet. She can't leave. She is waiting for something. She was always like that when she was going somewhere. I would be starting the car and she would remember something unfinished, or left behind, that she had to run back for.' He paused a moment. 'Could it help . . .? Maybe she wants all of us here at one time, all together with her, like on a feast day, before she can go?'

He was the kind of absolutely simple, direct man who was accustomed to looking for what was most practical, most right in the nature of things. He was a farmer – at home with gestation and birth, with growing and dying. His youngest son, strong and muscular, with a tender child's face, stood beside him. All day the two of them had been raising Mrs Warsoski's pillow, turning her to make her more comfortable, or holding her hand.

'Has she had the sacraments recently?' Christie asked.

'Recently. But I think it is right to do it again. Now,' he said.

'Who is your priest? Can I call him?'

'She likes Father Franciscus, the Catholic chaplain from the hospital,' offered the son.

'Who of the family can be reached?' Christie asked.

'All of them,' said Mr Warsoski.

'Well, let's call them. I'll page Father Franciscus.'

Mr Warsoski looked confirmed. An expression of elation came over his face. In this most important transition – leave-taking – he wanted everything exactly right. It was the last gift he could bring his wife.

By 4 p.m., five sons and two daughters had gathered. Those of the grandchildren who were of an age permitted in the hospital sat in the waiting-room lounge with Christie. Father Franciscus walked out of the elevator. Christie observed him with interest. Under the black anonymity of his priest's garb, his body moved with grace and power. He had the gait of a man who walked on a rolling deck: feet well apart, and a heavy, firm step. His eyebrows were thick and black. Beneath them his pale blue eyes seemed almost fierce.

99

Mr Warsoski greeted the priest. They spoke briefly; then he beckoned to Christie and the grandchildren to follow them. The small procession moved down the hall to Mrs Warsoski's room. The sons and daughters stood close to the bed. Two of them held her hands.

Mrs Warsoski had been hooked up for weeks with a nasogastric tube leading to a machine that pumped fluid from her stomach. This was used to relieve pressure and nausea. It was a large plastic hose which distorted her face and came between her and her husband when he attempted to hold her. He walked into the room with the priest now, and quietly introduced him to Christie. Then he waved his arm around the room and said, 'Our children.'

Mrs Warsoski's eyes fluttered. It seemed she saw Father Franciscus. He walked to the bed and took her hand. Her husband walked around to her other side and reached past the pump and the plastic tubing. He bent over his wife and began to speak. Then he stood up and spoke to Christie in a gruff tone of appeal: 'Is there any way this thing can be removed – *now*?'

Christie looked around the room at the Warsoski sons and daughters. Then she looked at Father Franciscus. The Warsoski family was a study in sorrow and acceptance. Franciscus returned Christie's glance with his pale hawk's eyes. The bushy brows lifted in a gesture that said, 'Get it done.'

Franciscus had absolutely no authority.

Christie nodded and walked out of the room. She found the head nurse and lied. She said she had been authorized to tell her to remove the nasogastric tubing. Knowing that the doctor had approved Christie's presence on the Warsoski case, the nurse assumed it was by his authority, and she removed it.

Father Franciscus observed the removing of the tube with satisfaction. For the family it was a moment of quiet joy. Mr Warsoski held his untrammelled wife in his huge arms. Franciscus annointed her forehead with the holy oil and said a blessing. Then he read a prayer of celebration from the

100

Psalms. The whole Warsoski clan embraced and kissed their mother, one at a time.

'Kiss Mother good-bye, Mrs Wilson,' Mr Warsoski boomed in his great basso voice. Christie went to the bed and kissed her. Mrs Warsoski breathed a long, happy sigh and seemed to sink more heavily into the pillows. It was then 5 p.m. She died when it was dark enough for the votive candle to make a shadow on the wall.

Chapter Eighteen

The tests Virgil Prince had initiated to determine the extent of Victor's disease were done over a period of several days. Between Victor's trips to the X-Ray Department and the blood laboratory he lay in bed and dozed, or sat in his chair by the window watching the sweep of the snow.

Since the two windows of the ward faced the brick wall of the West Wing, no more than a sliver of sun ever lit the room, so either Christie or Mary often took Victor by wheelchair to the little sunny alcove. He was no longer in constant pain and had gradually begun to look around him and observe the activities and sights in the hospital corridors. Each day Mary walked him slowly around the room to help him 'get his sea legs again.' She told him it was important to move as much as possible in order to build up his strength.

As he lay in his bed between activities, he thought about Virgil Prince and what his tests might reveal. He weighed over and over again the benefits that the poisoning of cancer cells might bring him. If Prince could reduce the cancer in his body – perhaps even obliterate it – what price must he pay? What other parts of him might be destroyed?

Each time he saw Virgil Prince, his distrust of him increased. A gut instinct which had never betrayed him rejected Prince as a healer. His private vision of Prince was that of a bully: not the species he had known in the alleys of his childhood or the shadows of the carnival, but a bully of the mind. He wondered why Prince had chosen to specialize in cancer and suspected it had to do with his face. Each time Prince came into the ward, Victor watched and listened to him carefully. His talk sounded like a religious incantation. A blizzard of medical terms in the smooth velvet tones of Prince's voice hypnotized everyone. It was as if the high priest of some ancient faith were uttering spells. Something beyond the ordinary seemed to reside in Prince. The patient could only have faith that the high priest would hold death at bay with elixirs and potions of poison. But something in Victor remained unconvinced.

That morning, Mary wheeled Victor to the sunny waiting room. As they passed through the area of the nurses' station and the elevators, a young woman he had seen around the Unit came up and spoke to them. Mary introduced her.

'This is Kate McGowan, Vic. She's a good friend of mine, the hospital's Home Care Coordinator. She works in the same department as Christie.'

Kate's eyes sparkled. Her mouth curved in a grin. She had a lot of red, curly hair and the kind of face Vic associated with independence and wit.

'Victor Vendetti!' she exclaimed, as excitedly as if she were meeting a celebrity. 'Wow! Mary and Christie have been telling me about you. The stunt driver!'

Vic warmed to her enthusiasm, then felt suddenly embarrassed. Some nurses and residents had looked up from their business at the station and were eyeing him curiously. But the attention didn't seem to bother Kate at all. She reached down and shook his hand.

'It's an honour to meet you, Vic. I'm going to stop in some-time and try to pick your brain. I don't meet many daredevils around here.'

Vic smiled. 'Come anytime,' he told her.

'See you!' She made a little pirouette and bounced away towards the elevators, smiling and waving back at them as she went.

As they moved along down the corridor, they passed a room with a sign on its door saying 'ISOLATION' in red letters. A cart stood nearby with a lot of equipment stacked on it.

'Isolation?' Vic looked up at Mary and frowned. 'What is someone in isolation for? Are there contagious diseases on this floor?'

'No,' Mary told him. She guided the wheelchair to a position by the window where Victor could get the full heat of the sun on his shoulders. Then she sat down on a sofa facing him.

'The isolation here is *protective*. That patient had a course of strong chemotherapy which reduced his white-blood-cell count to a dangerous level. He has to be in as sterile an environment as possible. Everyone who goes in the room has to wear a sterile gown, mask, and gloves. There is no immune system – or not enough – left in his blood for him to fight an infection.'

She read the impact of her statement on Victor's face immediately.

'Will the white cells multiply again?' he asked.

'The doctor stops the chemo for a while, hoping they will. Some patients whose white cells have been knocked out get pneumonia or . . .' – she paused a moment, thinking – 'other things.' She felt she had said enough, perhaps too much.

'Is Prince his doctor?'

'No. Some other oncologist in town. Prince isn't the only one. Just one of the best-known.'

Victor sat quietly. He shut his eyes and let the life of the sun warm him and ease the tension in his back and neck. But behind his closed eyelids the world of the patient in the isolation room began to take form. It was a surrealist landscape of masked, gloved, white-gowned spectres. He thought of how precious voices must be in that room. They would be the only real life connection. All of identity would reside in voices. He kept his eyes closed and asked another question.

'Have you seen anyone whose white blood cells were low die from an infection?'

Mary struggled in her mind with her need to protect Victor.

'Don't be afraid to tell me, Mary,' Victor said. He opened his eyes and looked at her. 'Remember,' he said, putting a shade of teasing into his voice, 'I'm a famous daredevil. I rode the Wall of Death.'

Her lips curved in a smile.

'You don't need any diagrams, Vic. I've watched you after one of our walks down the corridors. You can put things together as well as I.'

Vic chuckled and stretched his arms above his head. Then he relaxed against the chair. 'The sun feels good,' he said. 'When I came into the hospital I didn't care if I lived or died, you know. My life hadn't been worth much for a long time. Now I can think of reasons to live. I've been lying there looking into the snow, looking at the walls, seeing myself different than before.

'I keep thinking of the chemicals, and my mind goes back to the *wall*. I keep trying to figure out why the threat of the chemicals is so different. Maybe it's got to do with *style*. But I got a notion it goes deeper.'

Mary reached out and took his hand.

'I can't help you, you know. I wish I could. I debate it in my own mind all the time. I've discussed it before with Christie and Kate. None of us – as much as we've seen and experienced here – know what we'd do if we got cancer.'

'My tests have all been done,' he said. 'Prince ought to have reports and a recommendation by the end of the week. I'll have to give him a decision soon after that. One way or the other, I'll probably be out of here.'

'You'll make the right decision for yourself, Vic. I know you will.' Mary smiled, and her eyes looked confident. She looked at her watch and stood up. 'We've got to go, Vic. They'll be bringing up lunch trays soon.' She turned the chair around and wheeled it into the corridor. They moved along swiftly, passing the door with its red isolation sign.

When they came to the lounge area near the nurses' station, they found a large Latino family gathered there. One

104

of the older women was weeping loudly and pleading in Spanish. One of the men stood up and waved his fists at the room in general.

'She wants to know where Isabella's doctor is!' he shouted. One of the nurses left the station and walked towards them.

Mary turned into the East Wing corridor and they reached the ward. Charlie had come back from the X-Ray Department. He waved at Vic.

'You're getting around pretty swift these days, Vic.' He winked at Mary and grinned. 'Pretty soon you'll be leaving us, like Martin did.'

Vic crawled into bed and watched Mary straighten his sheet and blanket. She tucked them around him and adjusted the pillow under his head.

'I hope so, Charlie,' he answered. 'I sure hope so.' He looked out the window and saw that the light of the sun had diminished. More snow was building in the west.

Chapter Nineteen

Christie was on her way down the stairwell to her office when she heard swift footsteps overtaking her. Someone was jumping down the stairs three at a time.

'Mrs Wilson!' a voice called out. She saw the long legs, white coat, and blond beard of Dr Lindsay on the landing above her. She waited as he quickly negotiated the last steps. His rush down the stairs seemed out of character. She had thought of him as rather stiff and noncommittal. He peered intently down at her through the steel rims of his glasses.

'I've only been on this Unit a couple of weeks, but I understand you do counselling and the residents can give you referrals if the attending physician doesn't object.' He paused for a moment, studying Christie a bit shyly.

'I just made the rounds with Dr Bracebridge, and he's admitted a woman I think you ought to see.'

Christie was touched that Lindsay had come to her despite how uneasy he seemed to feel.

'You've spoken to Dr Bracebridge about my seeing her?'

'Yes, but she was admitted for surgery ... a bad surgery. Cancer of the jaw. Bracebridge called in Dr Shank, and he did a jaw resection.'

He stared at Christie and blinked his eyes. 'She's ... well, she didn't sleep all night. Another thing: she has a low pain threshold. She has ... er, uh ... she's really addicted to high levels of medication.' Lindsay paused again and coughed slightly. 'I thought, since you were able to talk with old Vendetti when he was mad at the world ...'

Christie listened to him carefully and noted the controlled agitation in his voice.

'Have you talked with her?'

Lindsay looked surprised, then confused. 'I'm a doctor. We don't take courses in how to talk to people. Our job is to get them well.'

'And if they can't be got well?'

There was a moment's silence. Then Lindsay smiled slowly and looked directly at Christie. 'Look. I don't intend to work with people who can't get well. My time on Seven Main is strictly a tour of duty.' He took a deep breath, and his face relaxed. 'I'm going to be an obstetrician ... or a surgeon.'

Christie saw the relief in his face. He wanted to be a dealer in life or, at least, to fight death with a scalpel.

'Thank you, Dr Lindsay,' she said gently. 'I'll go see the patient.'

'She is in seven twenty-one.' Lindsay pulled a pink referral slip out of his pocket. 'There. It's all legal.' He smiled again. 'Let me know how it goes. Her name is Jackie MacDowell.'

Christie wound slowly down the stairwell to her office on the ground floor, folding and refolding the referral slip.

That afternoon as she walked down the corridor coming

from her first visit with Jackie MacDowell, she noticed Stanford Bracebridge talking to Dr Bernard Shank who was shifting his broad, athletic body impatiently, as though he had been stopped in mid-flight. Bracebridge was speaking, his voice low and urgent.

'Bernie, your patient in seven twenty-one has an extremely low pain threshold. She's been through a great deal of trauma. The analgesic problem, balancing the medications, is –'

Shank interrupted, leaning into his face. 'Yeah, I know. I know all about her pain threshold and her addiction level.' He scanned Bracebridge with one eyebrow raised. 'As far as I'm concerned, you can fill a fishbowl to the brim with any kind of pill in the drug bin and let her eat them like M and M's. She's a junkie, and she's not my problem.' He waved his arm in a gesture of dismissal, leaving Bracebridge standing in the hallway. The older doctor's eyes locked with Christie's for a moment. They were filled with grief and something like shame. Then he turned away and walked into the nurses' station.

Christie didn't trust herself to stay on the floor. She had seen something rare and touching in Jackie MacDowell. The woman had beauty and dignity despite her pain and drug dependence and knowledge that the tumour had metastasized. Christie moved quickly to the nearest exit, breaking into a run down the stairway. Her refuge in moments like these was most often the chapel.

The action of Christie's speedy descent kept all dangerous emotions in check until she reached the chapel. It didn't matter if someone else was there. In the Social Services compound she had to guard herself from tears and anger, but the chapel was a sanctuary for pain and grief. It was the refuge of the powerless. The pressure in her throat relaxed as she entered the door and closed it behind her. She groped her way to a bench and fell on her knees beside it, her head buried in her arms.

She did not know how long she cried. She knew she felt limp and cleansed after a while. She became aware of the

107

bench beneath her arms, its mellow scent of old wood, and the texture of the carpet beneath her knees. Once a patient had given her a poem about Christ, and some of its words had remained in her mind: 'I am the path. Put your feet upon My stones.' It had given her a sense of safety and protection to think of God as a support beneath the ground on which she walked. These thoughts came to her again out of the silence of the chapel. Then suddenly she was aware that she was not alone. Someone was moving along the aisle. She felt a hand on her shoulder.

'Christie.' It was the voice of Stefan Franciscus. The cloth of his black sleeve brushed against her arm, and she caught the faint scent of shaving lotion. She opened her eyes and looked at him. There were lines like small gashes just below the corners of his mouth, and deep lines around his eyes. He lifted her to her feet.

'Sit down,' he whispered. They sat on the bench together. Christie pulled tissues from her pocket and blew her nose. Neither of them spoke for a while. Finally Franciscus turned to her.

'Can you tell me what it is?'

She bit her lip and stared down at her hands. 'Cruelty. Coldness. Arrogance. I can't stop it. I can't change it.'

'Who has been cruel?'

'There's a patient I've just seen. Half of her jaw was excised. It's only mutilated her. The cancer has proliferated. The surgeon doesn't give a damn.'

'Can you do anything for her?'

'We talked. Well, we actually *wrote*. She can't speak. I prayed with her. I'd never done it before. I . . . I don't really know God. I suppose it helps that I'm there. That I keep seeing her.'

Franciscus was silent. He stared ahead of him, past the velvet-draped wall. Christie turned to him, speaking earnestly – almost pleading: 'It's like digging out a bombed city with a teaspoon. It's like being on a battleground with wounded everywhere, and while you bandage them they are being wounded again.'

Franciscus watched her face as she spoke. Released from its tension by the weeping, it seemed young, but the legacy of age already resided in the eyes. He heard her voice again. She was speaking passionately.

'They are subjected to painful tests and surgery when they are nearly dead, to chemo when it compounds their misery. They are being tortured under official sanction.'

Christie searched his face. 'Have you noticed their eyes – the eyes of the patients? There is shame. Once a man said to me, quite humbly, "We who are *inmates* here ..."!' She stopped. She was weeping again. Franciscus spoke earnestly.

'I have thought about it in my room at night. I think about it as I drive between the church and the hospital. How could these doctors go on experimenting so single-mindedly if they saw individual persons instead of battlegrounds?'

Christie thought of Nippert and Bjord. 'Some of them can. Some of them suspend the battle if it is destroying the person.'

'Then thank God for them. They are rare.'

Christie looked into his eyes. She saw their fierceness and their gentleness and the history of many wounds.

'God has stopped speaking, hasn't He? He doesn't speak clearly anymore, the way He did to Moses or Paul?' Christie paused a moment, then asked in a whisper, 'Do you ever hear Him?'

Franciscus focused his eyes on the wooden cross on the altar. Several moments passed before he answered.

'Yes. Sometimes in the silence after my prayers. Sometimes in the words of others and in events. In my failures ... and my losses.'

Christie's face retreated into her own thoughts. Tight lines of bitterness had formed around her mouth. She began to speak again, almost to herself.

'So much of the treatment they give dying patients is useless. It gets in the way horribly, like Mrs Warsoski's tubes. It is more humiliating than helpful. It prevents them from living out their lives with the people who are important to them. There is something about dying that I sense is ...

109

is . . .' She paused and frowned, looking past Franciscus at an image in her mind. 'Well, it's like the last weeks and months of gestation. As important as being born. I'm afraid that all the useless treatments and the mental distortions they cause will abort this gestation.'

She saw that Franciscus knew. His eyes had locked with hers in an understanding too profound to be translated into words.

She needed to tell him something more.

'If God has ever spoken to me, He has spoken through things and beings: Gulls. The shapes in nature, and in people who have passed through my life.'

'Have you ever read Eliade, Christie?'

'No.'

'Well, he would understand what you are describing. He would tell you that at those times you are living in sacred time and walking in sacred space. Sometimes we move on holy ground when we are not aware of it. It is a thing I have to remind myself of.

'When I find myself angry with the Shanks and the Princes, I try to remember that they are not the source of the evil, only its instruments. There is a spirit which is the source of wickedness. It often uses people who have attained great personal power. If you understand that, it will keep you from being overwhelmed by them.'

Franciscus watched her face as she absorbed and weighed his words. He waited until she spoke again. Her voice was a whisper, but it was hard with the edge of urgency.

'The damage is there even if men are only instruments. What can you do with the anger? How do you live with the grief?'

He seemed to draw into himself the pain behind her questions. He spoke gently, putting weight into each word.

'Anger and grief will destroy you unless you can use them. They must be transformed. Christ is the Alchemist who can change lead into gold.'

He leaned forward now and looked into her eyes. 'Christie, you had the courage to pray for Jackie. Do it for

110

yourself. Ask God to transform the grief, the anger. Consign it to God, who can transform it into a blessing. That is what is meant by salvation.'

Christie was struck with this new meaning of the word 'salvation.' Franciscus' definition absolved it of its offensive images. The word had always evoked fear and the sense of punishment. She thought of her own sin, hidden and silent in her for years.

He reached for her hand and opened it with his fingers. 'The teaspoon you mentioned, Christie: bless it every day. It is better than empty hands.'

Chapter Twenty

Virgil Prince sat at the desk in his Broadcliff office waiting for Brenda to arrive so they could begin their rounds. He sipped a cup of coffee and looked down at a bleak view of the city with distaste. He and his wife usually flew to Jamaica every year at this time. Anyone in Brandenburg who could afford it took his vacation in winter and went south. This year he had lied to his wife – cancelling the trip, he claimed, because he was unable to find someone to cover his practice. The truth was that however bleak he found Brandenburg in winter, Jamaica without Brenda would be bleaker still.

Prince's wife, Dottie, had been terribly disappointed. Guilt nagged at him as he shifted in his chair and lit a cigarette. He had been sitting there for an hour going over the Vendetti test results. There was enough artillery contained in their contents to frighten the most arrogant cancer victim into a quick decision for *any* treatment. Vendetti's lung cancer had definitely spread to the bone. From there it would proliferate to other vital areas. He would offer Vendetti a combination of drugs that should

111

forestall such a spread. The treatment would make him sick as hell and might kill him, but there was a chance of a temporary remission.

Prince reviewed the case in his mind. Vendetti had become a model of decorum since the fiasco with the knife. But his attitude had created in Prince a low but constant level of anger. He had seen patients demur and ask many questions when they were told what their options were. But every patient he had ever handled, except Vendetti, had immediately assumed an attitude appropriate to his or her helplessness. When he confronted his patients with the facts, they looked up to him with a respect that approached awe. With more or less alacrity, they put themselves into his hands. He was their only hope of rescue.

Although Victor Vendetti had been disarmed and disciplined, Prince sensed that a secret arsenal still existed within him. Its undercurrents gave him the uneasy sense of being slightly off balance in each encounter with Vendetti. The situation puzzled and enraged him. It also added strength to his resolve. Vendetti had metastasized cancer. He was as weak as a cat and had no status socially or financially. Prince had, in the last week, enumerated these factors to himself like a devout Catholic fingering his rosary. Prince could present Vendetti with a sheaf of documents confirming that the cancer had spread, show him where it had spread and prove that it would spread more. Unless the man was insane, he would abandon whatever crumbling fortification he hid behind and surrender like the others. Whatever else Victor Vendetti might think, at the centre of his being must be knowledge of his own mortality.

Prince stood up and jammed the test results into their manila folder. He was pouring himself another cup of coffee when the door opened and Brenda walked in. She was wearing a long coat with a little hood rimmed in black fur. Crystal droplets of melting snow glistened on the fur and on her dark eyelashes. She smelled of cold, clean air and some delicious perfume. He put the hot coffee down on his desk, walked across the room, and pushed her against the wall, holding her there with his thighs. The hood slipped down, and he saw she had gathered her hair into a loose knot at the back of her head.

'Damn you!' he breathed against her hair. 'If it weren't for you I'd be out of this shitty climate, lying on the beach.' He moved his lips along her neck, nipping the soft flesh with his teeth.

Brenda raised her knee and moved him back by pressing it against his groin. 'Don't blame it on me,' she laughed and wriggled out of his grasp. Prince watched her as she removed her coat and hung it in a small closet. She slipped her long legs out of the knee boots and tied on white nurse's shoes. He began to feel less dragged out by the winter gloom. It was ridiculous, he told himself, to bother himself about an ass like Vendetti.

Brenda stood up and flashed her dimples. She smoothed her uniform over her slim hips.

'Is there a big agenda today? Are we still planning dinner together tonight?'

Prince kissed her on the lips and whispered against her face, 'At the Danville Inn. I reserved your favourite room. I told Dottie there was a late tumour conference.'

Brenda caught up a loose strand of hair and adjusted it into her knot. 'Good. Where do we begin?'

Prince retreated from her body, recalled to the challenge at hand.

'With Vendetti. I've got his test results.' He opened the door and they walked into the corridor. He waved the manila folder. 'Serious bone metastasis. I expect to start him on the protocol today.'

They matched steps and headed for the elevator, being careful not to touch each other. While they stood waiting for the doors to open, Brenda looked at Prince with the expression she reserved for about-to-be-confided secrets.

'I heard something about Vendetti that isn't in his chart,' she purred. 'Guess what his occupation used to be.'

'God knows,' Prince mumbled. They entered the elevator. 'He was a *stunt man*. A *death driver* in a carnival!'

Prince raised an eyebrow. The news was somehow disconcerting.

Victor had spent many hours mulling over all he had seen on the Cancer Unit. The patient who had affected him most profoundly was the one he had never seen: the man who lay behind the closed doors of the 'isolation' room. Father Franciscus had come to visit him again. He had made no attempt to preach to him or convert him. He had chatted with him quite easily, not with the attitude of an authority, but as an equal. Because of these things, Victor felt he could confide in him. He told him his dilemma concerning Virgil Prince and the chemicals; his conflict between his desire to live and his fear of what chemotherapy would do. Franciscus shared his concern. They discussed it at length. When he left, he told Victor he would pray for him to get the right guidance.

Victor had been dozing when he heard footsteps and the clank of the metal chart covers. Prince and Brenda had been joined by Dr Lindsay, and the trio came immediately to his corner of the room. Prince walked over and seated himself in the vinyl-cushioned visitor's chair by the window. Brenda and Lindsay remained standing at the foot of the bed. Lindsay handed one of the charts to Prince, who opened the manila folder and unhurriedly filed Vic's test results into it. Finally, he looked up and smiled. His attitude was smooth and low-key.

'How are you feeling today, Vendetti?' he inquired pleasantly.

Victor studied his face. Virgil Prince was always a man of great presence, but the sudden absence of his air of cold authority was puzzling.

'I'm pretty good,' Vic told him. 'A lot better than when they brought me in here. The pain medication – and the rest – has helped.'

Prince began to page slowly through the chart, pausing to read entries here and there. His mouth twisted to the side in a little smile.

'We're happy to hear that. Unfortunately, you had gone for some time with untreated disease and had become very weak.'

Vendetti looked up at Brenda and Lindsay, who watched expectantly. For a moment, he felt again the thrill of entering the arena. He coughed and took a sip of water.

'Have you got the results of my tests yet?' he asked.

Prince's tone was casual. 'As a matter of fact, I have spent a good deal of time going over all the reports this morning.' Prince paused and leaned his head against the back of the lounge chair. He pulled a pen out of his pocket and tapped a little staccato on the metal chart cover. His eyes explored Victor as if he saw him for the first time. 'I must say you are an extremely fortunate man, Vendetti. Your collapse in the street brought you to an acute-care centre where your problems could be diagnosed and where the most advanced medical treatment is available.' Prince's expression projected heavy concern. .

Vendetti leaned towards him. 'What do you know from the tests?' he asked.

Prince referred to the contents of the chart.

'The bone scan proved to be most productive. It revealed metastasis which is quite extensive. All untreated malignancies spread. It is regrettable that your lung lesions went untreated, and it is imperative that we begin treatment without delay.' Prince waited for Victor to absorb his pronouncements.

'The cancer is in my bones?'

'Yes. The scan was very clear.'

'And you say you have a treatment for that?'

Prince's face relaxed into a smile. 'Vendetti, there are plans on the board for Broadcliff to become a comprehensive cancer-care centre. I am waiting right now for confirmation of a grant from the Federal Government, which *I* will be administering. Brandenburg will have cancer facilities as fine as any in the country. We already have the finest diagnostic equipment. The most advanced chemical formulas from the research laboratories will soon be

115

available to me. Right now there is a protocol for every stage and combination of cancer invasion. We can begin your treatment *today*. I don't want to waste any more time.'

Victor listened intently, nodding his head from time to time as Prince covered his points. When he had stopped speaking, he lay back against his pillows and sighed.

'It looks like I landed in the right place. You got all the bases covered and you sure know your business.'

For the first time, Prince threw Brenda and Lindsay a quick glance. Then he looked back at Victor and waited for his next statement. Victor had turned his head towards the window and was staring out at the brick wall and a patch of dark sky that was visible between the ramparts of the hospital. He seemed to be lost in his own thoughts. Prince cleared his throat.

'We would like to begin your treatment with some intravenous injections of a new drug combination. It is administered slowly over three days and must be done in the hospital. If everything goes well you can go home after that, on a medication you will take by mouth. The treatment involves the same procedure repeated monthly.'

Vic turned from his introspection. He looked into Prince's eyes. 'I'm not sure whether I want any treatment,' he said. 'I haven't seen anything here to convince me that getting the chemicals would make me feel better. I have no doubt that your chemicals can kill cancer cells, but what will they do to *me*?' He looked around at all three of them. Lindsay's blue eyes blinked and glittered over the thin rims of his spectacles. Brenda and Virgil Prince glanced at each other. Then Prince returned his eyes to the subject.

'The purpose of medical treatment is to improve *the quality of life*.' There was a controlled edge in Prince's tone – a controlled, razor-sharp machete edge; then it blurred into easiness again. 'If I am to understand you, that is what you are driving at, Vendetti.'

Victor closed his eyes and folded his hands over his chest. A little smile played around his mouth.

'The *quality of life*. That has a good sound. . . . That's what

I hope to get and hang on to . . . as long as I'm breathing. I've had some time to lie here and think – and observe, Dr Prince. What I have to decide is too important to hurry. I want to be *sure*. It took a lot of poison to grow this cancer – inside poison, out of my own mind and feelings. I got to weigh out whether I believe more poison is going to save my life.'

There was a long silence. Prince didn't move an eyelash. Finally, he stood up and pushed back the visitor's chair with his foot.

'As you like, Vendetti.' His voice sounded neutral now, almost bored. 'You realize I am a busy man and have many other patients waiting. They all have critical problems. We will need your decision soon. *Quite* soon. Would you like to state when you feel you will complete this process?'

Victor pondered for a few seconds. 'Tomorrow,' he said. 'I'll know by tomorrow.'

Prince made no reply. He and Brenda moved towards the door and disappeared into the corridor. Lindsay paused on his way out and turned to Victor. He gave him an enlisted man's salute and went to join Prince on his rounds.

Chapter Twenty-One

Stefan Franciscus awoke in his small room at St Thomas' rectory with Victor Vendetti on his mind. He decided to try to see Victor first today. If Victor had been taken somewhere for tests, he would visit other patients, then double back and try again. He got out of bed, opened the window, and did his workout. Then he showered, shaved, and knelt by the bed to say his morning prayers. Lately he sometimes prayed aloud, as if it would enforce or make more immediate the channel between himself and God. Today he asked for the grace of an opportunity to talk privately with Vendetti. The sense of

Victor's captivity had grown oppressively within the priest's mind. Somehow, a liberation of Vendetti's spirit must be achieved. It must be achieved within, and in spite of, the bondage of his disease, and whether or not he decided on treatment.

As he drove to the hospital, scenes of the prison camp in Luzon mingled, as always, with problems of the dying and their families. He was amazed at the power doctors wielded over cancer patients and their families. He had seen desperate people waiting in the corridors of Broadcliff for hours in order to have a few moments of conversation with the doctor treating their dying wife, husband, parent, or child. Sometimes when they found the doctor, he stood on one foot giving minimal response to their questions, irritated at being interrupted on his rounds. The expressions on the faces of the patients and their families recalled to him the humiliation and the suffering of prisoners.

He parked his car in the ramp and proceeded into one of the turret stairwells leading to the hospital. At the lobby level, he parked his storm coat and boots in a cloakroom; then he took the elevator to Seven Main. It was a good time to catch Victor, he thought. He should have had his lunch. Tests were usually scheduled in the morning, and barring other visitors, he should find him alone.

When he walked onto the ward, the television was going. A hospital soap opera was engrossing the two men across from Victor. On the screen, a clear-eyed, handsome young doctor with a pained expression was leaning into the face of a lovely lady who lay in bed with her eyes bandaged. Violins played on the sound track.

Franciscus went to Victor's corner by the window and saw that he was sleeping and his face was peaceful. Weight loss had made all the bones prominent. As he studied Victor's features he thought of Thelma Zalenski, and a strange awareness intruded itself into his mind. He now carried with him the presences of all those patients he had known and who had died. They filled his consciousness like an invisible but eloquent congregation, quietly entering each new

118

situation he confronted.

Franciscus was torn in his mind as to whether he should disturb Victor. He thought of his agony the night of their first meeting. His logic told him to tiptoe away and let the man sleep. But intuition told him to awaken Victor. He sat down on the side of the bed and put his hand lightly on Vendetti's arm.

'Victor,' he called gently.

Vendetti's eyes opened and shut a few times, fighting the fog of sleep. Then he recognized Franciscus and came alert.

'Father. How long have you been here?'

'Just a few minutes. I almost went away and let you sleep.'

'No ... no. I'm glad you woke me up. I've got plenty of time to sleep ... later.'

Franciscus moved off the bed and took a seat on the small plastic chair. 'How are things going?' he asked.

Vic looked past Franciscus and his body tensed. The priest turned around and saw two nurses in the doorway: a tall one with long, streaked hair and a small blonde behind her. Behind them came Dr Prince and two residents.

'Burns,' Prince addressed the rearguard. 'We want some more blood studies if we begin the chemo today,' he said.

The young doctor nodded. The group arranged itself around the foot of Victor's bed.

Franciscus stood up. He inclined his head towards the group in a nod of greeting. 'Father Franciscus, Chaplain,' he said. 'Would you prefer I leave? I can come back. ...'

Virgil Prince waved to him to sit down. The group's eyes were all on Victor. No one spoke immediately. Then Prince opened a metal-covered patient chart and fingered through it.

'Well, Mr Vendetti, have you been able to reach a decision? Do you wish to accept treatment for your disease?'

Victor coughed and spat into some tissues. 'Yes,' he said. 'I don't want it.'

Dr Lindsay, Dr Burns, and Brenda exchanged glances. Then they all looked at Prince. His face was unreadable, but a slight twitch appeared at one corner of his mouth. The blonde nurse stared at the blanket on Victor's bed.

'Have you discussed this with your ... family?' Prince asked.

'I haven't got any family.'

Prince riffled through the pages of the chart to its beginning. 'A Stella Wassler is listed here as your next of kin.' He looked at Victor no more intently than before, but his voice undulated ever so slightly around the 'next of kin.'

'She's my housekeeper,' Victor answered evenly.

There was another pause.

'Oh,' Prince said. The metal chart case clanked shut. He handed it to the blonde nurse. He sighed slightly.

'That is regrettable. You are not a well man, Vendetti. I hope you have sufficient backup at home to carry you through whatever rigours result from your decision.' He waited a moment, looking down at Victor impassively; then he turned and led the procession towards the door. He paused before he exited. The entourage paused with him.

'One word of warning, Vendetti. Unless you change your mind and opt for active treatment, and a call is put in to my office to that effect, the Emergency Room of Broadcliff has orders not to admit you here as a patient. If I were you, I'd stay out of the streets.'

The group filed out through the doorway. Brenda remained behind. She walked over to the foot of the bed.

'You can be kept here no longer than a week. I would advise you to make your arrangements for transfer to wherever you're going as soon as possible.'

Franciscus watched her with interest. He did not associate her manner with nursing. She functioned more like a deputy – or a warden. She was a handsome woman. She smiled at him now, flashing even white teeth.

'Thanks,' Victor said. His face was impassive, but his eyes glittered. 'I plan to check out of this hotel well before the deadline.'

The nurse gave him a level stare. Then her eyes swept over Franciscus. She embraced her manila portfolios and swished out of the room to join Prince and his entourage.

Franciscus' eyes searched the room and its occupants, coming to rest on the drama enacted on the television screen. He watched it for a few seconds. The actors were building their climactic scene. The priest looked at Victor and began to speak. Victor interrupted.

'I know a place we can go, Father. I need to talk to you.'

Franciscus observed with pleasure the look of authority on Victor's face. It was an authority almost matching the power of his doctor – or his ex-doctor. He had been amazed at the coolness and confidence of Victor's response to Prince, contrasted with his utter helplessness the night of the manacles.

Victor leaned forward in the bed. 'Would you ask Mary, if you can find her – or the black orderly, Hugh . . . or the nurse – her name's Ann . . .' Franciscus saw him clocking off the roster of a small group he could trust.

'. . . Ask one of them, whoever you can find, for a wheel-chair. We can go down to a corner in the West Wing I know about.'

Franciscus stood up. 'Fine,' he said. 'I'll get the chair.'

Victor rested for a few minutes with his eyes closed. When he had told Prince he would give him a decision today, his mind had still been rocking between hopes for a possible benefit from the drugs and his fear of their consequences. But during the night he had had a strange dream. As it opened he had been young again and about to begin the evening performance of his act on the wall. It was in the time before Renée, and he was alone in the pit of the arena.

As he began his climb upward on the wall, other hands grasped the wheel. His own hands turned numb and paralyzed. They dropped uselessly to his sides. The strange hands guided the cycle upward evenly at first, but as they neared the rim he felt the cycle shudder violently. Then it plunged to the bottom of the pit.

He found himself aware and able to assess the damage. The vehicle was, incredibly, undamaged, but his own body lay disconnected around the arena: headless, legless, destroyed.

He had awakened in a cold sweat and had turned on his

night light. He seldom had nightmares, and as soon as he had cleared his head the sense of horror receded. A new feeling of calm came over him. It brought the same kind of comfort he felt in the presence of Christie and Father Franciscus. He lay awake for an hour or so warmed by this feeling of protection and peace. He began to realize slowly that the dream had come as a gift. The debate could be closed. He had been guided to the answer he would give Virgil Prince.

Now, just when he needed to talk to him most, the priest had arrived to visit. He leaned over to his locker and opened the door. He could just grasp the corner of his bathrobe. He pulled it over onto the bed. He would let Franciscus get his slippers. He still didn't trust himself to stand alone. He wished he could pray. He would have to trust Fransiscus to do his praying for him. God – the thought filled him with an uneasy nostalgia – had sent him a fine deputy. He needed a high-class prayer-maker to intercede for him. He needed two miracles: a surge of strength for a week or two, and something else, which this priest alone could help him to define.

His life was in motion again. He leaned back against the pillows. Small whispers of the old vitality moved along his nerves: a vitality he had known only when he grasped the handlebars, fighting the wind, holding the cycle tenuously on the rim of the wall. Riding the rim was the ultimate 'high.' Only a supernatural grace had ever informed him when the moment had come for bottoming out.

Mary helped Franciscus find a wheelchair. He arrived back at the ward to find Victor sitting on the edge of his bed with his bathrobe over his shoulders.

Franciscus slipped the sleeves onto Victor's arms.

'My slippers are on the floor of the locker,' he said.

Franciscus fitted them on his feet and helped him into the chair. He wrapped the blanket around his legs.

When they were rolling along the corridor, Franciscus asked Victor if he'd like to go down to the chapel. 'It's usually empty,' he told him. 'It's not fancy, but it's quiet and carpeted.'

'Okay,' Vic answered. 'I'd hate to tell you how long it's been since I went to church.'

They arrived at the elevators and caught one ready to go down.

'This is an interdenominational chapel,' Franciscus told him. 'It has a kind of anonymous feeling. I go there sometimes when I want a good place to think.'

They reached the ground floor and covered the short distance to the chapel. Franciscus opened the heavy carved wooden door. The chapel was empty. It was in the older section of the hospital and evidenced the luxury and formality of another era. There was a hushed, cushioned atmosphere – very welcome after the echoing cacophony of the wards and hallways of the East Wing.

Franciscus parked the wheelchair in an aisle and sat down on the bench beside it. Victor leaned back quietly for a few minutes and looked at the carved oak table at the front. It stood before some dark red velvet curtains and was bare, except for a wooden cross standing in its centre. Franciscus watched Victor as he looked at the cross. He seemed to be deep in thought.

'A cross without Christ's body,' he said, finally.

'Yes. This isn't a Catholic hospital. I understand that Protestants feel the empty cross symbolizes that Christ is now resurrected. They seem to put less emphasis on the crucifixion,' Franciscus commented.

'I guess I'm not even a Christian. I don't have any trouble believing somebody could be crucified and die, but I can't imagine a dead body being resurrected. I wish I could. I can't imagine heaven, either, or eternal life.'

Franciscus thought about the statement in silence. He himself was not sure what heaven would be like. There was a section in a symphonic poem called *Psyché*, by César Franck, which expressed his own concept of heaven in sound. The music brought tears to his eyes whenever he heard it. It conveyed the vision of a magnificent threshold, a door opening to infinite movement and possibility. For a few moments, as the music lived within him, the anonymity of the chapel was transformed.

'Father,' Vendetti said, 'I've never been religious. I haven't gone to Mass since I was a young boy. That's why I have to talk to you.' He paused. 'I . . . I'm not sure if there is any God, Mostly, I think there isn't. And I can't imagine what heaven is like.' He watched the priest anxiously, measuring his response. Franciscus rubbed his hand over his chin. His eyes narrowed. He seemed to be considering.

Then he asked, 'Have you ever felt really "up", extremely happy and full of joy, at some time of your life? – as if you could say to yourself, "This is heaven"?'

Conflicting emotions played across Victor's face, like ripples of wind disturbing water.

'Yes. Yes, I did. I felt superalive, superaware, strong – like I could move a mountain. I was in love and she loved me.'

'You felt vital, strong: as if you were opening up into all kinds of possibilities?'

Vic leaned forward, his eyes probing the eyes of Franciscus. 'Yes,' he said. 'Exactly.'

Franciscus appeared to be reaching towards some picture in his head. 'I think heaven is a door opening up into unimaginable newness.' He held out his hands and curled the fingers as if grasping something unseen. The timbre of his voice became richer. 'I think it is real. I think it has structure and substance.'

Now he looked at Vic and dropped his hands to his sides. He made a gesture of futility.

'I can't diagram it. I have never seen the details.'

Victor reached over and put his hand on Franciscus' shoulder. 'I think I know what you're saying. I hope you're right. If there is a heaven, I hope it's like that. You might meet up with interesting people there.'

They smiled at each other, each in his own mind forming the image of some rendezvous. Then Victor coughed, clearing his throat. His voice became urgent and business-like.

'Father, like I said, I can't pray. I . . . I feel that even if I had a strong faith, that something in me is . . . weak. I've been living for a long time in a lot of dread . . . terrible dread about things I've caused that are . . . irreversible.' He paused a moment. Then he went on. 'But since I came here, and in the midst of the hell you found me in, something . . . good, something like love, has happened. It wasn't just one person, though it began with you. A girl . . . Christie Wilson, comes to see me too. After I told her some things about my life, some of their meanings began to shift around inside my head. I began to feel lighter – here.' He pressed his hand to his chest. 'I don't mean the cancer's gone, or better. I still cough up blood. I still have pain. But there was a kind of miracle. You and Christie and Hugh and Mary just appeared. It was like I was in hell and then, suddenly carried up out of it into . . . into . . .' He was struggling towards something he hadn't yet processed. '. . . into a kind of release, a kind of heaven. Only I can't say "infinite possibilities." I know I'm going to die.'

Franciscus felt the gathering of a familiar stillness in his centre. 'What can I do to help you?' he asked.

'I know I'm going to get worse before it's over,' Victor said, his voice almost muffled. 'I saw Harold die. I got a woman at home. She's not my wife. She's been good to me for a long time. I've been hard to live with: half crazy, absent, living in the past.' He paused again and leaned towards the priest, a crucial question pleading in his eyes.

'I want a few good weeks to make some things up to her. Only God can give me those weeks; some strength to make it up. I don't know how to talk to Him because I don't know if He's there. You've got some pull. You're His deputy. I want you to do the praying . . . intercede . . . is that the word? – for me.'

Franciscus nodded, a grave expression in his eyes.

'You can do that?'

The priest took Victor's hand and grasped it.

'Yes.'

Victor took a deep breath, coughed, and spoke again. 'The girl I loved . . . she's dead. I used to think I killed her. Now I guess I don't think that. Maybe I really did give her . . .

125

something good. Christie thinks I did. Maybe it's all okay now between Renée and me.'

Franciscus watched the changes in Victor's face. Sorrow played over it, and relief, and a kind of joy. Then he leaned close to Franciscus. His face took on a firm expression. He spoke carefully.

'There's two parts to what I want you to do. The second part is in case the prayers don't work. Maybe God'll think I don't deserve what you're asking for me. If I don't get time to make things up to Stella, in case things aren't all right between me and Renée, can you give me the last rites before I go home? – the absolution? So everything can be evened up, so I can bottom out?'

Chapter Twenty-Two

Virgil Prince was driving towards Broadcliff with Brenda on the seat beside him. A late-February thaw had begun the day before, and the sun shone warmly. He turned and looked at Brenda. She had opened the window a few inches, and her long hair waved around her face in the breeze. The sun caught the highlights of her hair and played upon her face. He reached over and traced a finger, delicately, from her knee to her crotch. She shivered under the thin screen of her panty hose and crossed her legs.

They were almost to the parking ramp. 'What's first?' she asked.

'We're seeing Nippert in Radiotherapy. I've decided to lower the boom on him. The Hoffman case was the last straw. He's mincing around about radiation again, and Bjord is no better. I'm sick of their obstructionist tactics.'

There had been a subtle change in Prince since the day of Vendetti's decision to opt out of therapy.

Brenda had become aware of an increase in his naturally competitive personality, a hypersensitivity to the slightest disagreement. There had been a lot of aggression in their sexual relationship, deriving from certain ingredients in both their natures. Now Prince's approach had become even more combative, sometimes almost violent. It amused and intrigued Brenda. She welcomed the challenges of Prince's complex nature.

Prince guided the Mark VI into the cool cavern of the ramp and it purred to a stop. He retrieved an attaché case from the back of the car. Brenda was already ahead of him, proceeding towards the entrance. They stood together in the stuffy hallway. He pressed the button for the elevator.

Downstairs, Nippert stood beside one of his calculators, figuring out rad dosages for a young patient. He was bracing himself for a meeting with Virgil Prince. The keys of the computer were his ally in objectifying his mind before the meeting. He knew what Prince was coming down about, and he knew he would not be budged in his own decision. Furthermore, he had discussed the case with Gunnar Bjord. Bjord's opinion was as fixed as his own. It would be counterproductive, on a human scale of values, to irradiate Julius Hoffman. The old man had already received a palliative dose of radiotherapy, after several remissions on chemo. It was clear to Nippert that Hoffman could not be treated again without severely debilitating side effects.

He pulled the sheet of paper from the calculator and walked out of the small room, towards his office. His secretary followed him inside.

'Dr Prince and Mrs Stone are on their way,' she told him. 'I said they could wait here till you finished with the calculations.'

Nippert slammed a paperweight down on the calculator sheet and dropped into his swivel chair.

'Get us some coffee, Beth. I'll need all the props I can get for this one.' He smiled a wry smile. Beth nodded and hurried out to the coffee station. Brenda Stone preceded

Prince into the office. Before Nippert had seated himself, she swept him with her groin-to-eyeball glance, fondled her hair back from her eyebrow, and fingered his telephone.

'If you don't mind?' she asked rhetorically, 'someone is waiting on seven-o-nine.' She parked herself on the edge of his desk and dialled the digits.

Prince expanded fifty per cent on his mannerism of mixed archness and boredom whenever he was in Nippert's presence. In the realm of the practical, Nippert was employed by the hospital to run Radiotherapy and did not have his own service. Prince was employed by no one and therefore enjoyed the status of being above him in the professional pecking order. But by every social, cultural, and physical standard, Nippert was superior, simply because society put a large premium on physical appearance. Ed Nippert was handsome, by anybody's code. He was taller than Prince, broad-shouldered – an ex-half-back – and most of the nurses in the hospital had a crush on him. Part of Nippert's devastating charm was that he seemed unaware of his sexual power. He behaved in a gentle, gracious manner towards everyone. He never 'performed.' He was low-key and massively accurate in his work.

Beth walked in with a tray of coffee in cups, deposited it on the desk, and exited. Prince seated himself, with elaborate casualness, in an armchair to the left of Nippert's desk. He said nothing. He observed Brenda, who was talking on the telephone in a low tone, with several idle glances, looked once or twice at Nippert with an expression of mild recognition, and took out his gold cigarette case. He flicked his engraved lighter and took a long drag on a cigarette. Prince waited for Nippert to become uncomfortable and say something – anything. Nippert sat and made notes on the edge of his sheet of figures.

Gunnar Bjord appeared in the doorway and nodded, crisply, in Prince's direction, then spoke to Nippert.

'Esther Hanson is in one of the examining rooms. I'd like you to check what I'm seeing. There seems to be a vaginal lesion. She isn't ready to hear about it.' His angular face and sharp grey eyes were a map of concern.

'I'll be there as soon as I finish here,' Nippert told him. 'Beth should get her some coffee, or juice.' He gathered a few papers from his desk and stowed them in a manila folder. He stood up, stretched his arms, and yawned.

'You called to make an appointment with me, Virg. You must have a problem. What can I do for you?'

Prince leaned back easily in his chair. He glanced at Nippert with what appeared to be mild curiosity.

'I have no problem, Nippert. The problem is all yours. Are you running scared these days?'

'Let's not be cryptic,' Nippert answered in a tone of gentle annoyance. 'Come to the point. I have a patient in a critical situation waiting.'

'Let's not be sophomoric,' Prince countered. 'We all have patients in critical situations. They are all waiting. I am trying to get some cooperation from you to treat one. His wife is very upset. He is going downhill. She wants us to do something. Why have you written in the chart *"Not a candidate for radiotherapy"*?'

Nippert walked to his chair and sat down. He leaned back and placed his hands on the edge of the desk.

'It's very simple. Julius Hoffman is dying. I make it a principle never to subject anyone to radiation unless there is a good chance to remit them; to buy some good living with whatever the radiation costs.'

Prince chuckled, as if mildly amused. 'Who can say if Hoffman is dying? Patients have fooled us before. I was under the impression you sometimes irradiate for palliative reasons. If it shrinks the largest tumour, it could relieve some pressure.' Prince toyed with his cigarette case and watched Nippert.

'I often irradiate palliatively. To treat Hoffman would not be palliative. It would add to his debility.' Nippert enunciated the words with a fine edge to his tongue.

'If he is as close to death as you say, doing something, pursuing *some* treatment would at least help us. It would get his wife off our back.' Prince turned a bit in the armchair and

129

held his cigarette at arm's length. He watched the column of smoke snaking upward in a graceful coil. Then he looked at Nippert with his sidelong glance, and continued.

'Anyone married more than a year tends to accumulate guilt. "Pulling all the stops," you know, is a massive palliative for lingering guilt.' Prince paused again. Nippert had leaned forward and was listening with an electric attention. Prince glanced idly at Brenda, who had finished her call. Her eyes were flashing from his face to Nippert's, as if she were watching a fencing match. Brenda's presence always put him on his mettle.

Nippert continued to watch him with total absorption.

'Of course, you are aware we are inevitably treating the spouse when we treat the patient,' Prince said softly, almost languidly. He reached over and stubbed out his cigarette in the tray. Brenda had dropped a saccharin tablet into one of the coffee cups. She added powdered cream and handed it to Prince. She looked at Nippert with a slightly teasing little grin.

'Yours is straight, if I remember?' Nippert gave her a curt nod.

'Do I understand you to take the position that we irradiate Julius Hoffman, even though it can only debilitate him further, because to treat him until he dies will be psychologically palliative to his wife?'

Prince sipped his coffee. His long, thick fingers were very graceful. With one hand he described locked circles in the air, like a lazy figure-8.

'What is palliative to Mrs Hoffman will be palliative to Julius. She is begging him to live. The responsibility will be lifted from him and onto the linear accelerator.'

There was a brief silence. Prince continued to sip his coffee.

'You're mad,' Nippert whispered.

Prince glanced at Brenda briefly. Her eyes were huge. She blew delicately into her paper cup, flared her nostrils, and sipped the coffee.

Prince leaned back with his elbow on the arm of the chair.

He gazed meditatively at Nippert. Nippert's pale blue eyes glared back.

'You are extremely competent in your field, Nippert,' Prince began, in a ruminative tone, 'but you tend to be annoyingly simplistic. Dying is not a simple matter. Cancer is even more complex. It is a metaphysical phenomenon.'

'You are mad,' Nippert said again. This time it was not a whisper.

'Stan Bracebridge and I have had this simplistic obstructionism to deal with before. We may decide, one of these days, to go to the Joint Commission and report you and your partner, Bjord, who shares your disease, for refusing our patients treatment.' Prince rose gracefully from his chair as he spoke. When he finished, he slipped his cigarette case into his pocket and put the cup back on the tray. He glanced over at Brenda, who was fingering her hair and hugging the protocols to her breast.

'Are you going to irradiate Hoffman?' he asked mildly.

Nippert pushed back his chair with some force. It coasted backward on its rollers and banged against the wall.

'No,' he said. His voice was very low. 'Make your report to the Commission, Doctor. The only palliative treatment to enhance life, or to remove guilt, that the Hoffmans will receive from me is time. And hopefully, someone with time to encourage them to share their fears and feelings with each other.' His eyes belied the control in his voice. They were blazing with rage.

Brenda glided to Prince's side and dusted one of his lapels. She plucked an imaginary thread from his coat sleeve.

'As you wish,' Prince replied. He sauntered towards the door, Brenda following just behind him. 'I will refer Mrs Hoffman to you for an explanation of why we are abandoning her husband's treatment.' He spoke over his shoulder as he disappeared into the hallway. Brenda turned and threw Nippert a tight little smile.

'It was a fun show,' she murmured throatily, swishing her hips as she joined Prince to continue their morning rounds.

Chapter Twenty-Three

Victor's pact with Father Franciscus was honoured before they left the chapel. After a brief prayer mentioning Victor's personal intentions, Franciscus performed the sacrament of the anointing – formerly called the 'last rites.' As he listened to the prayer and as Franciscus touched him with the oil, Victor felt as if some very personal relationship had been formed between himself and an incomprehensible God. The first step in that relationship had been taken the night Franciscus had addressed his desperate physical needs without a word of prayer.

That night Victor called Stella and told her he was ready to go home. Neither Victor nor Stella owned a car. Arrangements were made for their neighbours to bring Stella up to the hospital a few days later and help her to take him home. Victor fell asleep with a new sense of peace and a new feeling of balance and poise.

The day of his departure was clear, cold, and sunny. The early March weather had been a congenial respite from February's cruel and bitter storms. Mary and Hugh helped him pack up his gear. There wasn't much. Stella was bringing his street clothes, including a warm woollen sweater she had knitted. He tucked the free hospital lotion into his shaving kit.

After Stella arrived with Victor's clothes, Hugh helped him dress while Mary and Christie took Stella to the conference room. Christie had heard descriptions of Stella bandied about the Unit shortly after Victor was admitted. She found that Stella, in the flesh, contained more than her detractors had indicated. She and Mary poured coffee and invited her to sit down and talk with them. Stella removed a faded paisley scarf from her head. Her thin grey hair escaped in wisps from a knot at the back of her neck. Her pale blue eyes expressed a touching appreciation and surprise. It was evident she was unused to consideration or deference.

'It's sure nice of you ... the coffee, and you all taking time to talk to me. Vic's told me about his friends up here. He don't know how to thank everybody enough. I thought he was a goner for sure when I come home from work and his bed was empty and him out there somewhere in the snow. He took it into his head he had to walk.' Her eyes were sad, and tired; more than tired, they expressed an infinite weariness. Christie sensed it had begun long before Victor.

Mary smiled at her reassuringly. 'Victor's really done pretty well. He seems better than when he came in, and he's anxious to go home again. He's spoken to us about missing you.'

Stella's face lifted a little; a touch of life animated the flatness in her eyes.

'He has?' Stella ran her fingers over her skirt where it covered her knee, erasing imaginary wrinkles.

'You must promise to call us and let us know how he is doing,' Christie told her.

'Oh, I will ... and Vic will write or call, when he ... can.' Her eyes now questioned them both.

'We want to know if you would like us to arrange some home nursing care for Vic. He may not feel well enough to bathe himself. It would give you security to know a nurse would check on him and help you out once a week or so.'

Stella leaned forward, frowning. 'No ... no. Thanks, but ... it's hard to explain. Vic, he's a funny guy. He ... well, he don't want no strangers around the house. He don't even like that he had to be took care of in a hospital.' She paused a moment and then went on with a thin little smile of pride curving her lips: 'What him and me can't take care of together, well ... it goes by the board. But we got some neighbour friends – they drove me up here today, and I can call them if push comes to shove.'

'We understand, and we hope you won't need outside help. But later on, if you think a visiting nurse would help, we'll find a way to arrange something,' Christie said.

'About Victor's pain problem; even if you can get along without nursing help, he has the kind of pain that's pretty constant,' Mary began. It was important for her to make sure Stella understood how to give the new pain medication. Victor had confided to her his wish that Dr. Nippert could manage his case, and when Victor had announced he was going home, she had approached Nippert. He had been sympathetic to the situation and had written prescriptions. Mary took the slips from her pocket and gave them to Stella.

'One of the doctors has written some prescriptions for you to have filled to give Victor at home. One should do a good job of controlling pain. It's called Brompton's Cocktail. Make sure you give it to him regularly, before the pain gets bad. Read the directions when you get it. Dr Nippert thinks it will keep him pretty comfortable.'

Stella listened to this carefully. 'That's good. I was worried about what we could do about the pain at home. Vic used to take aspirin and whiskey. I'll get the prescriptions filled, and I'll give it to Vic real regular.'

Stella folded the prescriptions and put them into her cracked plastic purse.

'There's something for his cough, too,' Mary told her.

There was a light knock on the door and Hugh peeked in.

'Victor's all ready to go, Stella. Your neighbour's wife just called and said her husband has his car on the second deck of the ramp.'

Stella stood up and buttoned her worn navy blue winter coat. She tied the scarf over her head.

'Thanks again for all you girls and Hugh and the doctor done for Victor. We'll sure let you know how things go.'

She picked up her purse from the table and left the conference room with Christie and Mary. Victor came down the hall in a wheelchair pushed by his neighbour, a fat, jolly-looking woman wearing a red knitted beret. Hugh walked beside the wheelchair carrying a duffel bag, his hand on Vic's shoulder.

Victor had subtly begun to take on the gentle and dignified patina of an elder statesman. He sat quietly in the wheelchair, a grave smile on his face, his eyes twinkling. They all stood around him, waiting for the elevator. He reached up and grasped Mary's and Christie's hands. His eyes were moist with tears. The elevator doors opened.

'So long, Victor,' Mary said. 'Stella promised to let us know how you're doing.'

Christie bent down and kissed Victor on his forehead. 'I know you'll be all right, Victor. Stella will take good care of you. Don't forget to sit in the sun. Put yourself by a window where it comes in.'

Victor looked at her with affection and concern.

'You stay in the sun too.' He reached up again and pressed her hand. 'I think the worst of the winter is over for us.'

The wheelchair rolled into the elevator. They arrived at the ground floor, and Hugh waited with Victor in a small vestibule while Stella went to collect their neighbour and direct him to the departure exit.

Hugh stooped down and tucked the blanket more closely around Vic's legs. He laid his hand on Vic's shoulder and cleared his throat. His eyes were grave, almost troubled.

'I . . . I've been trying to find you alone, Vic, before you left the hospital. I've had something of yours ever since the day of the fight. . . .' He reached into his pocket, pulled out an object wrapped in tissue paper, and placed it in Victor's hand. 'I'm going against orders by giving this back to you,' he whispered, 'but after I looked it over I knew it was a one-of-a-kind, a real keepsake.'

Victor removed his gloves and unwrapped the tissue. Renée's mother-of-pearl knife lay in his hand. God! In all the hassle and horror following his debacle, he had forgotten to wonder what had become of it! Hugh was speaking again.

'Vic, Dr Prince told me to confiscate it. But I couldn't do that, when I saw it had a silver plate and read the engraving.' He paused. They both looked down at the knife. Neither one spoke for a while. Hugh put his hand on Victor's shoulder.

'It shouldn't ever be thrown away. Put it in a safe place.' His eyes took on a mischievous glint. 'Hide it in the chandelier,' he said. Victor wrapped the knife back into the tissue very carefully and shoved it deep into his overcoat pocket.

'Thank you,' he said. 'I really appreciate this. I wouldn't want to wake up in the middle of the night and realize I'd lost some more of my life.'

Hugh held out his hands and Vic grasped them. Then Hugh opened the door. He had heard the car pull up outside the vestibule. Stella and the neighbour came in.

'Stay cool, man,' Hugh said. He stood on the kerb as the car pulled away. He watched it until it had pulled out of the driveway and disappeared behind the federal buildings on its way to the other side of the river.

PART II

Chapter One

Summer had arrived in Brandenburg. The ice had finally melted even in the darkest caverns of the parking ramp. The hospital windows were open, and a breeze from the big lake fluttered the medical notices tacked to office walls. The scent and finally the heat of summer wafted through the patients' rooms, evoking memories of trees and roots, of touches and voices; the perfume of lost treasures.

By July a true heat wave had settled in. One scorching afternoon Mary left the building late. The ramp was still simmering. Tar bubbles burst beneath her feet as she walked across the driveway to the deck where she parked. In summer the days were very long – heaven if you could be at the lake, but hell in the city. Between the decks of the ramp the ceilings were low. The day's heat mingled with exhaust fumes and lay trapped in breathless pockets between the concrete floors. Mary hurried into her car and opened the windows. As she wound down the turns to the exit, she thought of the cottage she and her husband had at the dunes. She had been trying to arrange a way for Kate and Christie to go up there with her for an extended weekend, if they could synchronize their days off.

This heat wave had been unusually long and intense. At Broadcliff only the operating rooms, intensive care units, and administrative offices were air-conditioned. At the end of the day everyone wanted to head for a cool place to level off. The nearest rendezvous was the Pirate's Cave. Mary drove towards the Cave now. She was looking forward to relaxing over drinks and dinner with Kate and Christie.

When she walked into the cool darkness of the Cave, her eyes searched the crowd and saw Kate's profile etched by a candle flame. She had evidently managed to get a corner booth, out of the main traffic. Mary sank into the leather cushions next to her and sighed. 'What are you drinking?'

'A Salty Dog. They replace lost sweat. I sweated a quart today in that dog-hole of an office.'

The waitress had stepped up to the table.

'I'll have what she's got.' Mary pointed to the drink in Kate's hand. 'What's in it?'

'Vitamin C – grapefruit juice; an analgesic – vodka; and salt. You get a lime, too. Where's Christie? I thought you'd come together,' Kate said.

'Christie's going to be late. We had a bad day on the Unit. I lost track of her around four.' Mary's drink arrived and she took a long sip, licking the salt from the edge of the glass. 'Mmm, nice,' she murmured.

'And therapeutic, child.' Kate patted her arm. 'Eat your lime. It'll make you shiver. So what happened to delay Christie?'

'I heard she was staying for a while with this patient's wife – to talk with her. It's a rotten situation.'

Kate was lounging back in the corner cushions chewing on her lime peel. She squinted into the candle flame, 'They're all rotten.'

'Well, this guy went on a silence strike a week ago. The crisis began today when he yanked out his Foley twice and shredded his urethra. Prince put him in leather restraints. He half made it out of them.'

Kate whistled gently through her teeth. 'Jeez. He sounds like Sampson.'

'Well, he's real sick, past middle age and has been bald a long time,' Mary stated.

They were both silent for a while. The cool, dim interior of the Cave, its candlelight flickering over the walls, created a sheltering womb. The vodka began to relax them. Often it seemed to Mary as if the imprisonment and pain of the patients flowed into her own spirit and flesh. Only the closeness and support of comrades made it bearable. She heard Kate's voice close to her ear.

'What in hell can Christie say to mitigate that situation?'

Mary thought for a moment. 'Just be there. Just be *with* them. Maybe help his wife not to feel too much guilt.'

'Yeah, guilt. Why do we all feel guilty when we see people dying?'

Their eyes met, probing the depths of the question. Mary broke the silence first.

'Not everybody feels guilty.'

Kate pulled out a cigarette and lit it. 'What do you think Prince's plans are for the patient?'

'To keep the I.V.'s and chemotherapy going; to keep him in restraints until he's sure he won't tear his various tubes out,' Mary replied. 'Is there any *other* way to go?' she asked.

'Palliative care – like a hospice,' Kate answered. 'But it should have been begun before this.'

'Could anyone get Prince to do just palliative care?' Mary shrugged. 'He didn't even read the material Christie gave him. It had all the guidelines on hospices, including the composition of Brompton's Cocktail.'

Kate sipped her drink and made a face. 'A hospice would lose him a bin of money. What oncologist would promote it? It's a conflict of interests. Especially for Prince. He needs statistics for his research grant.' They sat looking at each other.

'Protocols until the bitter end.' Mary's voice was flat and angry. Brenda the Protocol Bearer, she mused to herself; the Bearer of the Law. It was like a new religion. The two of them, she and Prince, always seemed to descend from some Orwellian Mount Sinai.

Mary felt a touch on her arm. Christie had arrived and was standing beside her. She slid into the booth, looking a little more drained than the heat would account for.

The waitress appeared again. Christie checked Mary's drink.

'Give me one of those,' she said.

'How is Mrs Hoffman?' Mary asked.

Christie took a deep breath. 'After I talked with her, she was just about to leave for home when she ran into Prince and Brenda. I was in the station and heard the conversation.'

Kate and Mary both spoke at once. 'What happened?'

'She walked up to him and asked if she could speak with him in private. Brenda was standing there. He said, "Mrs Hoffman, I have patients who are waiting to see me. I am due at a project meeting in one-half hour. Come to the point. We have had too many pointless meetings in the past."'

Christie paused and began making designs on her place mat with a knife. Then she went on.

'But she wasn't scared off. She said, in a voice firm and clear enough for everyone in the station to hear, "Dr Prince, I want you to stop my husband's treatments and get rid of the tubes. I want you to give him enough pain medication to keep him comfortable. I want you to stop all the chemotherapy. I heard from the resident that you were going *on*, possibly to further combinations. I don't want you to do that. Whatever is happening – *has* happened – it is clear that my husband is fighting it, and fighting ... us all. I am going home to take a bath and rest now. I'm glad I ran into you. I would like to rest knowing he is in the hands of God."' Christie paused and took a sip from her glass.

'What did he say?' Mary whispered.

'He looked at her with that sidelong glance and said, "It is good to know that *you* can *rest*. Your statements are not relevant to any kind of logic. You have retained me as your doctor on this case and I am managing it on the basis of the best protocol oncology has to offer. It is *his* life that is at stake. If you try to stop his treatment, it will be noted, officially, as against my will and he will have to be removed from this hospital."'

All of them watched Christie draw on the mat with her knife. The waitress came again and they waved her away. They sat looking at each other and sipping their drinks.

'He knows his curse-magic,' Kate muttered under her breath. Christie's voice was uneven as she continued.

'By the time he got to the end of his speech, she was over on the sofa with her head buried in her hands. Prince left by the stairwell exit. I took her to the conference room.'

Kate's eyes narrowed. She leaned towards Christie. 'Has she got the guts to take him out of there?' she asked.

'She couldn't lift him around alone at home,' Christie said.

'He has to be catheterized without the Foley,' Mary added.

'They can't afford private nursing care.' Christie stared at the candle flame. 'I wonder if he would begin to speak again if he got out of there. He was unsteady on his feet when he came in.' They were all searching around in the facts for some hope of a better solution for the Hoffmans.

'Where is she now?' Mary asked Christie.

'I had tried, earlier, to convince her that she had to minimize her losses; that she had to take care of herself; that she wasn't crazy in her perceptions. After her scene with Prince, she was pretty bad. Hysterical. The resident ordered a Valium for her. I went out to get her a glass of water and saw Father Franciscus getting out of the elevator. I knew the Hoffmans weren't Catholics, but I asked him to talk to her anyway.' Christie paused again.

Her voice was always a betrayal. One always knew by her tone when she was going to wade into deep water. They sipped their drinks and waited. The candles on the table guttered and flickered every time the door opened and a new casualty dragged into the Cave to cool off and refuel. Finally, Christie began to speak again in a careful voice. 'Do you believe that dying could possibly be a ... kind of gestation? That on the other side of dying could be a better vision of ourselves that we had earned ... or, or ... worked out?' She was feeling around for words and trying to express something she'd never told them before. She watched their faces a bit anxiously. They were listening intently. She went on. 'Well, we develop all our lives and hopefully, *grow*. But maybe dying isn't just a throwaway thing, an anticlimax to life. Maybe it is terribly important.' She was very earnest now, searching their eyes. 'Could we come to things in dying that we can't come to any other way?'

143

'Do you mean reincarnation?' Mary asked.

'No ... I ... I ... I'm not sure. Maybe ... but *something* is next.' Christie was thinking it out.

'Aren't you Catholic?' Kate asked.

'No. I just went to a Catholic college.'

'What does Father Franciscus think?' Mary wanted to know.

'Well, he sure as hell doesn't believe in reincarnation!' Kate pontificated. She'd been nurtured in the bosom of Our Lady of the Assumption Convent. She lit a cigarette and took a long puff. 'If you came back here over and over, you'd get too many chances to screw.'

Christie's shredded look suddenly disappeared as she shook with laughter. They had heard stories about Kate's cold showers and inspecting her own conscience twice a day under the watchful guidance of the Sisters of the Assumption.

Mary persisted, 'I really wonder *what Father Franciscus thinks.* He must have done some isolated thinking about dying during the time he's been travelling with his sacraments to all these people.'

Christie stopped laughing and wiped tears from her eyes. She thought for a minute before she replied. 'You ought to talk to *him.* I let him know if there's someone scared or depressed. The trouble is, most of them are afraid to tell anyone how scared they are.' She paused again; then she said, 'I can tell you a lot about what he doesn't do. He doesn't ever say, "You are going to die, you know, and you'd better get right with God."'

'We need about ten of him,' Kate said. 'I've seen patients turn on the light for help because they woke up with a flyer on their chests with red letters saying: "ARE YOU READY TO MEET YOUR MAKER IN HEAVEN, OR WILL YOU SPEND ETERNITY IN HELL?"'

'I've never heard him mention hell,' said Christie. 'I think he is too full of love.'

'Did you hear what Franciscus said to Mrs Hoffman?' Kate asked.

'No, I left them alone,' Christie answered. 'But I went in to see Julius. No one was with him. He had been bathed and his bed had fresh sheets. When I go in there, I always say, "This is Christie," and I touch his head or put my hand in his. Anyway, I sat there awhile, trying to give him some sense of love, and of ... good *passage*, I guess.' She looked down at her drink and stirred the ice with her finger. Her eyes had filled with tears. She swallowed hard and paused until her voice was steady. 'Then Father Franciscus walked into the room with Mrs Hoffman.'

'How was she?' Kate asked.

'Very calm. She looked ... eased,' Christie answered. Her face brightened and she leaned towards them, looking from one to the other as she spoke. 'I started to leave, but Father Franciscus motioned me over to the bed. I looked at Mrs Hoffman, and she took up my hand and pulled me over beside her. Father Franciscus walked over to Julius on one side of the bed and motioned me to the other side. He said, "Julius, this is Stefan Franciscus." He put some oil on his hand out of a little vial, and put his hand on his head. He knew he was too sick to swallow bread and wine. He said, "I am a priest, and your wife, Pearl, is here, and Christie Wilson is here. We are all asking God for what you need most: to be made whole, according to His will." It was quiet, very quiet. Franciscus had taken his hand and reached for my hand across the bed. Mrs Hoffman took my hand and we made a closed circle. We stood there, silently, and we all prayed. Mine didn't have any words, exactly. We all just wanted him to be let *loose* – out of the restraints.'

Kate had stubbed out her cigarette and was pressing the palms of her hands against her eyes. Mary said, 'I bet he knew you were all there, even if he didn't speak.'

'I don't know,' said Christie. 'I don't know. But I looked at his wife and I felt as if *she* had just shed some leather straps and metal buckles. Franciscus put his arm around her and said, "I'll take you home now."'

Mary got up to go to the women's room. When she returned, they had ordered pizza and another drink.

Kate raised her hand and asked for silence.

'Okay, everybody. I want to tell you some good news. When Margot hauled me into her office this morning to give me the latest poop as transmitted by DeHogue, I really did the old "My God, thank you for helping me" number! She got in a very good mood. I gave her a lot of strokes.

'Then I told her Christie and I wanted a long weekend off, including Friday and Monday, to go to the dunes. Can you believe she okayed it?'

'When?' Christie asked, astonished.

'Next weekend,' said Kate.

'Is it okay, Mary? Can we go then?' Christie reached out and touched Mary's hand.

Mary felt a quick flash of joy, then suddenly remembered there was one more hurdle. She had to get permission from the Nursing office to take that time off.

'I'll try to get the time off, but if I can't, I'll just write out directions and give you the key.'

'You'll get the time off,' Kate said, as if it were a pronouncement, and crossed herself.

They sipped their drinks and dealt with their private thoughts for a bit. Mary was the first to speak again.

'What does Father Franciscus call the sacrament he performed with Julius Hoffman?'

'The anointing,' Kate stated, being the Catholic in residence.

'The sacrament of the person,' said Christie. They all exchanged glances.

Kate said, 'That's one the Sisters never told us about.'

Chapter Two

Mary hated the three-to-eleven shift. When she was on it, her husband usually picked her up. That night he couldn't. She particularly hated the parking ramp, with its poorly lit, narrow, multilevel maze.

Mary entered the stairwell hoping a rapist wasn't lurking in the abundant darkness between the cars. Visiting hours were long since over. She was almost to the level where her car was parked when she heard voices. It sounded as if a fight were in progress. For a second, she thought someone had been trapped just ahead of her. Then she recognized one of the voices. It was Brenda Stone's. She moved further down the stairs to a curve near the bottom. From there she could see out the double-doored exit and into the ramp. In the shadows she could make out the figure of Brenda. She was standing against one of the ramp supports. Every noise always amplified hollowly in the reinforced concrete of the ramp: horns, tyres squealing, people's voices. Brenda was speaking.

'What are you going to do about it?' she was saying evenly, measuring out the words.

Mary froze. Whom was she talking to? It wasn't beyond her image of Brenda to imagine her in a standoff with a sex maniac.

'You've got to stop it, Brenda,' a ragged male voice responded. There was a silence. He went on. 'Everybody is talking.'

God. It's her husband, Mary thought. She had heard that voice before. It was Frank Stone. She'd seen him around the hospital with Brenda or Stanford Bracebridge.

Brenda laughed. The joke must have been cosmic. She shifted to a philosophical tone.

'Everybody is *nothing*. You wouldn't understand that.'

'Even if *no* one else knew, *I* know. You're gone all the time. You're with him around the clock.'

'So?'

'It can't go on.'

'Oh? Just watch me.'

'Do you want a divorce?' There was a lot of pain in it.

'Do whatever pleases you.'

'Whatever *pleases me*! My God! Don't you have any plans? He's married too. He has five kids. Is *he* getting divorced?'

There was a weird play of light. The place where Brenda stood was almost totally in shadow. But the neon sign above the Space Shuttle Cocktail Oasis flashed on and off, illuminating the ramp and throwing her face into fierce psychedelic spasms. Stone was out there somewhere, beyond the path of the light, a totally invisible presence.

The beam caught her again, and Mary saw her lips curl down in a grimace of contempt.

'Divorced!' Brenda laughed, shortly. 'Even in a count-down you pounce on trivialities. What's the difference whether he gets divorced or not? If *you* want a divorce, get one.'

She spat out the words like bullets – like some precious poison, saved for too long. Mary knew she had blundered into an overdue confrontation.

'What do you *want*, Brenda?' Stone sounded like a prisoner begging his torturer for a sip of water. 'What haven't I *given* you? What has he got? His . . . He is . . . Can you fall in love with a man that . . .?'

Brenda's voice came out of the black now. It was as dark and rich as a jungle night. 'God, you're simple,' she breathed. 'Did you ever know anything about *power*? Did you ever learn anything about *me*? You fight . . . Mickey Mouse wars. You're like a *child* battling with tin soldiers on his bedspread.' The light impaled her again. Her handsome face was twisted with contempt. 'A crippled child.'

'Crippled!' His voice showed a touch of strength now.

'Crippled,' she repeated, tiredly. 'Inept. You play mild games.'

There was a groan from the cavern where Stone was standing. Then he said, with a strangled sob, 'And if I am crippled ... what is *he?*'

'He?' Her voice had dropped about two octaves. In the neon's dark phase it was menacing, like some primordial growl. 'He ... is more than God.'

There was a long silence. The light washed over her again. Her eyes had narrowed. She had flattened her slim body against the pillar.

'You're crazy, Brenda.' Stone's voice had steadied remarkably. It sounded even, and kind. Then his tone shaded slightly, with a kind of shrewd patience. 'How, Brenda? *How* is he more than God?'

The tension had pinned Mary to the railing. She gripped it now, as if for assurance.

'*He* is fighting something *big*: a large war,' Brenda said, with tedious patience. 'He is fighting *Death* – around the clock; not arguing boring cases in a courtroom and kissing the ass of stupid politicians. He isn't pounding his butt around on a damn horse. He is ... fighting death *itself.* He is using poisons – he is using cobalt. Do you know the power in six thousand five hundred rads? What is death now?' She paused a minute. 'You wouldn't know,' she laughed. 'You couldn't know. Death is *Cancer*. Cancer is *Death*.'

Mary began to feel dizzy. The heat curled up like a serpent. She wondered if the door was open at the top level. There were some stairs from the outside. If she could get to them, she could get to her car – hopefully without passing through the relentless beam of the Space Shuttle Cocktail Oasis and mucking up the denouement of the Stone confrontation.

She started to climb back up through the semigloom. The air was suffocating.

Don't pass out, she told herself. She tried an old trick she used to use as an emergency measure when she was in a bind. She dug her fingernails into the palms of her hands. She shrugged up the straps of her shoulder bag. She was almost there. She got to the top and turned the knob. It opened. Thank God. The door wasn't locked from the outside.

She walked over to the edge of the ramp. The wind – the blessed west wind – was blowing from the lake. It caught her hair and the skirt of her uniform. She stood there and breathed and turned her face to the sky. Tears ran down her cheeks. 'What the hell am I crying about?' she whispered up at the sky. A cloud was scuttling over the moon, and a splash of raindrops began to fall. That incredible fresh scent of air mixed with summer rain washed through her. She stood there a minute, in the feel and smell of the rain. As long as she could remember, it had made her feel relaxed and healed, as though something tight inside her had come unbound.

She heard the thunder beginning to roll. A flash of lightning illumined the hills, the freeway, the federal buildings, and the steeples.

Mary wondered if there was a Church sacrament involving summer rain. Someday I'll ask Father Franciscus, she promised herself.

Then she spotted the entrance to the outside stairway and ran for her car.

Chapter Three

The wind was blowing like crazy when Christie and Mary got down to the lake. Kate would not arrive till the next day. Mary hoped the bad weather wouldn't last all weekend. They pulled into the driveway at the back of the house and walked in through the basement entrance. Even in that short space, the wind blew off their scarves. It had just begun to rain.

They walked into the large living-dining-kitchen room. The front was all glass, with sliding doors. It was just about sundown, the weather a mass of contradiction: sun piercing through turbulent clouds. Breakers were crashing down on the sand, while rain poured onto the roof and deck.

They stood watching it all through the glass.

'Maybe it's going to stop,' Mary said.

'It's beautiful,' Christie answered. 'I don't mind if the weather isn't sunny.'

'The weather is crazy in this climate,' Mary commented. 'It could clear up tomorrow – even tonight.'

The torrents were already drumming a little less loudly on the deck.

'I'm going to build a fire,' Mary said, suddenly feeling brighter, 'and put the groceries away. But first, I'll show you where to dump your gear.'

She led Christie back into one of the guest bedrooms. Mary and John had no children, and there were four separate bedrooms. Sometimes they were all filled with guests.

Christie looked around the small bedroom. It had a double bed with a lot of coloured pillows at the head. There were wicker baskets and well-worn tables. Mary had furnished most of the cottage with things she had picked up in secondhand stores. One large window overlooked the beach, facing north-west. The rain was rolling down the glass in sparkly rivulets. Christie ran her fingers through her hair and stood there looking out.

'You're lucky, Mary. What a place to be able to come to.'

'Yeah, I guess I am,' Mary answered. 'My husband's parents had this place and turned it over to us when they couldn't climb the steps anymore. It was old and pretty run-down when we got it. We've spent a lot of time fixing it up. John's an amateur carpenter. He put in the sliding doors and remodelled the kitchen.'

Christie walked over to the bed and flopped down. 'I can

151

see the beach from my bed! I can lie in this bed and watch the waves!' She wiggled her toes.

'And sometimes the moon,' Mary said. 'Watch out for that. It can make you crazy.'

They both giggled.

'I want to get the fire going.' Mary started out of the room. 'When you get yourself settled, come on out and we'll mix some drinks. Then we can roast wieners in the fireplace.'

She pulled on her jacket and went out the side door to a lean-to where they kept the wood dry. She took the logs two at a time to the woodbox, beginning to feel the relief of her distance from the hospital. On the trip down she had told Christie about the argument between Brenda and her husband she had overheard the night before. That scene was so layered with significance that she still couldn't get it off her mind.

She could hear the shower running in the guest bath while she stood the logs in a tepee structure and watched the flames climb up the curves. She went over to the counter and unpacked the groceries, then filled two glasses with ice; she set out some bottles of Scotch, gin, and vermouth and put some celery and carrot sticks into a bowl. Then she fixed herself a martini and curled up on the sofa, lighting a cigarette. She watched the fire and tried to fit the pieces of Virgil Prince together.

'He is even more than God,' Brenda had said. It sure as hell explained Brenda. Mary was an agnostic, but it gave her the shivers. She watched the fire and wondered what it felt like to crawl into the sack with someone you felt was more than God and watch him get down on his knees to enter you.

Christie walked in wearing a T-shirt and jeans. Mary had never seen her in old clothes. She looked revived. She dropped down on the floor and said, 'Yum. Goodies. I want a dry martini. Wow. Mary, what a lush life – lying by the fire, fifty feet above the lake. I'm really going to sleep tonight.'

'I always sleep better with rain on the roof,' Mary said, snuggling into the sofa. They clinked glasses.

'To the vacation,' Mary toasted.

'To the sun,' said Christie.

They picked up carrots and nibbled them.

Mary was thinking of Brenda's face flashing on and off in the beacon from the Space Shuttle Lounge. Her mind drifted back to their earlier discussion in the car.

'I can tell you one thing: Brenda's fascination with Prince is rooted in a power trip.'

Christie stared thoughtfully into the fire.

'Prince is very strong. He symbolizes power to a lot of people. I can imagine Brenda's husband would seem powerless in comparison.'

It was getting dark outside. They were sitting between the flames of two fires. The one on the hearth was always mirrored, at night, in the glass. The water beyond the windows gave the illusion of a small lake of fire. There were shadows and lights dancing around on the ceiling, and Christie's face was washed by them.

'Let's get some more logs,' Mary said. They put logs on the grate, fixed themselves a second drink, and curled up at opposite ends of the sofa. Mary watched Christie's face as she stared at the fire.

'Christie,' she began, 'I've often wondered how you came to be working at Broadcliff. You don't seem like a social-worker type.'

Christie laughed. 'You aren't the institutional-variety nurse, either.' She leaned back and turned her glass around in her hand, watching the ice move. She seemed to be drawing back into what had been unspoken and unknown between them.

Mary broke the silence.

'I'm sorry – I brought up something you don't want to think about.'

'No. It's okay.' Christie's voice was low. 'It isn't like the past is something you choose not to think about. It is part of your bones and your blood. I spent a lot of time in a kind of death-in-life ... while I was married. Now I can understand anyone in limbo: not wholly alive, not completely dead.'

'While you were married?'

'I married when I was pretty young. I had only been in college a year.'

'Do you know what went wrong?'

Christie avoided Mary's eyes. She stared into her glass. How could she describe to Mary the alienation she had felt in the wilderness with Joe, or the terror of knowing about the child? The memory of the drive in the blizzard returning from the doctor was frozen within her. The snowstorm had carved the child's tomb and inwardly, her own. She sipped her drink in silence for a time, hoping she could convey something of her experience, something of her feelings, without disturbing the white silence that enclosed the child. She began to speak slowly.

'It was all wrong from the beginning. Joe and I were too different. I was alone a lot in the winter. I was trapped once on a hill in a snowstorm. After that I was afraid to drive in snow.' She paused and looked at Mary before she continued. 'It was like a big invisible wall around me kept slowly closing in and I was all alone in the centre. I began to have terrifying feelings that I wasn't real, that I didn't exist.' There was another silence; then she said, 'You don't know who you are when there is nothing left to love.'

Mary's throat had been tightening as it often did on the Unit when she saw someone dying. Christie's eyes looked hollow and haunted.

'What kept you going?' Mary whispered.

'Knowing that summer would come, and reading my books. I loved Carl Jung and Martin Buber. I had a close friend for a while. But the books were my salvation. When summer came, it was very brief. But I could love the trees, the insects, and weeds and stones. I could be near the lake.'

Christie's story explained for Mary the strange remoteness she had always sensed in her. It was present even when she laughed.

'When did you decide to leave him?'

'Something happened – something terrible ... I can't talk about it. It gave me the courage to leave. My parents were dead, but I called my aunt. She told me to pack up and come

154

back to the city for a visit. I never returned. I stayed with her for a while. I enrolled in college again. I read a book about some people who were working with dying patients. It seemed that all I had experienced, all my isolation, had prepared me for this work.'

Christie turned and looked at Mary now.

'Maybe you always earn something through pain. Those years, they weren't for nothing if they helped me to feel for someone else.'

A cold fear crept into Mary's mind. It was almost as if she saw Christie drowning, even in her escape from isolation, even as her face reflected the bright fire.

Mary suddenly lifted her glass, with the remains of her drink in it. 'I propose a toast!' she said, injecting a tone of heartiness into her voice. Christie picked up her glass and lifted it.

'Here's to earning through hardship,' Mary said. 'May you have earned yourself some real love and life – some strong arms around you!'

Christie laughed and stood up. They touched glasses and drank. Then Mary turned to the tray and put one of the wieners on her fork.

'The fire's just right,' she announced. 'Let's get this show on the road!'

Christie walked over to the sliding glass doors and opened them. The rain had stopped. The wild surface of the lake was settling into rhythmic breakers rolling onto the sand. The wind was clean and fresh, almost cold.

'Look there!' said Christie, pointing over the rim of a pine tree by the deck. 'A full moon coming through the clouds. What do you bet? Will it be sunny tomorrow?'

'I won't bet,' Mary said, watching her hot dog sizzle. 'I won't even glance at the moon. If I pretend not to see it, it will wear out the clouds and tomorrow will be a sunny beach day.'

'Kate should be here by afternoon,' Christie mused. She stuck a wiener on her fork. 'We can explore the dunes. Tomorrow morning I'm going to see what's down the beach.'

She waved the impaled wiener in a wide sweep around her head. 'Tomorrow,' she predicted, 'I'm going to do *everything*!'

Chapter Four

Christie awoke to the reflection of sun on water. Patches of sun spilled on the sand beneath her window. She stretched her whole body, wriggled her toes and fingers, and then lay there for a few minutes, enjoying the thought of where she was. She looked out the long window. Two swans glided by, about ten feet from the shore.

There was no sound from Mary's room. She decided not to waste any more time in bed. She would make a takeout breakfast, put on her bikini, and explore the beach. She wanted to climb into the dunes and just lie there and wait for the gulls.

It was one of those blue and golden days she remembered from her time in the north. Every surface, every ripple in the lake, the curve of the hills on the long peninsula several miles across the bay, all were magnified by a marvellous clarity. After the heat and stench of Broadcliff, and the dark, steady downpour of rain, she felt as if she were emerging into a supernatural world. She looked up and saw the first gulls. They were wheeling high above her with the sun on their wings, a luminous white against the sky.

She walked along the beach, carrying a wicker basket for collecting driftwood and eating an egg sandwich and watching the gulls. When she finished the sandwich, she tied the sleeves of the robe over her shoulders and broke into a run. She ran until she was out of breath, then stopped and looked around. The lower, grassy dunes near Mary's cottage, which were full of small pines and juniper bushes, had given way to long upward sweeps of sand. These were the real dunes, the ones she loved, with ledges and slopes and long, level plateaus curving behind protective mounds of sand.

She climbed upward along the first rise until she came to a wide, flat promontory, where she stretched out her robe and put her basket down. Then she stood and looked around her. She was high enough above the beach for the cries of the small sand birds to seem remote, yet the dunes still arched further up behind her. Her promontory felt like a citadel. The darkness of the deep woods crowned the tops of the dunes and filled black canyons behind them where no sun ever penetrated. The only sounds were the faint voices of the sand birds and the sharp cries of the gulls. She could see no cottages around the curves of the nearest dunes.

She decided it would be marvellous to feel the touch of the sun and wind over her whole body. She unhooked the halter and dropped the pants of her bikini suit, and threw them into her basket. Then she stretched out on the sand and looked up at the sky.

Some gulls were circling, not very high and just above her. She wondered if any of them would come close. She had always considered them mystical creatures, the bearers of good omens.

Around her were fragile sand weeds. She stretched her arms in the safe warmth of the sun.

At the water's edge was a castlelike stand of large rocks. It shone wetly in the sun, a glistening fortress bereft of its commander, perhaps inhabited by shore creatures. She thought about Carl Jung. He said the fragility of the sand weed and the power of stone were God's thoughts.

She wondered if dragonflies ever came to the dunes. At the small inland lake in Canada there had been blue dragonflies. They had loved the sun and the stones at the water's edge. Sometimes a dragonfly had landed on her arm or her leg and she had marvelled at its beauty, the energy emanating from its tiny body. The dragonflies were avatars, as well as the

157

gulls. But the gulls brought only benedictions and courage. The dragonflies were healers.

Sometimes, when Christie stood by the bed of a patient none of the chemicals had cured, she wondered whether if, at the silent, mysterious inception of the cancer, a host of blue dragonflies had suddenly covered him, the cancer would have been aborted. She had even dared to wonder if the energy in their touch, the embodiment of their love, could reverse a growing cancer, one that had already metastasized.

The vision of dragonflies at the bedside was so impossible it amused her. She sighed and felt the warmth of the climbing sun penetrate the bones of her arms and legs, the skin of her face. The breeze lifted strands of her hair. She lay there, sleeping and waking. The shadows of gulls passing the sun made a ballet on the sand.

She must have fallen asleep, for she was startled by a sudden motion. There was a ruffling of feathers, the beating of wings, and a gull flew up from the sand very close to her feet. It called out in its sharp voice as it curved towards the water. She sat up and shielded her eyes, watching it go higher and farther away. She felt an acute sense of loss, and wondered how long it had been so close to her. Then she sensed a different presence. She heard the sound of a branch breaking, up near the top of the dune. She turned in the direction of the sound and pulled her beach robe up around her. A figure was flying above her in a long broad jump. It landed about ten feet away, skidding to a stop in the stem-christie position of a snow skier. It was a man, and whoever he was, he had leaped from the top of the dune. He stood grinning at her. His blond hair stood wildly on end, and his dark body shone with sweat. He was shirtless, with the gnarled muscles of a wrestler above his baggy white shorts.

Christie's first thought was 'I'm naked.' But the gentle surroundings, the sun, the water, and the gulls all seemed to wipe out any fear at his sudden appearance. She held her beach robe up to her chin and stared at him. He trudged slowly over to her and looked down at her, still grinning.

Christie squinted up at him.

'You scared my gull away,' she said, with honest regret. It seemed the only appropriate remark.

'Sorry about that. Sorry if I scared you.' He looked serious for a minute, then added, 'I could have climbed down around the side and sneaked up on you, but I never sneak up on naked ladies.'

Christie knotted the sleeves of her robe across her shoulders.

'Well, I'm not naked now,' she answered.

She studied what she could see of his face behind his sun goggles and decided he didn't look depraved, just wild. Then she glanced down at the shore to see if anyone else might be coming by, who could distract his attention while she put on her robe.

He saw her eyes combing the beach and read her mind. 'Don't worry. I'm not a mad rapist who lives in the trees up there.' He sat down on the sand beside her. 'I'm just a harmless neighbour boy out to enjoy the morning sun.' He glanced up at the gulls circling against the deep blue sky. 'I was afraid the monsoons would keep right on through my holiday.'

So he was a neighbour. She relaxed a little. She knew there were more cottages, some big, expensive ones, around the next dune in a kind of cove. Mary had mentioned that.

He picked up a fork-shaped piece of driftwood and began drawing in the sand with it. He drew clusters of geometric shapes, like hieroglyphics. She watched him as he covered the ground around them with his strange mural. Then he moved the stick over to Mary's wicker basket and deftly lifted the top of her bikini onto one prong of his driftwood stick, and the bottom onto the other. He dangled them in the air in front of her.

'Is that all there *is*?' he asked, in a tone of stagy horror. Christie fell back on the sand, clutching her beach robe around her, shaking with laughter. She wondered how he could make her laugh when she was sure he was capable of racing off and throwing both pieces into a tree.

The intruder sat watching her. He amused himself by

tossing the suit into the air and catching it with his driftwood fork until Christie stopped laughing and looked up at him. He took off his large sun goggles and stared back at her. She saw that he had brilliant blue eyes with heavy lids, almost Oriental. It was an odd combination: the fair hair and blue eyes of a Viking, darkly tanned skin, and Oriental eyelids. He had the broad face and nose, the high cheekbones of a Mongolian.

'Is the bikini all you had in your basket, little girl?' he asked, with mock seriousness. 'What a pity. But you have met up with a good, pussycat wolf.' He continued to stare at her steadily with his narrow blue eyes. He did look a little like a wolf, she thought. A half-breed wolf.

She shivered a little, trying to stare him down. His muscular body and strange intense eyes frightened her.

He suddenly broke the eye contact. 'If you'll promise to stay here and play in the sand till I get back, I'll run up to my kitchen and get us a lunch.' He looked at a watch on his wrist. 'It's high noon, and I'm hungry,' he growled.

Christie felt more secure. She liked the idea of a man's getting food for her in his own kitchen.

'How far is your kitchen from here?' she asked.

'I can drop down on it from the crest of this dune' – he pointed to the top of the dune and gestured along the ridge and to the south with a thick finger – 'in five minutes. I can do the whole thing in twenty ... okay?'

Christie smiled at him and held out her hand. 'Give me the suit.'

He drew in the air between them in some kind of ritualistic gesture, like a priest with a censer. Then he placed the bikini, one piece at a time, in her hand. 'Agreed?' he asked.

'Agreed.' She nodded her head.

He jumped up and made a 'V' signal with his fingers.

'If you disappear before I get back, there's a horrible curse on you,' he warned.

Christie watched him bound up the steep slope of the dune – not at an angle, as she did, but straight up, the muscles in his legs bulging as his feet gripped the sand. He turned and waved to her at the top, then loped across the ridge, vaulting small bushes and finally disappearing behind a stand of tall pines where the dune curved into a cove.

She pulled the bikini back on with reluctance. It cut into the middle of her belly and the tops of her thighs. She had never before felt the freedom of being nude in the sun and the air. It had been delicious. For the first time she wondered how long this man had watched her sleeping. She didn't even know his name, and now she had agreed to stay and have lunch with him.

She lay back on the sand, shut her eyes, and slipped on her dark glasses. They offered a certain security, a mask to put her at one remove from close scrutiny. The word 'mask' evoked, suddenly, the face of Virgil Prince staring from the enigmatic mask of his own scars.

She had been unable to respond adequately to Mary's story about Brenda the night before. It was understandable that Brenda would conceive God's power to be less than Prince's. Her own sense of Prince's dichotomy was too complex to put into spoken words. If this disfigurement had been an accident of birth, then that accident had been the genesis of his power; a curse which had garnered the strength and mystery of duelling scars. She was convinced that his face had a mystical significance to him. She wondered if the mark had caused his conflicts, or if some profound inner dichotomy had stamped its symbol on his face.

Her mind went back to the appearance of the stranger. She decided to wear the sunglasses when he came back with lunch. The sun was getting really hot now. Not a single cloud interrupted the intense blue of the sky. The big lake spread out in iridescent ribbons: pale jade, turquoise, cerulean, and finally cobalt blue at the greatest depth. Some of the gulls climbed higher, higher, soaring in circles. A few were sharing the beach with the small sand birds. She counted seven on the rock castle. They sat motionless, serene and self-contained, watching over the water.

She thought about the gull the intruder had startled. If gulls were avatars and messengers, perhaps it had come to

161

announce him. The intruder was an odd combination of mannered charm and alarming barbarity. There were mongrel contradictions in his face. No doubt, he was the issue of some accident; the legacy of an extremely irregular passion. Maybe a delicate Nordic lady, a princess, had been carried away by Attila or one of his guards at the time of the Mongol invasions. She wondered what his father and mother were like.

A hissing sound in the sand alerted her again. She looked behind her to see him sliding down the dune in slow-motion strides, carrying a picnic hamper. He dropped down beside her, leaned into her face, and smiled.

'I'm glad to see you're a lady of your word,' he said. 'Now look.' He opened the basket. 'Aren't you glad you didn't run away?'

It was evidently not the first picnic lunch he had put together. There were cold fried chicken, Port du Salut cheese, dark rye bread, pears, a caddy full of ice, a bottle of champagne, white · pottery dishes, and glasses for the champagne.

He removed the checked cloth and spread it out on the flattest section of the sheltered ledge. He set down the glasses, plates, and napkins carefully; then the ice bucket and the champagne. Christie wriggled around on the sand until she sat opposite him on the edge of the tablecloth, and watched him set out the food. She was fascinated by the grave, ritualistic way in which he performed certain acts. He carefully loosened the cork in the champagne bottle, then let it blow off towards the top of the dune. He looked at her levelly and unsmiling as the cork shot into the air. Then he filled the two glasses. He pushed his sun goggles up on his head, picked up both glasses, and held them in his hands.

'What's your name?'

'Christie.'

'*Chris*-tie,' he repeated, caressing the syllables with his voice. 'And the last name?'

'Wilson,' she said. 'And yours?'

'Lance,' he answered. 'Lance Bohrman.' He frowned, but

looked at her through blue, narrowed eyes that glittered with amusement. 'The famous Hun,' he added. He had said the whole thing on a long, low breath, in a sinister tone, his lip curled, like a villain. Then he smiled happily again and handed her the champagne. She felt herself struggling for the sense of safety she had been basking in when she was alone and half asleep. Now she was aware of every inch of bare flesh above her halter top and above and below her bikini pants.

'Chris-tie,' he repeated, sipping his champagne and squinting at her. She was suddenly aware of another feeling: how long had it been since she had heard a man's voice saying her name with tenderness?

Lance Bohrman touched his glass to hers.

'To meeting in the sun,' he said.

'To meeting in the sun,' Christie repeated. They clicked their glasses and sipped the cold champagne. She realized how thirsty she had been.

'How often do you come up here?' she asked.

'Oh – on and off all summer,' he said, removing the chicken from its plastic wrap. He pulled some devilled eggs out of a covered dish and handed her one, holding it up to her mouth. She took a bite. It was delicious. She began to relax again. He put the rest of the egg in his mouth and licked his fingers. Leaning back on the sand on one elbow, he nursed his glass of champagne with his other hand, and sipped it slowly.

'Tell me where you came from,' he said. 'You were out here pretty early.'

'I'm visiting a friend, Mary, down there. She has a cottage.' Christie pointed down to the right of their promontory.

'Mary ...?'

'Yes. Do you know her?'

'We're neigbours who yell "Hello" and talk about the weather. Her husband jogs on the beach. How do you know Mary?' he asked.

'We work together – in Brandenburg, at a hospital.'

She sensed a small increase in his attention.

'You're a nurse?' he asked.

'No ... no. I'm a ... a medical social worker. A counsellor.'

'A *counsellor*?' he repeated. He had taken another devilled egg and was speaking while chewing. He swallowed hard and lay back on the sand laughing.

'What's funny about counsellors?' Christie demanded.

Lance stopped laughing by degrees and looked down at her feet and then over the rest of her, slowly.

'Nothing,' he answered, growing instantly serious. 'Nothing. Who do you counsel?'

'Well, sick people. Very sick people. I work on a cancer unit.'

Lance was silent for a long few seconds. 'Cancer unit? What can you say to anyone with cancer?'

Christie thought she detected a new tone she hadn't heard before. She waited a moment, feeling the sudden chill of a minor impasse.

'It isn't what you *say*. ... They are alone ... in their disease. ... It's hard to explain.'

She leaned over and took a piece of rye bread. He unwrapped the cheese and carved it like a sculptor. Christie's nose was perspiring under the weight of the dark glasses.

'Are these people *dying*?' he demanded, in the new, guarded voice.

'Yes. In one stage or another,' she said. She felt uncomfortable, sensing his sudden shift of mood. She leaned back and curled her legs under her. She sipped the champagne and turned her head upward to locate the gulls.

She sensed him watching her. He reached over and placed a heavy hand on her thigh.

'*I* almost died once,' he said in one of his earlier voices; intimate and intense. It announced a mystery.

'When?' Christie asked. 'How?'

'I hanged myself,' he said. His mouth twisted into a crooked smile.

'Hanged ... *yourself*?' She couldn't stand the impediment

164

of the glasses. She wanted to risk really looking at him now, even if it gave him the advantage of seeing her clearly. He was smiling his wry smile and looking at her levelly. She wondered if his volatile confidence ever slipped.

'Why?' she demanded. 'What saved you?'

He sipped the champagne. She saw the hair on his hand glinting like gold in the sunlight, the little beads of perspiration like crystals. The barrel of his bare chest was a tangled mat of blond-and-grey hair. The tight muscle of his arm moved as he revolved his glass. Finally, he turned and leaned forward. He faced her squarely, holding his glass in both hands. He stopped smiling.

'I was about seven or eight. I loved going to movies. I had a lot of time to fantasize. I went to this movie where the hero got hanged. It was a tense scent. They marched him up these stairs. Some guys at the bottom of the platform were rolling drums. A lot of people wanted to save him, but nobody did. They showed a dim-lit surrealistic scene of his body at the end of the noose in this spasmodic dance. It really blew my mind. One Sunday afternoon I was suffocating in that Midwestern small-town childhood boredom, and I decided to try to reenact that hanging scene myself. I got a rope and a ladder and I tied the rope around the branch of our apple tree, near the back porch.'

He paused a minute, quietly looking at Christie, but withdrawn, as if he were absorbing something from inside himself.

'I made a knot in the noose just loose enough to squeeze over my head. Then I jumped off the ladder.'

Christie was watching him with horror and fascination; remembering her own childhood, remembering loneliness, remembering boredom – all the vacancies, all the depressions, all the limbo of many Sundays.

'Go on,' she said.

'Well, the rope choked me. It didn't feel dramatic, or good. No drums were rolling. I was trying to hold the rope away from my neck with my fingers. I had just made a regular knot. Didn't know how to do a slipknot. I was trying to get my feet back on the ladder, and trying to yell. The ladder fell over and crashed, and the racket startled my mother in the kitchen. She raced out, yelling for my father, and she held me up till my father cut down the rope.'

Christie took a long, deep breath. Lance broke the mood by a burst of laughter.

'I've learned to find some cheaper thrills since then,' he said. 'Hey, let's have some chicken.' He picked up a crisp drumstick and handed it to Christie. She took a large bite. She realized now she had also been very hungry.

'Have *you* ever done anything crazy? Do counsellors ever do anything crazy?' Lance demanded. He buried his teeth in a large chicken breast.

'I was just remembering when I was nine and I nearly drowned from the garden hose.'

'Come on ... the garden *hose*!'

'I had a mean little friend. We were both bored ... at my grandmother's ... and it was *hot*, steamy hot.'

The champagne and the sun were easing knots in her body. Piece by piece. From her head to her shoulders, her chest to her legs. It was easy to remember the moment. She felt like a child again, swapping secret stories with a playmate.

'Well, I was playing with the hose,' she continued. 'I had finished watering the flowers. I was thirsty. I took a drink from the hose, and I lay down on the lawn. I was fooling around, spraying the hose up in the air and getting wet; then I turned it down to a trickle, just to keep myself wet. I let it run on my face, all over me.'

Lance finished the chicken and leaned back on his elbows, watching the slow exchange of the gulls' positions on the rock castle.

Christie went on. 'So I was thirsty, and I had the idea of letting the hose trickle down my throat – just enough to swallow; and I lay down flat in the grass and slowly drank the water, looking at the patterns of the leaves. They made designs on the sky.'

Lance stopped looking at the gulls. 'And then?' he asked.

'Well, it was like an explosion in my body. In my head. I

couldn't breathe. Then I saw my father bending over me. He turned me upside down. I was vomiting water.'

Both of them were silent. Lance was watching the lake again. Christie was aware that her heart was going too fast. Maybe the sun, and the champagne.

Lance finally leaned over and picked up the champagne. He tapped her glass with the neck of the bottle.

'So who exploded the hose nozzle?'

'It turned out that my little friend saw me lying down playing with the hose and wanted to splash me in the face. She didn't know I had the nozzle all the way back to my tonsils.'

He poured the champagne into her glass. 'So both of us nearly died in childhood by our own hand. Well, it's nice to know that about you. I was afraid you might turn out to be the average counsellor.' He threw back his head and laughed. He filled his own glass and reached forward to touch hers.

'Here's to crazy,' he said. She was aware of the hard curve his lips made when he smiled.

She lifted her glass and they clicked. After a few sips she knew she had to move.

'I want to cool off in the water,' she said. She jumped up and looked down the dune. Little shimmer waves of heat were rising from the sand. She wondered which way to go to the water. Could she leap – the way he did? Could she jump first, from the promontory?

She saw him standing just below her, poised, his legs almost together. He was finishing his glass of champagne. He looked over his shoulder and tossed his glass back onto the tablecloth.

'Follow me!' he yelled.

He began to ski down the dune, digging in his heels, in a skating motion, and she followed, never having done it, but doing it exactly the same way, the sun and the champagne bestowing grace, never falling. It was like flying; down, down, down.

They were finally at the edge of the water. She watched

him leaping and diving into the waves. The wind had come up more than they had felt on the promontory. She felt a sharp pain of regret that she could follow him only down the steep dune, not into the deep water. She had never learned to swim. The waves frightened her when they came near her face. The movement and the depth seemed overwhelming.

Suddenly he turned around and swam back towards her. '*Chris-tie*!' he yelled. 'Come on! Come on in! I'll hold you up!'

Chapter Five

Mary and Kate were walking down the beach carrying a picnic basket when they saw Christie standing on a little rise near the shore, and heard Lance calling to her. By the time they got closer, he had waded out, picked her up in his arms, and carried her, kicking and screaming, into the lake. Now he struggled back.

'I'm sorry, Christie! God! I didn't know you were really scared!'

Christie's heart was pounding, and angry tears poured down her cheeks.

'I don't know how to swim!' she sobbed. He put his hands on her shoulders and pulled her face up to him.

'And you nearly drowned in the hose.' He was trying to look into her eyes, but she was wiping tears with the back of her hand, looking away from him. Lance ran a hand across his shoulder.

'God. You drew *blood*! I've got teeth marks! You're a dangerous commodity, baby.' He held up his bloodstained fingers for her to see.

Suddenly, he threw back his head and laughed.

Kate and Mary had walked up to them now. The heat of

Christie's rage and fear had obscured everything else. She had not seen them approaching.

She hugged Kate and turned to Mary, who was holding out her basket of food to Christie.

'We were counting on hunger to drive you home,' she told her.

Kate scrutinized Lance closely, while she said to Christie, 'We thought we were going to have to do our rescue-squad number, but it looks like you have the strength of ten, Cookie.' She reached up and touched Lance next to the bite. She examined his wound carefully.

'You'd better wash that and get some antiseptic on it. No telling what she could carry from the hospital,' she warned in a tone that implied hoof-and-mouth disease. She winked at Christie.

'Are you a nurse?' Lance asked her. He looked over at Mary and broke into a wide grin.

'It looks like some of us have already introduced ourselves,' Mary said.

'He dropped out of the sky on me while I was taking a nap,' Christie explained. 'He said he knew you.'

'Yeah, I know Lance,' Mary said, smiling. She introduced him to Kate.

'Hi, Lance.' Kate grinned. She reached for the basket. 'Hey, I'm famished. Let's put this blanket down and dole out the food. Okay?'

'Give me the basket and blanket,' Lance said. He reached over and relieved them of their burdens. 'Come on. Follow me. We've got a place up there where sand won't blow into the food.' He slung the basket over his shoulder. 'It's a soft nest with a view,' he said.

'He has a kitchen nearby,' Christie told them. 'He brought a whole picnic lunch. And champagne! There's even some left!'

'Hey-hey-hey!' Kate gave a slow whistle. 'We'll give you some of our lemonade, won't we, Mary?'

'I'll give you a Band-Aid, too,' Mary said.

The four of them trudged up the dune with Lance in the

lead. As usual, he went straight up. The women lagged behind, stopping once in a while to get their breath.

Lance arrived first at the promontory. On the way, he had come by a long, weathered wooden stick that looked like a discarded flagpole. Christie saw him stoop over and pull something out of her beach-robe pocket. It was her green-and-blue scarf, the ribbon colours of the water along the shoreline. He knotted a corner of it around the top of the stick and then stabbed it into the ground.

'Welcome to our bastion!' he yelled down at them, holding the pole with one hand, his body gleaming with sweat and his pale hair flying wildly in the wind. The scarf fluttered like a flag above his head. He looked to Christie like some triumphant savage who had just taken possession of a sweet and coveted terrain. She reached the 'bastion' first, and Lance stood with one arm around her, the other holding the flag. As Kate and Mary climbed upward, they seemed to be greeted by two hosts.

'Well ...' Mary exhaled a long sigh of relief and flopped down on the blanket. Lance had already spread it beside his tablecloth. '... you have made a little *home* here.'

'Checked tablecloth, glasses, plates!' Kate nodded appreciatively. Lance poured the champagne.

'Help yourselves to ice,' he told them. 'There's still some in the caddy.' Kate and Mary munched their sandwiches and savoured the slightly diluted champagne. Kate leaned back on one elbow and squinted out over the lake.

'God, what a view! I wonder what the poor devils working back at the hospital are doing now.'

Lance had just put an egg in his mouth. 'Why would anybody decide to work in a hospital?' he asked, with some difficulty.

'Everybody's got to be somewhere,' Mary commented.

'It feels so good when you stop,' Kate added.

'And for now – we're here.' Mary's voice was hollow with mystery. 'Tonight we build a big bonfire, go swimming in the firelight, and roast corn and stuff.'

'And then we sleep until noon,' Kate ordained.

'Look!' cried Christie. 'Here come some swans!'

'See the one closest to the shore?' Lance asked them. 'That one is the male. He stays on the inside because that's really the outside, where danger might be.'

'Are you a bird-watcher?' asked Kate, licking mustard off her fingers and thinking it was the last thing she'd have credited him with.

'I spend a lot of time near water, so I know about water birds,' Lance replied. He jumped up. Christie wondered what his record was for being in repose.

'Hey, I'm going down to see if they'll feed.' He picked up some bread crusts, jumped clear of their ledge, and went foot-skiing down the dune, a wake of fine sand spray behind his heels.

'Wow. What a dynamo!' Kate whispered through her teeth. 'I wonder what fuel he runs on. He came straight up this dune like a jet taking off.'

'He's always been a big athlete,' Mary said. 'At least, that's what the rumour is. All I know about him is what the rumours are. He's out of our financial and social ball park.'

'Is he up here a lot?' Kate asked. She glanced over at Christie. She hadn't moved. Her expression was unreadable behind her large dark glasses. She was evidently watching Lance. He was at the bottom of the dune walking slowly along the sand towards the swans. He began to tear off pieces of bread and throw them into the water. The male swan came gliding towards the bread. He ate two pieces and then moved towards his mate. Soundlessly, a message was conveyed, and both moved towards the bread, the female always eating the pieces furthest away from the shore, the male keeping his body between her and Lance.

'So what do you know about him, other than that he's rich?' Kate said to Mary.

'That he drives an Italian sports car too fast and lives in a big contemporary beach house, just over that dune.' She pointed towards the end of the ridge. 'They sometimes have big parties,' she added.

Lance stood up and waved. 'Chris-tie! Come and feed the

171

swans!' Christie stood up and drank the last champagne in her glass.

'I'll be back in a minute,' she said to Kate and Mary. Then she slid down the dune, imitating the downhill skiing slide Lance had used for his descent.

Kate and Mary ate in silence for a few minutes, watching the two figures on the beach below. Lance had given the bread to Christie, and the two swans were moving very slowly along, picking up pieces of bread from time to time.

'Something tells me he's bad news,' Kate said.

'Mmmm,' murmured Mary, sipping the champagne.

'You know something else?' Kate persisted.

'Why do you say "bad" news?' Mary asked.

Kate threw her a loaded look. 'He's got too damn much energy. I think he's got an ego a mile wide. I think he could hypnotize her and make mincemeat out of her.'

'*That* bad?' said Mary, a bit rhetorically. 'Well,' she sighed, 'I guess I would worry less about Christie if she fell into a deep hole in the lake.'

'Also, he's married?' Kate asked, touching her paper cup of champagne to Mary's.

They sipped the champagne silently for a while.

'It's one of those loose-jointed marriages that will probably last forever,' Mary said, finally. 'They live together when they aren't off in opposite directions.'

'What's she like? Have you met her?'

'Not exactly. I told you we're out of their orbit. I've seen her on the road driving in. I've seen her picture in society columns. She spends most of her time in Chicago.'

Kate nudged Mary and pointed down at the shore. The swans had gone gliding off and Lance was on his knees, mounding sand up into a heap and drizzling water on it. Christie was sitting cross-legged in the sand, picking up stones and sorting them.

'What does she look like?' Kate asked.

'Like a horsy dame with frosted hair, a year-round tan, and a high-society overbite.'

'Fat? Thin?'

'Athletic, thin, and flat-chested.'

'She sounds like a real sexpot.'

'She has her charm. She's supposed to be a big brain.'

'Why is the marriage loose-jointed?'

'Separate interests, I guess. She's into dabbling in politics. She's a political patron. She wrote a column in the paper for a while and sponsors some aspiring congressman.' Mary picked up a sandwich.

'Yeah?' Kate looked absolutely absorbed. 'And what turns *him* on?'

'Well, he runs a foundry that his father turned over to him. He has a huge racing boat and a crew. And he's seen with girls; girls who can move as fast as he does.'

'Kids?'

'Two. Away at private schools most of the time – or vacationing in Europe or Africa, or somewhere.'

Kate sat looking into her champagne for a while. Finally, she said, 'I always thought Christie must have had a bad experience with a man. We've never had a friendship outside of Broadcliff, but ... I don't know ... it's like something in her ... the woman in her, is closed off; like she's asexual.'

'She's had a bad marriage,' Mary said. 'She told me about it last night. The men in her life are Martin Buber and Carl Jung. They're both dead.'

Kate stuck her cup in the sand and lay back on the blanket. She threw a towel over head. 'Swell.'

'Let's go down and get wet. Let's see what they're building.' Mary stood up and walked to the edge of the ledge.

'Okay – let's try sliding à la Lance.'

Both of them jumped onto the steep slope and half-running, half-jumping, half-sliding, they made their way to the bottom, then fell into the water, laughing.

They both stretched out in the shallows and looked back at the beach. Lance and Christie were totally absorbed. They were building an intricate structure made of rock and sand. Lance called it a castle, and Christie corrected him.

'It's a Druid thing. It's going to be like an open place for the moon to shine through and cast shadows,' she said.

'Okay. Then let's call it "Moon Castle",' Lance suggested.

Kate had come dripping up to them to inspect their progress.

'Has this been in the design stage for quite a while?' she asked Christie, who was placing some pillar-shaped rocks with serious concentration.

'Yes,' she answered. 'It's *my* house. It's the house I want to live in. It's my real home.'

Everybody was quiet. Lance had done all the foundation work, packing the wet sand. He was helping with advice, or in balancing a certain stone. There was an improvisational character to the proceedings. And yet it was plain that Christie knew how it should look when it was completed. It had a broad, sweeping stairway made of long, flat rocks. The structure itself was on several levels. The roof was held up by rock pillars. A few rocks formed intermittent walls, but it was mostly open on its sides.

When it was finally finished, Christie wandered halfway back up the dunes gathering small blue-green sand weeds with lacy fronds, and sprigs of juniper. She placed them along the stairway and at the front entrance. Some of the tallest became stately trees.

'They are guarding it,' Christie said. She sat back and looked at it for a while. Then she waded into the shallow edge of the lake and let the water wash over her. Finally, they all stretched out in the sand and fell asleep.

The sun was getting low when Mary woke up and called Christie and Kate. Lance had disappeared with the remnants of his own contribution to the picnic, but the driftwood pole was still flying its scarf flag at the edge of the promontory. The ramparts of the Moon Castle were casting a shadow on the sand. Christie stood looking at it.

'It's beautiful, isn't it?' She looked at Kate and Mary.

'It's not long for this world. If the wind comes up, it'll be buried in the sand,' Kate said.

Christie walked back a little distance and studied it in silence. Finally, they both helped Mary gather up the blanket and began walking along the sand towards the cottage.

174

No one had mentioned Lance. Christie was obviously lost in her own thoughts.

Finally, as they got to the wooden stairs and began to climb up, Mary asked Christie, 'So what did you think of Lance Bohrman?'

Christie remained silent. As they reached the top and walked onto the deck, she turned to Mary and Kate. 'What did you think of him?'

Mary traded a glance with Kate and said, 'Well, I saw more of him today than I have in the three years we've had this place.' She paused, and then said, 'Number one, he's probably the biggest dynamo I've ever run into.'

Kate looked at Christie. 'So what did *you* think of him?'

'I think I wonder if he fits anywhere. I wonder where he would really belong. He's in the wrong time.'

Kate thought a moment. Then she said, 'You're right. I can see him on horseback somewhere; like leading the Charge of the Light Brigade.'

They all walked to their rooms.

The sound of the guest shower came on, and Kate's voice singing.

Mary was brushing sand out of her hair when she heard a tap on her half-opened door. Christie was standing there, holding her white terry robe in front of her. She looked steadily into Mary's eyes. 'He's married, isn't he?' she asked.

Mary nodded. 'How did you know?'

Christie's grave look didn't waver. 'Well, he disappeared as suddenly as he came. Maybe he was only a hallucination.'

Mary had difficulty meeting her eyes. Christie had always seemed to her like an exile, a displaced person who created temporary homes in strange terrain. Yet she had seemed at home on the beach as if the Moon Castle were in fact her real house.

Mary slapped her on the fanny. 'Get in the shower. I want us to be out on the deck to see the sunset.'

Chapter Six

Mary had all the makings for drinks out on the deck by the time they were dressed. It was still hot, but the late-afternoon wind and the low sun made a passage into dusk. The light was soft, not yet twilight above the rim of the big lake.

Christie and Kate had put on shorts and T-shirts, but were still barefoot. Mary wore a long yellow jersey beach coat, with her brown hair hanging down her back. The others whistled when she came out.

'God,' Kate sighed, 'I've never seen anyone in anything but white uniforms or lab coats. It's affected my brain. I think I'm meeting strangers when I see them in their own clothes.' She sank into a lounge chair.

Mary mixed the drinks.

'Since you're being bartender, Christie and I will do the log rolling,' Kate said.

'Where are the gulls?' Christie wondered aloud.

'Bohrman probably harnessed them to fly him over the dune to his lair,' Kate laughed, sipping her drink. The sky was getting redder. Clouds with gold edges ballooned against the pale lavender sky.

'Hey, Kate,' Mary said, 'any hot news on Broadcliff?' Kate didn't answer right away.

'It's easier with a martini in my hand,' she said, finally. Her voice had a tinge of something Mary had never heard in her before. 'Remember Mr Kessler?' she asked – 'the old man with the tracheotomy and jaw cancer who went home to die? He lived in a trailer.'

'Of course.' Mary had an instant picture of three things: a

convict's calendar, a turquoise ring, and a crippled wife, who was fairly old herself.

'We were all afraid he would be so intimidating to his wife, what with the trach and the cancer being so bad, that she wouldn't be able to keep him at home,' Kate continued.

'I remember. I remember! What happened?' Mary leaned forward.

'Well, about a week after I got him home, the nurse from the Health Department phoned and told me they were doing fine. Get this: she said, "His wife not only isn't scared by the trach, she says she is sleeping well for the first time since he had to go to the hospital – with his arm around her."'

Kate was now speaking quickly, in the manner of a witness who had a hard story to report. She took another sip of her drink. There was a long silence. Everyone was watching the spectacular sky. The sun was now a huge coral globe descending into lavender-grey clouds.

'Mrs Kessler called the nurse very calmly, yesterday morning, and said, "Mr Kessler died last night." The nurse asked, "Are you all right? Were you alone?" and Mrs Kessler said, "Everything is all right. Mr Kessler must have slipped away some time during the night." He brought her some tea at bedtime, and she had brushed his hair and rubbed his back until he fell asleep. When she woke up, he was dead on her arm. She said, "He must have gone so easy – and we had such a good evening together."'

Kate paused. She bit her lips and blinked a few times. 'The nurse said the whole thing was kind of unique in her experience.'

All three were silent now, and watched the sun, which had grown more crimson, falling slowly into the lake.

'We shouldn't cry about the Kesslers,' Mary said. 'Let's drink a toast to them.' The three of them walked to the edge of the deck and clinked glasses.

'To the Kesslers,' said Mary.

'To loving someone,' said Christie.

They sipped their drinks and watched the sky.

'The sun is getting pretty low,' Christie told them.

177

'Shouldn't we start preparing the fire?'

She and Kate walked around the deck to the log pile and dropped a dozen good-sized logs down the bank. Mary brought out the shish kebabs and a picnic blanket.

'I'll dig a fire pit,' Kate offered.

By the time they had filed down the steps, it was almost dusk. Mary had decided to make a separate charcoal fire to grill the food. When the charcoal was hot, they began to roast their shish kebab. The disappearance of the sun had cooled the air a lot.

Kate stood up. 'I'm going to get some sweaters.'

'I'm going to get another blanket,' Christie said.

Mary curled up at the edge of the picnic blanket and ate pieces of steak and onions and mushrooms in her hand.

It was really dark now. The moon was not yet high enough to clear the woods behind the dunes and the cottage. The only light was a pale grey horizon where the sun had been, and the glowing charcoal. She had picked up another skewer of food to begin roasting it when something moving off to her left caught her attention.

Some distance down the beach and halfway up the steeper dunes she saw something that looked like a flare, a flickering orange flame, moving down the dune towards her. It was eerie and exciting to watch – a disembodied, bright entity coming towards a target.

As she watched it, she heard Kate and Christie on the stairs behind her.

'Hey, what's that – some ground meteor?' Kate called out.

They walked up to the charcoal fire and dropped the blanket and sweaters.

'It's Lance Bohrman,' Christie said. 'He must have seen the light from our fire.'

'Ahoy, there!' yelled a voice. The torch waved back and forth. It was now close enough for them to make out the figure carrying it. He was still wearing the baggy shorts he'd had on earlier, but had put on a blue velour shirt which hung open down the front. His torch was a pine branch he had soaked in something that gave off the orange flame tinged

178

with blue as it burned.

In the flicker of the torchlight, three things reflected and glittered: his eyes, his teeth, and a silver goblet he carried in his hand. He walked up to the charcoal fire.

'I could smell the meat cooking all the way down the beach.' He smiled and glanced around at them. Kate noted a subtle mutation in his brash demeanour when he looked at Christie. God, she thought, is it possible something could give him a touch of shyness? He walked over to where Christie stood and put his arm around her blanketed shoulders. She tugged at the blanket, looked down at the fire, and then back up at him. The torchlight revealed more than Kate wanted to see.

'Have you had dinner?' Mary asked Lance. 'We have plenty of food cooked, and more to go.'

'No,' Lance answered. 'I had to drive over to the harbour to check out my boat. We're racing tomorrow.' He stopped and planted the torch, smashing wet sand around it to make it stable.

Christie watched him securing the torch.

'Is the Moon Castle still standing?' she asked him. 'Did you pass it on the way down?'

'I came down to check it,' he told her. 'It's still there.' He walked over to her and held up the silver goblet. Everyone could see it more clearly now, closer, in the leaping light of the torch. It was fairly large, and etched around its sides were various designs. Kate and Mary watched him. His face became severe and grave.

'To the Moon Castle,' he said. He took a deep draught from the goblet. Then he held it up to Christie's mouth, indicating that she must drink from it. For a moment, she stared up into his eyes. Then she steadied it with her right hand and took a sip. She expected some unidentifiable, exotic potion.

'Hey, Lance, what witch's brew have you got in there?' Kate asked.

'It's just Cutty Sark and branch water,' Lance said, grinning. 'Have you girls got drinks? I can go up and get some booze . . . .'

179

'We've got our drinks here. We had cocktails while we watched the sunset,' Mary told him.

Lance walked over to the fire pit, taking in the heaped-up tinder and logs.

'Hey! You've got the makings for a great bonfire!' he shouted.

'Let's start it now,' Kate said.

'You all have to back up first,' Lance said, glancing around at the setup.

Kate jumped up. 'I want to light it! It's the first bonfire I ever helped build.'

Lance bowed low and handed the torch to Kate with a flourish.

'The ceremonial torch,' he said in a hushed voice. 'But you have to make an Intention before you light it. Lighting fires is important. You have to light them for something.'

Kate stood very still with the torch in her hand. In its light, her green eyes sparked red flecks.

'God!' said Kate. 'This is the second dedication we've done tonight. I feel as if I'm invoking the gods too much.' Everyone laughed, then fell silent. Kate lifted up the torch.

'This fire burns for courage.' She looked straight at Christie and then at Mary; then she touched the torch to the tinder. She looked at Lance as the driftwood began to crackle and snap. She walked over to him and gave him back his torch.

'*You* don't need any more courage,' she laughed.

Lance gave her a questioning look, followed by his slow smile. He accepted the return of the torch and again braced it carefully in the sand. Mary and Christie had dragged the picnic blanket and food a safe distance from the bonfire and were now sitting cross-legged, watching the flames from the driftwood licking high around the logs.

Kate circled the fire, admiring it and commenting about it. Lance circled just behind her. Christie watched the way he moved. He had a curious way of walking; a look of secret attention in his face, in the way he held his head. He walked like a hunter in the woods, like a man who is stalking

180

something. He had an aura of intense, controlled anticipation. Christie suddenly thought of cats she had seen, paying rapt attention to sights and sounds no human could see or hear.

After he walked around the fire, he sat down on the blanket next to Christie. He did not put down his goblet. Between sips, he held it in his hand. It shone silvery in the flames, glowing as if it contained its own pale fire. Christie reached her hand out to touch the goblet.

'May I look at it?' she asked. Lance placed it in her hand. She sat turning it and examining the figures etched on it.

'There is an owl,' she said, 'and a butterfly, and . . . is this a stalk of wheat?'

'Yes,' Lance told her. 'The owl is for wisdom, the butterfly is for joy, and the wheat means abundance – it means to be fruitful and flourish.'

Christie held the goblet and turned it, examining the etched figures closely.

'I love it,' she said. 'It looks very old. Where did you get it?'

'It came through my mother's family. It belonged to her father's mother, and to her father before that, and beyond. It is very old. It is a chalice. I think it is a magic chalice.' He looked at her through narrowed eyes, smiling, studying her face.

In this light, the chalice gave off a luminous glow. Christie wondered who had drunk from it, and why. What vows had they taken? It would be wonderful to find a goblet from which you could drink wisdom, joy, and abundance.

Mary had been unwrapping the food. The aroma of steak, onions, and garlic mixed with the scent of the wood smoke. They put the food from the skewers into the foil and ate from their laps. After a while, Lance pulled a corner of the blanket off Christie's shoulder and asked her to share it with him. He threw it over his head and spread it out on either side of him, like a huge bat. Then he swooped down on Christie, sliding behind her in the sand and wrapping both of them snugly in the blanket's folds. He reached around her with both arms and lifted her so that she was sitting between his legs. She felt warm and secure, and totally encircled. From time to time, his arms and thighs would tighten around her. He had an alarming strength.

Kate and Mary had been eating. Now they were lying on their backs, watching the stars and trying to name them. Lance had some food beside him, in its foil, and alternated putting bits of steak, mushrooms, or onions into his own mouth and then into Christie's. Sometimes he would pick the chalice from the sand and lift it to Christie's lips, then to his own.

Lance put his mouth next to Christie's ear and whispered, 'How long will you be here?'

Christie felt the distance between the night, now, and the Cancer Unit.

'I'm going home early Monday.'

Lance seemed to ponder this; then he said, 'Today is Saturday. I have a crew racing with me tomorrow. I have to leave for Chicago tomorrow night. Can I call you from there?'

Suddenly, Christie's mind was at war with her body. The time at the dunes had taken her out of her mind, and made her aware of her body in a new way. Only in childhood could she remember that simple relationship between herself and nature, between herself and the world. Only with certain patients had she acted almost entirely by instinct. Here, she felt both free and beautiful. She looked up at the night sky. Its velvet clarity and the millions of stars seemed almost within the reach of her hand.

Now there was the strange, comforting feeling, tinged with dread, of strong male arms and a warm body cradling her own. A faint litany in her head repeated that this man belonged to someone else; and yet he seemed to belong to no one. He seemed to follow some intricate and secret pattern within himself.

'Christie? Are you asleep?' His lips moved little waves of ice down her spine and her legs.

'No. I'm awake.'

'I want to take you to my house.'

182

The noise of the fire was dying down. The driftwood had been consumed. There was the hiss of the crimson logs, and the soft, lapping sound of waves breaking on the sand.

'I should help Mary gather up the stuff.' Christie suddenly sat up straight.

'All the stuff is in the basket. There won't be any logs left to take back,' Mary's voice answered.

'I'd like to take Christie up and show her the house,' Lance said. 'I'll get her back at a decent hour – by torch or by car.'

Kate said, 'I've had enough exercise and excitement to wear me out. I'm going to bed.'

'Hey, look!' Mary called out. 'A shooting star!'

They watched it make its arc across the sky and disappear above the horizon.

'There are star showers in August,' Lance told them. 'You can see them because it's much clearer here than in the city.'

Lance stood up and wrapped the blanket over Christie's shoulders.

'Follow me,' he said. Holding his torch in one hand and his chalice in the other, he headed towards the Moon Castle and the ridge of the high dune. Christie knotted the blanket over her shoulders. She was aware that a breeze had risen. It blew the blanket around her body rhythmically. She knew the joy of her legs pushing against the sand. She followed behind Lance Bohrman. He almost immediately began the slow cross-ascent to the ridge. It seemed they would not pass by the Moon Castle.

Chapter Seven

They climbed to the pine-covered ridge and then descended a winding path through the woods to a tall house of timber, set halfway up the dune. They walked onto a broad deck lit by

Tiki torches that made leaping shadows of light across the dark planking. They stood at the railing, and Christie saw that the moon had climbed from behind the dune and now spilled a path of silver onto the lake. Even though the house was nestled into the side of the dune, it was considerably higher above the lake than Mary's cottage.

Lance put his own torch into a holder on the railing. He put his arm around Christie and said, 'Welcome to Pacifica.' He led her through open double doors into a long room lit only by pinpoint lights in the ceiling, and a wood fire. She stood just inside the doorway and looked around the room. She had read about *déjà vu* in books, but had never experienced it herself. Now, an eerie sense of more than foreknowledge flooded her. She had never been in this house before, but her heart and her spirit knew it. It was as if she had returned to a place where she had lived through profound experiences; as if some meaning her mind could not identify was laced and woven into the fabric of all that the room contained. She stood motionless at the edge of the white carpet. Lance was staring at her. She had forgotten his presence in the impact of the house.

'Are you okay?' he asked. 'Did I race you up the dune too fast?'

'No,' Christie said, 'I'm just looking at the room.'

The blanket had slipped from her shoulders and was lying on the floor around her feet. Lance picked it up and threw it over a black-and-white-plaid chaise longue next to the fireplace. Christie's eyes turned to the fireplace and to the brick wall above it. Hanging on the wall was a half-furled handwritten musical manuscript, and next to it a large child's watercolour of a clown in vivid colours. She walked over to the painting and studied it. In the lower left corner, in a child's uneven print, was the name 'COLLIN'.

Christie turned and saw Lance standing behind her shoulder. She looked at him closely. He was squinting at the painting, his expression blank. She walked to the chaise and turned around to see the rest of the room. One wall was mostly books. On a low table beneath it stood a tall, slim woodcarving of a cowl-draped figure. A flat wooden bowl filled with stones lay beside it. At one end of the room was a grand piano. A tall earthen vase on its surface held several twisted bare branches. There were low sofas scattered with fur-covered pillows. The floor was dark, polished wood. The white rug curved around the room in a free-form pattern. Beyond the piano was a built-in bar, of the same driftwood-coloured panelling as the walls.

Lance put his chalice on the bar. Then he bent down, selected a record, and put it on the turntable. He uncorked a bottle of Scotch.

'Would you like a drink?' he asked. 'What do you prefer?'

He was an urbane and mannerly host. She almost forgot the savage. She ran her fingers through her hair. It was hopelessly tangled by the moisture and the wind.

'The same as yours, only light,' she answered.

While he was mixing the drinks, Christie studied the room again.

'Your wife has very good taste,' she remarked.

'My mother furnished this house,' he answered.

Christie walked over to the fireplace wall. 'Who is Collin?' She touched the manuscript lightly with her fingers. It was yellowed with age.

'Collin was my brother,' Lance said. He walked over to Christie and gave her the drink. He looked into his goblet, shaking it gently.

'Collin painted that when he was five. He wrote the étude when he was twenty-one.'

Christie continued to stare at the clown. It expressed a whole spectrum of gaiety and tragedy in the spare whimsy achievable only by children.

'He was my half-brother,' said Lance. He walked over and stood beside Christie. 'Collin's father died,' he said, his voice slightly uneven. 'Collin was killed at Anzio.'

The room was suddenly filled with music. Lance had put on a swirling, heady South American record. Someone with a gruff, shaded accent was singing. His voice was sexy and slightly flat. Christie watched Lance walk around the room, lighting candles. His rumpled white shorts; his tanned, heavily muscled body; his wild, grey-blond hair were a dramatic contrast to the room, but he was as much at home here as he was in the dunes. Once having entered the door, his slow, ritualistic persona took over.

The candle flames flickered in the air from the open doors. They made shuddering patterns of the long, bare branches.

The music curved and danced. Its resonance echoed from the beams in the ceiling, and in the base of Christie's spine. She walked over to the black-and-white chaise again and sat down on her blanket. The room was warm, but the breeze entering the doors was cool, tinged with water and the moon.

The room was filled with presences. Suddenly, she was overpowered by it. She got up and walked out onto the deck. She lifted her head and took deep breaths. The feeling of being surrounded, of hearing messages, of coming home would not leave. She wiped away some tears with the tail of her shirt and felt Lance standing beside her. The hair on his temples brushed her ear. She felt his arms around her shoulders. His mouth, for the first time, brushed against hers. His lips were firm and gentle. They searched her face without kissing her mouth, like a wordless speech. Moving, moving, and making no sound. His face covered hers. His arms closed off her perception of space. Then she was lying on something broad and soft, a bed of fur. Lance was above her, but weightless, like a bridge, joining all that was known in her to all that had never been.

'Christie,' he said, 'Christie . . .' She opened her eyes. The other voices, the other presences were gone. She saw beyond his face a row of glass shelves. Covering them were rows of golden trophies, smooth and shiny; a horse being taken over a jump by a woman in a hunter's hat. A skier beside it, bright in the beam of a spotlight in the ceiling. And a slim female figure caught in a high leap with a raised tennis racket.

Christie heard the sensuous undulation of music in the background. She saw Lance's hair and his strange eyes against the sheen of the trophies.

His face moved away very slowly. He sat back on the bed,

and she was able to look around her. She was in a beautiful room. On all sides, she saw Lance's body and her own, both of them in beach clothes, both with dishevelled hair. There were multiple images, multiple beds of fur, brown and taupe and white. There were a thousand reflected images of golden women performing feats with horses, clubs, rackets, and ski poles. The room was mirrored on all sides.

'No,' she said. 'No.'

'Christie ... please.'

'I have to go back.'

'Just let me hold you!'

'No ... not here.'

'Why not ... Then where?'

'This is your wife's house.'

'This is my mother's house.'

'You live here ... with your wife.'

'Christie' – his voice was husky, almost muffled – 'I need you ... Christie. ...' She felt his mouth again, moving over her face and hair, finding her mouth and exploring it. His arms held her in an iron grip.

'I want to leave,' she whispered. 'Whatever happens to me in this room will not be mine.' She twisted her body away from him. He stood up and looked down at her. She felt suddenly hollow, as if part of herself had been withdrawn.

He took her hand and lifted her up, leading her out of the room. He scooped up the blanket from the chaise, draped it around her shoulders, then led her outside. He pulled his torch from its holder, walked to the far end of the deck, and jumped down into the sand, immediately taking a path near the top of the ridge and below the pines. When they had left the shadows of the trees and were bathed in the light of the full moon, Lance stopped and planted his torch in the sand.

'We can find our way by moonlight now,' he said.

They began the cross-descent, going down across the dune towards the water. The lake was now the deep, shimmering grey of wet stone. Slow foam moved along the shore. The sand was cool and silky on her feet as she followed him. His hair was silvered by the moon. His shoulders looked huge, moving just ahead of her below. Her heart pounded. She was aware that she followed him almost in a trance, without question. Free of the interruption of the mirrored room, they were back in their own time.

They were approaching the level area of the beach. She could hear the hushing sound of the waves. Just beyond Lance she saw the outlines of a small structure breaking into the pale expanse of sand. It was the Moon Castle, distant enough from the water not to have been washed away. She was surprised that no passerby had knocked it down. Lance stopped about four feet from it, and moved over to Christie. He took the blanket from her shoulders and spread it on the sand. Then he lifted her into his arms and began to walk with her, circling the Moon Castle slowly.

She wrapped her arms around his neck. She had almost the same feeling she had experienced earlier when he had taken her into his strangely familiar house. But beneath the relief of this homecoming there lay dread; the awareness of a critical leap into darkness.

His arms held her tightly. He was lowering her gently onto the blanket, and she saw the castle clearly. It was sculptured by shadows. Seen from her position flat on the sand, it seemed to have grown gracefully and mysteriously to human size. The stairway to the structure curved upward in a long, wide sweep. The trees guarding it stood like tall and venerable sentinels. The slender pillars that encircled it filtered pale light in rhythmic patterns. The rocks that formed its walls and ramparts seemed solid and firm as mountain cliffs.

She felt the wind from the lake on her arms and legs, and shivered. Lance was kneeling above her, unbuttoning her shirt. He removed his velour jacket and put it around her. He slid his arms under her body, cradling her loosely against him. His lips touched her eyelids, closing her eyes, pressing against her hair and moving along her throat. His body warmed and surrounded her. No longer aware of the wind, she drifted in the security of his strength.

Then she felt him move away. He sat down on the blanket

beside her and deftly and unhurriedly removed all their clothes. He threw them behind him in the sand. His figure bending above her was in shadows, but she saw the undulations of her own body gleaming whitely in the full moon. Lance began to trace with his fingers the structure of her bones: her neck, her shoulders, her rib cage, her hipbones, all the concave hollows between. He traced the convolutions of her body as if he were moulding it. His lips now followed the long line of her legs. He held her feet and stroked the high curve of the arch. He followed the structure of each foot with his fingers. He leaned back and explored her carefully with his eyes. His head was bowed, but the moon etched the concentration of his face with shadows.

His features took on a kind of purity. She thought, oddly, of the faces of choirboys. Her body shuddered. Lance kept his position away from, and above her, touching her only with his eyes. She was aware of a sensation like pain engulfing her. She had never known this strange kind of pain. She closed her arms tightly around her body and drew up her legs against her stomach. She heard her own voice in a muffled cry.

Suddenly, Lance was surrounding her. The rigid muscles of his arms pinned her against his body. Something like torment, something like relief filled and shook her. He was moving over her, around her, within her. He seemed to devour her in some dark, flameless fire. When she felt she would die, or be consumed, he released her; retreating, leaning away from her, stroking the curves of her breasts, her waist, her stomach, tracing her, again, with his eyes.

When the pain mounted, and she could no longer wonder at his face, he surrounded her, impaling her on the fire. She writhed against it. She thrust upward to embrace it. Suddenly, the fire exploded in her centre. Her whole being was wrenched into spasms of relief. They came and went, gripping her into tension, then releasing her. She felt hot tears running down her cheeks. Her body shook and was still.

After a long while she became aware that Lance was

189

holding her in a close, weightless embrace; speaking to her, saying her name. His mouth travelled over her face and her eyes, blotting the tears. She felt that all that was material in her, every hard edge and tension, had been melted and absorbed, like water, into the sand. It was a strange, free sensation, as if she were at last liberated from the weight of her body.

'Christie.' Lance was saying her name again. He had moved to her side and was leaning on one elbow, looking down at her. He pulled the edge of the blanket up and wrapped it around them.

'You won't leave me? I'll see you again?'

'Yes.'

'Christie . . .' – he seemed to be groping for words – 'you slow me down. Thank God. You slow me *down*.' His voice had a ragged relief in it, as if someone had dragged him from a car with no brakes that had been headed for a precipice.

She opened her eyes and looked at him. There was no mocking flirtation in his eyes, none of the heat of sexual need. Their eyes held each other with the tenuous closeness of everything in them that was inexpressible by touch.

She reached up and pushed the hair from his forehead. She stroked his head. He lay down beside her and pulled her onto his arm, cradling her head on his shoulder. She felt his hair against her cheek and brushed her lips across it. She ran her fingers through the thick, wiry hair on his chest. He had drawn the blanket snugly around them, and the warmth of their bodies allowed her mind to wander.

Just beyond Lance's head, her glance fell on a low clump of juniper bushes, scraggly and half barren from the wind. Something bright glistened from it like slender filaments of diamond thread. Its tiny creator rested serenely at its centre, his feet clinging to delicate skeins, his body moving as the web moved in the wind.

A rush of love for the spider and his home filled Christie, and a dark knowledge of the vulnerability of silken webs.

The spider had spun his web at the windward edge of a vast lake, not in a dark corner of a cave, not in a warm closet.

She partook of his frail existence. She was a sister to the spider.

Lance moved slightly, and a thin eddy of wind blew between their bodies. The blanket fluttered. He put his lips to her ear and kissed her.

'Christie,' he whispered. His voice was husky with earnestness, and a tinge of pain. 'I love you. I love you more than I've loved any woman. Christie ... I think I will love you for a long time.'

He paused for a moment. His voice had grown unsteady. Her heart pounded slowly and heavily. She looked past Lance's head at the spider. He pulsed in the centre of a breathtaking microcosm. He vibrated in his web like a tuning fork. Tiny diamonds of dew sparkled in the skeins surrounding him like a miniature constellation. She fell asleep watching the spider and his web, and listening to Lance's slow, regular breathing.

Chapter Eight

Since his return home from the hospital, Victor Vendetti had entered a period of remarkable peace. He had experienced a gradual release from his pain, which he attributed to Franciscus' unblocked channel to the ears of the Lord. He had apparently been granted some 'good time', as he'd requested; time in which to ponder his life with Stella and the turn of events in his life, beginning with his sojourn at Broadcliff.

Stella had been working at a big packaging plant long before his hospitalization. When she knew he was coming home, she had requested to have her shift changed so that she could spend more time with him. She worked between three-thirty and eleven and had his dinner ready when she left for work. These hours allowed her to spend most of the night with him, too. Their neighbours Arline and Stan looked in on him while she was gone. They had assured Victor that they were available anytime help was needed.

When he had first arrived home the weather was still cold, but the snow flurries were punctuated with intervals of sun. Stella had moved a daybed alongside a south window in the living room, and Victor spent his days there, lying in the sun. Shabby and lacking in luxury as it was, his home was a blessed haven compared with the hospital. As the last days of winter relaxed their hold on Brandenburg, Victor lay on his daybed emptied of the bitterness and guilt of the past. He was at peace about Renée. He no longer thought of himself as the instrument of her doom. Their relationship now seemed to him fulfilled.

He felt as if his mind and spirit, and even his body, had been released. He dozed and woke through the lengthening days of spring. He closed his eyes and let the sun warm his face. It shone with increasing strength through the bare branches of a maple tree. The delicate shadows of the branches quivered over his blanket. New ideas came to Victor in his hours alone with the tree and the sun. Many of his thoughts now concerned Stella and her needs. Released from his old outrage and bitterness, he had become aware of Stella's hurt and her sad isolation. He saw how thoroughly he had locked her out of his life.

One day in April, she had been sitting at the foot of the daybed in a rocker. Some mending was in her lap, and as she worked, the moving branches and the sun cast lights and shadows on her face. He watched her as she bent over her mending, wondering how one went about the task of reversing the years, and feeling that he was seeing Stella for the first time. She looked up and saw him watching her. She seemed startled, then smiled uncertainly.

'Stella,' he began, then waited for whatever words would come. She raised her eyes again from her mending and put down her needle. He knew she was expecting some request; water perhaps, or a pain pill.

'Stella,' he said again. The name felt awkward on his tongue. He realized he hadn't called her by *any* name for many years. He cleared his throat and smiled at her.

'Your eyes are the colour of the lightest turquoise I ever saw in Phoenix,' he said. She looked startled. Her lips parted slightly, and colour came up in her cheeks. She stared at him for a moment, then went back to her mending. He saw that the hand holding the needle shook slightly.

'Stella,' he repeated her name a third time, 'you have been good to me – good *for* me. I haven't been having so much pain lately. Now that it's getting warmer I want to plant some seeds for you, maybe a rosebush.' He waited for her response. 'Would you like a rosebush?'

Stella again put down her mending and looked at him with a mixture of hope and doubt.

'Roses bloom year after year,' he went on. 'You don't have to do replanting. Just a little pruning.'

She searched his face, and her mouth softened. Her rocking chair was still.

She looked out at the brown grass. Here and there small spots of green were appearing. The yard was barren except for the maple tree outside the window. A broken lattice that had been the grape arbour was still half attached to their old garage.

'I always wanted a rosebush,' she said. Her voice, usually flat and toneless, now had some pale colour, like the first patches of green in the winter grass. 'A *pink* rosebush,' she added. She put down her sewing on the foot of the bed and stood up to look out at the yard. Next to the broken arbour and the garage, a low grey fence bordered the alley. Her eyes brightened, imagining something. Victor followed her glance.

'Stella, I'm going to take Stan up on his offer to repair the grape arbour. The grapes rotted on the ground last summer,' he said. She patted his blanket-covered foot and smiled.

'Arline wanted me to make jelly with them last year. This summer we could have plenty for them – and us.'

Victor nodded. He closed his eyes and sighed. He felt

Stella's hand touch the top of his head and stroke his hair. She had stopped touching him a long time ago, feeling his resentment, his silent drawing away. She knew, though he never said it, that her crime lay in being herself instead of someone else.

'I'm going to check on supper,' she whispered, withdrawing her hand. He reached up and caught it in his own, then pressed it against his cheek. He could accept its warmth and its comfort now.

'I'm hungry,' he said. 'I can smell the soup.'

She smoothed the wrinkles from her apron. 'It's almost ready,' she answered. 'I'll turn the fire down.' She moved away to the kitchen. He could hear the reassuring sound of her footsteps, of the lid rattling against the soup pot, the dishes clinking as she set the table. Now she was humming to herself, some old tune from the forties, a little off key. He closed his eyes and felt tears roll down his cheeks. He could feel tenderness again. He could love Stella because she was Stella.

Chapter Nine

By midsummer Christie and Father Franciscus had been visiting Victor Vendetti at home from time to time. Christie's visits were not official, since hospital employees were not supposed to follow patients who had been discharged. Social Services discouraged its staff from continuing relationships, believing it destroyed professional objectivity. Christie said nothing to the staff about her visits, except to Mary, Hugh, and Kate.

Christie's relationship with Lance now occupied most of her thoughts. He called her almost daily and was planning to come to Brandenburg in a couple of weeks. His business in Chicago had kept him tied up there. She had plenty of time to think about him, as she seemed to have fewer and fewer patients. Her referrals had diminished, as if cut off at the source.

After her return from Mary's cottage, she called Victor and went to see him one Saturday afternoon. Stella had just cleaned up the lunch dishes and was getting ready to go to market. Christie had noticed a gradual change in her over the months since Victor's homecoming. Now she was like a butterfly which had emerged from its chrysalis after too prolonged a metamorphosis.

Stella greeted her at the front door, wiping her hands on her apron and smiling. Her eyes, which before had been dim and dull, had come alive. Their pale blue colour contained a sparkle. She had curled her hair and wore it in a soft style that flattered her features. Her colour was enhanced with a little makeup. The sense of defeat and poverty that had clung to her in the past was gone. There was a dignity about her, even grace.

'Come in, come in!' she sang. Her voice was alive now, too – a radical change from the apologetic monotone Christie remembered.

Stella led her towards the back door. 'Victor's anxious to talk with you,' she said. 'He wants to know all about your little vacation at Mary's. Father keeps him posted on all the news, you know.'

Christie felt a small sinking sensation as she followed Stella into the backyard. Lately, as she walked around the hospital on her calls she had hoped not to run into Franciscus. She would not know what to say to him, since she could not summon the courage to tell him what now filled her thoughts. Victor was different. She would feel less guilty speaking with Victor about Lance. The priest lived in a state of grace from which she had long since fallen. Victor had lived with two women, maybe more, and had not been married to any of them.

Stella walked with Christie over to an old lounge chair

where Victor lay drowsing in the half-shade of his maple tree.

'Victor' – she touched his cheek gently – 'wake up! Christie's here. She's back from her vacation.'

Victor opened his eyes and looked up at them with eager expectancy. Stella also looked forward to Christie's and Father Franciscus' visits. They injected news from the outside world. The conversations Victor had with them seemed as strengthening to him as plasma. She had the feeling that part of what he received from them was that they enjoyed and appreciated what he had to say.

Christie settled down, cross-legged, in the grass next to Victor's chair.

'There's iced tea and cookies in the house if you'd like some refreshments,' Stella said. 'I'm going down the street to do some shopping.'

'Your yard looks beautiful!' Christie called after her. She looked around at the flowers. 'I've never seen such big zinnias and morning glories. Oh! Look at the roses!'

'Go smell the roses and pick one for yourself,' Victor told her. 'The sun brings out the smell.'

Christie wandered over to the small garden. 'I hate to disturb them,' she replied. She watched some bees browsing drunkenly among the warm flowers.

'Stella will cut some roses for you before you leave,' Victor told her. 'The more you pick them, the more they will bloom.' He watched Christie bend over to smell the delicate petals. He thought she looked thinner. He studied her closely as she walked back towards him and sat down on the thick grass. She was very tanned, and in spite of being a little thinner, she had a healthier look. Something was different. She seemed more earthbound, more substantial. They smiled at each other and were silent for a few moments. Christie spoke first, feeling a bit self-conscious under Victor's X-ray gaze.

'Stella looks terrific, Vic. She looks like *she's* been on a vacation. Something's made her look ten years younger.'

As Christie spoke with him, she thought *he* seemed thinner. But his face was tanned. He was obviously relaxed and

196

in no pain. He smiled and looked up into the maple leaves.

'It's just that I've had enough peace of mind myself to think of her. She's been neglected – like the yard here used to be.' He looked over at the fence and the grape arbour. They had been repaired and were painted white. The tendrils on the grapevines were loaded with tiny, hard new grapes.

Christie watched him fondly. She looked at the bushy grey eyebrows above his keen eyes and remembered him guarding his self-constructed bed on Seven Main. She had admired his courage even then, knowing it would get him nowhere, knowing he would be punished for it. Now she felt as if she were discovering new facets of his nature each time she saw him. He was speaking again, very earnestly.

'Christie, I'm glad she's been promoted. I know she'll be promoted again after a while. And I want her to have some experience of success so she won't feel lost when I'm gone. Right now God's just loaned me some time. Some *good* time. Better than I hoped for when I asked Stefan Franciscus to pray for me.'

'You asked him to pray for you?'

'Before I left the hospital. I wanted some time to make things right. After I talked to you about Renée you helped me to see myself and her – in a different light. I wanted to be able to live awhile . . . not like old Harold, winding down like a broken clock, but to live awhile well enough to make . . . reparations, I guess you'd call it. It's important that a man leave behind him *less* pain, not more.'

Christie felt her throat constricting. 'Do you pray, yourself?' she asked him. Victor considered the question for a time before he could answer.

'When I asked Franciscus to pray for me, I couldn't imagine a God who could have anything personal to do with us – with men. I figured that if there *was* a God who could hear He'd more likely be reached by a man like Franciscus, who was a cut higher than the rest of us.

'Well, now at least I know God's *there*, because Franciscus reached Him and he must have thought it was a good idea to give me this time.' Victor folded his hands and rested his chin

197

on his knuckles. He sat there thinking, a slight frown wrinkling his brow. He wanted to describe to Christie all that had been happening inside him.

'When I came home here at the end of the winter I laid on the daybed in the *sun*, like you told me to. I was just weak and tired from all my battles – empty. Somehow, gradually, lying there over the days and the weeks, thoughts began to come to me. Sometimes something that felt like love, or an unbelievable kindness, seemed to touch me – to *fill* me. Maybe it was God. I'm willing to believe it was God. Anyway, the pain lessened. I even got a little stronger. Strong enough to plant a rosebush, to hold up the trellis while Stan hammered nails in it. Maybe God can't touch you, can't deal with you, till you're *empty*.' He leaned back in the lounge chair, looking again up into the maple leaves. They were both silent, within their own thoughts.

'I guess I have never really been *empty* – or empty enough,' Christie said after a time. 'I'm always full, or half-full, of *some*thing. I guess I too need someone like Franciscus to intercede for me.'

They both fell silent again. Some pale yellow butterflies flew into the space between them and executed an intricate ballet in the air.

'Christie,' Victor began, and his eyes narrowed and glinted, 'how was your vacation? When you walked into the yard there was something new about you, something like you saw in Stella. I'd have sworn I was looking at a woman who had fallen in love.'

Christie had been watching the butterflies. Now she looked back at Victor and her face flushed.

'I'm right!' Victor leaned back in his chair and laughed gently. 'I've never been mistaken about that look.' He watched her mouth curve into a smile. 'Who is it?' he teased. 'Did you finally run into a resident who had some moxie?'

Christie twisted a corner of her skirt around her finger and shook her head.

'No. It's nobody around here. I met him at Mary's. On the beach. He's different from anyone I've ever met. He's smart and wild and – tender. He helped me build a Moon Castle!

He was announced by an avatar ... a gull! And—'

Victor raised both hands. 'Wait! Let me catch up! You're throwing around some big words there.' He watched her face. As she spoke her eyes had grown soft and very bright.

'And,' she continued, 'he lives too far away for me to see him often ... and he ... he ... belongs to someone else.' She folded her hands in her lap and straightened her shoulders. She stared into Victor's eyes and waited for his response.

'You love him?' he asked.

She bit her upper lip and nodded her head vigorously. He had never noticed before how square her jaw was. He had always known she was capable of great commitment – or great stubbornness. What he knew of her responses in the hospital proved that. He wondered if she really knew what she was committing herself to now.

His own sins of commission and omission moved in his mind.

'Then you must go with it. See where it leads. Maybe you will find you must turn back. Maybe you won't.'

Christie's face filled with the intensity of her emotions. 'I think, Vic ... I think he's given me my *self* back – like you did with Renée. He makes me feel, for the first time in years, that I have a body. He teaches me how to run, how to play. He makes me feel that I have substance – as well as spirit! He makes me feel real. He might ...' Tears spilled from her eyes and ran down her cheeks, and her voice faltered as she went on. 'He might even *make me feel real in the snow*.' She wiped the tears with her skirt. 'Can you *understand*, Vic? I know *you* must understand!'

He stretched out his arm to her, and she grasped his hand. His voice was hoarse with what he knew, what he remembered, and what he feared.

'I understand,' he whispered.

She stood up and looked down at him, pressing his hand tightly. Her voice was very soft. 'You always told me I needed to have something in my life, more than the hospital. Well, now I *do*. As long as he has room for me in his life, I'll go on seeing him.'

Victor managed a smile, camouflaging the uneasiness and

concern he knew had registered on his face. They heard the screen door slam and Stella came walking towards them, her printed cotton skirt blowing around her legs. She was carrying a tray of iced-tea glasses and a platter of cookies.

'It's good to be back in this breezy yard,' she said. 'It was hot in the store.'

Chapter Ten

Martin Kiley had been readmitted to the Seven Main Cancer Unit on Thursday, the day Mary and Christie left for the dunes. He did not live in Brandenburg, but came from a small town about thirty miles away. He had been doing fairly well on the new treatment Virgil Prince had switched to after his tests in February. But he had suddenly become quite ill, developing severe symptoms, and Prince had told him he must be hospitalized for tests. It was apparent from the increasing yellow colour of his skin that the cancer was spreading to his liver. He had succeeded in obtaining a private room. He still looked strong, with his heavily muscled arms and legs and broad, thick chest. He had piercing grey eyes, almost the colour of his hair. He was fifty-five years old.

Martin had been commuting for weekly treatments. Now his wife had begun daily trips to be with him in the hospital. They had six children, four from his first marriage.

Mrs Kiley was a quiet woman. She seemed, somewhere along in life, to have achieved a vast patience. She attended her husband silently at his bedside. She was not a talker. Her conversation was limited to her husband's interests and needs.

Prince received the report on Martin Kiley's liver scan the Monday after his readmission. He eased his silver-grey

Mark VI into his reserved space in the doctors' ramp at Broadcliff, mindful of the little talk he would have to present to Martin Kiley and his wife. The next step on the protocol for treatment was a liver infusion. He was sure that Kiley wanted to live. He had been a strong man, and several of his six children were still at home. Moreover, he had lived only six years with his new wife. So Prince anticipated no trouble in following through with the data. The presence of Brenda on all his calls augmented his own power. Her aura of arrogant beauty, mixed with the immaculate authority of her nurse's uniform, dramatically complemented his own presence. He realized that together, they presented a formidable bulwark of wisdom and authority. While he spoke to the patients about their test results and his proposals for treatment, Brenda stood attentively and reverently erect at the foot of the bed. He often thought of her in fantasy as a high priestess who guarded their mobile tabernacle.

He arrived in the Broadcliff lobby and made his way to the Pathology Laboratory. He examined the test results of his patients, noting the bad news of Julius Hoffman, who had died the night before. He left the lab and headed down the hall to his office to pick up Brenda. When he opened the door, she was on the phone with her back to him. He laid his attaché case on the desk with enough noise to announce his arrival.

Brenda half-turned from the phone. 'Okay. I'll tell him. We'll be up in a minute.'

She put the phone back on its cradle and looked at him with a level, matter-of-fact stare.

'What's up?' Prince asked her.

'The head nurse reporting that Joan Bentley has been crying a lot again. She still can't eat anything.'

'Let's go,' Prince said. Brenda picked up her portfolio of patient protocols. She walked over to him and straightened his tie, deftly sliding a finger under his shirt between the buttons and putting a fine, scalpel scratch along his chest with her sharp nail. He shivered, and grabbed his stethoscope off the doorknob. Brenda went ahead of him as they walked to the elevator. It was filled with the usual morning crowd of nurses, residents, secretaries, and visitors. Prince and Brenda rode in silence up to Seven Main. They walked into the nurses' station.

'Where do you want to start?' Brenda asked in her customary crisp hospital delivery, pulling the charts out of their slots.

'With Kiley,' Prince replied. 'Anything new in his chart?'

'Yes. Evidently he was hallucinating last night,' Brenda announced.

They walked towards Kiley's room.

'I wouldn't expect that in his stage of liver disease, or with his potassium level,' Prince observed. He stopped walking and picked up the chart, paging through it to the last lab reports. 'No,' he concluded, 'I don't understand it.'

'Well, he's hallucinating,' Brenda insisted. 'He may be developing a schiz psychosis. He told two of the nurses, one on the eleven-to-seven shift and one on the seven-to-three, that he saw Jesus in his room.'

Brenda employed her favourite gesture of punctuation. She took her right index finger, lifted a long shaft of hair from her cheekbone, and tossed her head.

'Jesus?' he said, lifting one eyebrow and staring at her over the top of Kiley's metal chart case.

'It's all in the Nurse's Notes,' Brenda replied.

Prince shifted his shoulders around under his coat and his collar. He put Kiley's chart back on the stack. He turned his head slightly and studied Brenda from his profile stance.

'Well, from the perspective of his present predicament, it could be wishful thinking,' he commented dryly. They proceeded on towards Kiley's room. He thought a moment, and added, 'Did his visitor make any conversation?'

'According to the reports, he told Kiley that he shouldn't be afraid, that everything was going to turn out fine.'

Neither of them spoke. They kept walking. They were almost to Kiley's room.

'You know the agenda. I have to propose the liver

infusion and explain why,' Prince said.

Brenda nodded.

'The hallucination could work either way,' Prince went on. 'It could make him agree quickly and feel confident the treatment would cure him.' He paused, considering.

'Or' – Brenda picked up on his logic – 'it could give him the confidence to refuse treatment and wait for a miracle. Is he religious? I mean, has he been religious before?'

'He's on the record as a Catholic,' Prince replied.

Brenda seesawed both hands in the *comme-ci, comme ça* sign.

'Yeah,' said Prince. They both stood in front of Kiley's door and looked at each other. Brenda squared her shoulders, tossed her head, and opened the door.

There were three people in the room. Martin Kiley filled the bed with his huge, muscular body. His eyes were closed, and a peaceful smile curved his lips. His wife was sitting in the large visitor's chair leaning forward and talking to Christie Wilson, who was perched on the footstool. Mrs Kiley was asking how to collect total-disability insurance.

Christie stood up when she saw Prince and Brenda.

'I'll come back after the doctor leaves,' she told Mrs Kiley.

Mrs Kiley nodded. Martin opened his eyes at the word 'doctor' and held out his hand.

'You don't need to leave,' Prince said, waving his arm at Christie.

'I'll be back,' she said to Mrs Kiley. She moved towards the door and glanced back at Prince. 'I'd like a minute to talk to you, later.' Christie left the room, giving a little smile and salute to Martin as she went out.

The patient leaned forward in his bed and made a host's gesture to Prince.

'Sit down and relax a minute, Doctor,' he said. 'You and I never really get a chance to chat man-to-man.' He threw subtle glances at his wife and Brenda, as he drew his I.V. away from Brenda's probing fingers.

Prince took a seat in the plastic upholstered visitor's chair Mrs Kiley had vacated.

'Well, Dr Prince, you must have come here with some news. Did we get some results from all those tests you ordered?'

Prince leaned back easily in the chair and slowly paged through Kiley's chart. Finally, after a pause which was long enough to engender uneasiness, he began to talk in his best casual, chatty style.

'Ye–es ... we have some results here, and we can pinpoint some of the reasons for your pain and the anorexia. The liver scan turned up the presence of more disease, and the further blood tests showed the white-cell count is down. These are things we don't like to see, but fortunately, we have treatment for them.'

'More disease?'

'Your lung disease has extended itself to the liver. I was hoping the drug therapies we had on your programme would forestall that, but it often happens. When it does, we move the treatment to a direct infusion through the hepatic artery. It is most effective.'

Martin Kiley had fixed Prince with the full weight of his direct steel-grey gaze.

'Infusion – that means something going into an artery – the drug?'

'The metastasis is involving the liver. With this treatment the drug is dripped directly into the liver itself, for maximum concentration and effectiveness.' Prince maintained a demeanour of casual, almost lazy, nonchalance which was always the nucleus for his presentation of the bad news and the antidote. It implied the opposite of crisis. It offered logic and control.

Kiley leaned back on his pillows and looked out the window. His far view was partially obstructed by the freeway interchange, but the freeway interchange had now become for him a kind of holy ground. He had been looking at it when the angel appeared.

He looked back at the group around his bed. His wife was standing beside the bed with her hand on his pillow. He could read her love for him in the lines of anxiety etched on her face. Everything his frivolous first wife had not been, all

204

the hurt she had dealt him, had been erased and healed by Gretchen. She was from solid German stock and had taken over and reared his children with stern discipline and abundant affection. Only Josh had stayed with his mother. The Church had never recognized their marriage because his first wife was Catholic and alive. But Gretchen was, as far as he was concerned, his one and only wife, and he had had two more sons by her, and she was praying for him to be healed. On the way home each night, she stopped by the Catholic church and lit a candle for him. She was not Catholic, but knowing that he was, she felt the prayer, and the consistency of her visits, would move the Lord to intercede.

Kiley's glance moved to Virgil Prince, who sat studying the pages of his chart. What a curious and tragic disfiguration he had been saddled with. The perfect half of his face was as handsome as a movie star's, the features fine and sensitive. The good side of Prince's face had always reminded Martin Kiley of someone, but he couldn't remember whom.

Suddenly Prince turned from perusing the chart and looked at his nurse, and it struck Martin that he looked like *David*. His first wife had had a print she treasured of an old Italian painting. The face was David's, the young boy, before he became King.

Ever since his remarkable experience the day before, Kiley had been infused with an almost supernatural grace and confidence. It was as if he saw people in an illuminated way. He looked at Virgil Prince's face and was moved to a deep compassion.

He leaned forward in his bed, his eyes slightly misted. 'Dr Prince, I wish you and I would have time to speak alone some day.' He paused and glanced at Brenda, then went on: 'What do you want me to do?'

Prince cleared his throat. He appeared a bit – ever so slightly – uncomfortable. His voice was even and low.

'The optimum-treatment protocol for the condition of your disease calls for immediate infusion of the liver with . . .' He named a combination of chemicals that Martin Kiley did not try to remember. Kiley sighed and looked at his wife and then at the nurse. He wished he could talk with this doctor in his hometown tavern over a glass of good whiskey, or before his fireplace at the farm. Above all, he wished he could talk with him alone, without the impersonal presence of this nurse hovering over the scene. He wanted to share with him the miraculous appearance and the message he had received from Jesus.

Virgil Prince shut the metal chart case with a sharp crack. He smiled and stood up.

'Mr Kiley, why don't you discuss this with your wife, and let the head nurse know your decision. I would like to get started with your infusion this afternoon. My nurse, Brenda, will call in later to see if you have made up your mind.'

Martin looked at Prince intently. 'And if I say "No infusion"?'

Prince's smile twitched slightly to one side. 'We all know what your disease will achieve if it is not treated.'

'And the liver infusion: what does *it* achieve?'

'It will, hopefully, retard the metastasis. We treat to improve the life quality of the patient.'

Kiley looked down at the bruises on his arms. His I.V. had gone subcutaneous a few times. They always had to try several times to get a good vein when they came for the daily blood tests.

'More chemical treatments mean more blood samples?' Kiley asked.

'We have to keep close track of your blood-chemistry changes.' Prince had been moving towards the door. Martin Kiley looked down at his own large hands, and appeared to study them.

'We'll check later, Mr Kiley. You and your wife think about it. But don't delay too long.' Prince held the door ajar as Brenda passed through.

They both moved silently down the hallway towards the room of the next patient. Finally, Brenda spoke.

'Well, what do you think?'

'I think something has made him less cooperative. It

would be difficult to class his behaviour just now as psychotic.' He threw her a meaningful look.

'He acts like someone who is taking charge of his own case,' Brenda answered, matching his look with one of her own. 'Where do you think his wife is at?'

'She will persuade him to keep on being treated.' Prince paused and picked up Kiley's chart again, paging through to the Nurse's Notes. 'I don't think Kiley's celestial visitor has called on her yet.'

'Well, a person can act perfectly normal between hallucinatory episodes,' Brenda remarked. 'What was Mrs Wilson doing in there?'

'I think someone asked Social Services to come up and help his wife work out Medicaid claims,' Prince said.

Brenda gave him a penetrating look. 'Let's hope that's *all* she does in there. If she winds up dealing with Kiley's personal problems, we'll really have a bucket of worms.'

Prince detected the steely tone her voice always took on when Christie was mentioned.

'What harm can she *do*?' he asked, in a tone of bored distraction. 'I've told you I've got nothing but good feedback from patients she's seen. She's never been known to discourage anyone from treatment.'

Brenda planted her feet apart and folded her arms across her chest, clutching Joan Bentley's chart. Her eyes narrowed and flashed. He remembered the scratch on his chest, which still smarted. Brenda's face was so close to him that he could smell her cologne. The thought of the night ahead with her sent a wave of heat through him, and for a moment he felt dizzy. He watched Brenda's lip curl under, revealing a row of small, even white teeth.

'What harm can she do?' Brenda hissed. 'She's a *flake*. Ask Mildred Schultz. How can *she* straighten out someone who's hallucinating? She thinks angels are strolling around Broadcliff herself. Ask Mildred what she said to that old guy they had to put in restraints because he thought he was on trial in a courtroom and kept jumping up to go find an attorney.'

An afternoon of calls lay ahead, and Prince couldn't take time for a hot go-round on Christie. He enclosed Brenda's upper arm in a just-short-of-bruising grip, at the same time pressing the back of his hand into the side of her breast. Then, fastening his eyes on her teeth, he spoke to her in a low whisper.

'Tell me tonight,' he said, slowly increasing his pressure. He felt Brenda gradually go limp, and released his fingers. He glanced both ways down the hall. No one was in sight.

Brenda stepped back and rubbed her arm. She gave him a tight smile that promised infinite retaliation.

'Carry on, Dr Prince,' she said, in her smothered voice. She handed him Joan Bentley's chart, and they opened the door of her room into darkness and weeping.

Chapter Eleven

Randy Hoekelman was a new member of the Seven Main nursing team. She had become very close to Julius Hoffman during her two weeks on the Unit. Last night he had died in her arms. The event had made her even more sensitive to the needs of the other patients on her wing. One of those who concerned her most was Martin Kiley. Randy was one of the nurses he had confided in about his vision. She had asked Christie to meet her in the locker room at the end of her shift to talk about Martin. She had seen her talking with a dying patient the week before, and some of the things she had heard convinced her that Christie could help Martin.

There seemed to be several matters troubling him. His marriage had not been in the Catholic Church. His wife was worried about the medical bills, and also knew she had to apply for his disability income. She was confused by the maze of insurance rules and hospital rules connected with his case. Randy knew from his prognosis that he didn't have long to live. For the last two days, he had been in almost an euphoric state, following the appearance in his room of a person he believed to be either an angel of annunciation or Jesus Himself. When Martin had told her about it, his wife, Gretchen, had been there. Gretchen hadn't expressed disbelief. She had only set her mouth in a narrow line and looked down at the floor. Randy had a feeling she was afraid this new turn of affairs would cause her husband to baulk again at signing papers declaring permanent disability. It had been very difficult for him to accept the evidence that he would never work again; particularly in view of the fact that Dr Prince was actively treating his disease. Randy was not sure what to say to either of them.

She had just arrived in the nurses' locker room and was changing her shoes when Christie walked in.

'Hi,' Randy said. 'I'm glad you could meet me here. I'd rather talk about the patients in private.' She had never talked to Christie before, and was relieved to see that she had an easy, friendly manner.

'You're new on the Unit, aren't you?' Christie commented, then added quickly, 'I've seen you with Julius Hoffman a lot.'

Randy sat on the bench and looked down at her shoes, carefully untying the laces. 'Yes. He ... when he died he asked me to hold on to him. He died ... last night.' She wiped her eyes with the back of her hand. Christie sat down beside her and put her arm around her. There was a box of tissues on a table, and Christie retrieved it.

'I've been thinking how – what a miracle it was you came on the Unit when you did. There was something about you that comforted Julius. You were one of the few he trusted.'

Randy blew her nose and nodded her head in agreement. 'He said I helped him to ... to die sooner. It ... it was a *compliment*. He wanted to die – because he couldn't *live*.' She looked into Christie's eyes and saw that they were wet. For a few moments they sat there quietly. Then Randy spoke again.

'Christie, I asked you to come here because I've heard you talking to patients who were very ill, and there's a man in seven-eighteen I . . . I really think he has a lot of problems and things are . . . are happening to him that . . .'

'Martin Kiley?'

'Yes! Do you know him?'

'Well . . . just a little. I was sent up by Social Services to help his wife on a financial problem.'

'Have you talked to him about . . . himself any?' Randy asked anxiously.

'I haven't had a chance to, yet. Right after I got there, Prince and Brenda came in to tell him about the hepatic infusion.'

Randy stood looking at Christie for a few seconds. Finally, she said, 'He's going to die. He's going to go downhill fast, or slow. If he's lucky, he'll get a fatal pneumonia. But he's going to die.'

Christie lowered her eyes. 'Perhaps we could ask Father Franciscus to see him,' she told Randy.

'Has he ever seen Martin?' Randy asked. Her tired face brightened.

'He may have met his wife at St. Thomas' Church. She told me she goes there to pray. I'll talk to Franciscus about his problems. He said he'd come down to the hospital this afternoon.' She put her arm around Randy and hugged her. 'I'm going back to see Martin myself in a few minutes. Prince should be gone now.'

'Good,' said Randy. 'I'll sleep better knowing you and Father Franciscus are seeing the Kileys.'

Christie held on to her hand. 'Thanks for telling me about Martin,' she said.

Randy waved goodbye and left the locker room.

Christie walked over to the open window and looked down at the city. The network of the freeway interchange droned with the beginning of rush-hour traffic. The two churches interrupted the monotony of the skyline with their steeples. One featured an angel in mid-leap heralding some announcement to the sky through a slender trumpet. The other was St Thomas'. Its spire ended in a plain gold cross which caught the sun at certain hours. Beyond St Thomas', west of the river, was a neighbourhood of grey wooden houses. In one of them Victor Vendetti was working out his reparations and living into an unexpected remission. At the end of the cluster of houses the first lush hills began, rolling westward in soft green waves. On this midsummer day she could see faraway ranges that bled, like a misty watercolour, from dark grey to blue to lavender as they came closer to the big lake and its dunes. She thought of the beach and the Moon Castle.

Since Lance had entered her life the atmosphere of the world seemed to have changed. It had suddenly become more vivid, more charged with meaning. Her body felt stronger too. Lance's strength and power seemed to have entered her own nerves and bones. A sense of sin, an awareness of his wife had become a thin, minor undercurrent beneath the vital force that now strengthened and coloured her life. And yet, Lance sometimes seemed like a fable she had read, until the phone rang and she heard his voice.

When she thought of him, sometimes without willing it, in places like the cafeteria line or the nurses' station, a sudden reflex of her nerves would make her shiver and send a surge of strength through her body. Then the heat, the odours, and the oppressive aura of death, would recede from her as she walked through the hospital corridors.

She deliberately summoned his image now. He stood watching her, his brown body etched against the sand and the lake. He was bare to the waist, wearing his baggy white shorts.

Christie smiled to herself and squared her shoulders. She went to the small sink on the wall and splashed cold water on her face. Her watch told her it was 4 p.m. Prince should surely be well into his other hospital calls by now, or out of the building. She hurried down the hall to Martin Kiley's room.

His door was slightly ajar. He was alone, lying in his bed with his eyes shut. Christie tiptoed around the bed, studying his face. He had a strong, square jaw and stubborn nose. His hair was grey and still thick. His large, thick-fingered hands were folded over his chest. A strong yellow tint had invaded the healthy tan of his skin.

He became aware of Christie's presence and opened his eyes. The whites of his eyes were coloured with the same yellow tinge.

Kiley held out his hand.

'You're the lady who came in here a while ago to talk about disability payments,' he said. 'My wife just left for home. She has to check the kids out, but she's coming back tomorrow morning.'

'I came to tell you that I contacted the expert in the hospital's Finance Department, and he said he will be happy to help you and your wife work out details, and answer any questions you have. Just let me know when is a good time, and I'll ask him to come up here,' Christie told him. Martin Kiley smiled and indicated to Christie to take a seat. She sat down on the side of his bed.

'May I sit here?' she asked.

'Sure,' Kiley answered. 'What do you do at the hospital?' He looked at the badge on her lab coat, and read aloud, 'MEDICAL SOCIAL WORKER.'

'I don't do anything medical,' Christie explained. 'But usually people who are sick enough to be in hospitals have needs that aren't strictly taken care of by drugs and surgery ... like the question of your disability benefits – and other things.'

Kiley's grey eyes were intelligent and intense. He looked at her closely, as if he were making an assessment. 'Do you talk a lot with people who have cancer?'

'The only place I work is on this Cancer Unit,' she told him. He looked at her intently again, for a few seconds.

'What is your religion? Are you religious?' he asked.

'I don't go to a particular church,' Christie said. 'But I guess you would say I am religious. I believe in God. I went to a Catholic college.'

'You met my wife. Well, I'm a Catholic but she isn't. She's

212

my second wife. I was married to my first one in the Church, but she ran off with another man and left me with our kids. When I met Gretchen and wanted to marry her, the priest said we couldn't be married in the Church. Well, we were married in a civil ceremony. I felt bad about it. I was pretty bitter, too, seeing as my first wife left me and all. Now I have cancer ... ' Kiley's voice was getting husky. His eyes filled with tears. 'It isn't good to be alienated from your church ... I thought I was separated from God ... out of His reach ... '

'I understand your wife has been talking to the Catholic Chaplain ... Have you met him?' Christie waited for him to get control of his voice. Finally, he continued.

'Yes ... yes ... this priest ... Franciscus ... he came in the other day and talked to me. He said ... ' Martin Kiley's voice faltered again. He laid his head back on his pillows and bit his lip. Tears ran down his cheeks. Christie reached over and took his hand. She pressed it between both of hers and sat quietly.

'I was never no crier,' Kiley said, summoning strength into his voice; 'but a lot of things happen to a man that ... ' He looked at Christie, and his glance eloquently completed the sentence.

'Father Franciscus understands your situation?'

Kiley nodded his head. 'He said the Church don't take that position no more. He said he is going to marry me and Gretchen. I guess we'll have a wedding right here in this hospital room.'

'That's wonderful, Mr Kiley. What good news! I know Father Franciscus. He's a good man, and a good priest. I'm glad you've got to know him.'

Kiley leaned forward and read Christie's badge again. 'CHRISTIE WILSON, eh?' he said. 'Can I call you Christie? You call me "Martin," because there's some things I'd like to tell you, and I don't want you to keep calling me "Mr Kiley" – I'm Martin.'

'Fine, Martin.' Christie smiled.

'Can you take time to talk for a little bit?' Kiley's face

213

suddenly shaded over with concern.

'I have lots of time,' Christie said. 'To listen and to talk is what I'm here for.' His face relaxed. His tears and her unhurried interest had broken a tightness in him. He sighed and leaned back against the pillows again.

'I've had a lot of bad things happen to me, and side by side with those, some real good things, some ... *amazing* things. You see ... I thought I was separated from the Church ... from the sacraments ... and from God. And then I got cancer. If it hadn't been for this cancer, I wouldn't have known I could be married in the Church now. I was bitter and didn't go back to church. I wouldn't have met this priest if my wife hadn't gone to pray about the cancer.

'Life is funny,' he went on. 'I mean it's *strange*. You think you got everything figured out, and then, wham. It's all gone the other way.' He looked down at his hands – large and calloused – and held them out to Christie.

'See these hands?' he said. He turned his hands over and twisted his arms at the wrists. The hard muscles in his arms flexed. 'See these arms?' he said. 'I used to lift huge engine blocks that weighed a hundred and fifty pounds. No matter what I lost – even when I lost my wife – I never lost these hands and these arms, and all the strength of my body. I could beat up two men at a time – hold one off and beat up the other. Once, two guys picked a fight with me in a bar. I racked up both of them.'

Martin Kiley paused a moment and then continued. 'I was the best auto mechanic within two hundred miles. I had a strong, healthy body. I hadn't been sick a day in my life until this cancer.'

Kiley's face fell. A cloud had enveloped his animation. He stared at Christie.

'And now,' Kiley went on, 'now this Dr Prince tells me the cancer is spreading. I've been driving all the way down here, taking some new cancer drug from this cancer specialist, and the cancer is spreading to my liver, he says.'

Christie nodded her head. 'That's what I understand.'

'And now he tells me he has a new card up his sleeve. Some

214

kind of infusion into the liver. I have to make up my mind whether to agree to it. You see these bruises?' He showed her his arms. 'You know, they keep having to take blood samples to see what these drugs are doing to my blood.' He paused. Christie reached out and touched his arms lightly on the bruised places. Then she took his hand.

'It's a very difficult decision. You have a lot to balance out.'

Martin Kiley sighed a heavy sigh. Christie felt he was trying to decide not only the course that was right for his body, but the course that would not jeopardize his soul. Kiley was studying his hands and the bruises above his wrists. He looked up at her, his eyes pleading for understanding.

'This is hard to explain. I don't know if I can say it right, but . . . ' His voice took on a desperate earnestness, laced with thin steel. He leaned forward and took her hand, holding it tightly.

'I didn't go looking for cancer, Christie . . . No doctor gave it to me. I didn't smoke. So I guess you could say this cancer came from God.' He paused. His eyes held hers.

'Now, these bruises, and this chemotherapy, all that I've contracted for myself. And this new infusion thing I would have to contract with a doctor to do to me, in order to stop this cancer.'

Christie looked into Martin Kiley's eyes and saw a pit of agony. And he read in Christie's face, mirrored back, the true lineaments of his own inexpressible conflict, and its pain.

'You know,' he said. 'I see you *know*.' His voice was a whisper, but it was rich with the tones of discovery and relief.

'There is something more,' he said. 'I wasn't going to tell you this, because I told it to one nurse and she looks at me now like she's afraid of me. Then I told it to another, but I don't think she believed me either. They think the drugs are getting to my brain – or the cancer. Now my body's so polluted it'd be hard to figure out which.'

A swishing sound interrupted Martin's speech. He looked

215

up and saw a nurse coming through the door with a tray of blood-sample tubes. Something clicked inside his mind. He had, for the first time since his illness, suddenly entered a kind of time and space in which he could talk about the dread, about this precarious moment of pressing decisions, without oppression. He was about to tell her what he had sworn he would tell no one else.

He cleared his throat and spoke to the nurse. 'Please leave me alone. I am in the middle of something important and personal. Come back later.'

The young nurse looked shocked, but she recovered quickly. 'It's time for our blood sample, Mr Kiley,' she said brightly. 'It's important to our recovery to keep track of our blood, isn't it?' She approached the bed and lifted the syringe and rubber catheter from the tray. She gave Christie a meaningful glance, lifting her eyebrows.

'Come back later. I don't want to be interrupted,' Martin said. His voice was strong and firm. The nurse seemed to be wavering between incredulity and determined intention. She looked from her patient to Christie and back again.

'You refuse to have a blood sample taken?' she finally asked.

'For the time being,' Martin said.

The nurse threw Christie a shocked glance. She put back the syringe and catheter, and wheeled out of the room with the cart.

Christie looked at Martin. 'You know what that means?' she asked.

'I know that it will go on the record with any other remarks that make them think I'm crazy,' said Martin.

He eased back on his pillows again and sighed, trying to recapture the mood. 'There's something more.' He thought a minute. 'You're not a Catholic?' he asked Christie.

'I'm not technically Catholic ... I ... I'm a Christian,' Christie said.

'That means you believe in Christ.'

'Yes.'

'Do you believe in angels?' Martin asked. He leaned

forward and fastened her with an intense look.

Christie hesitated a moment.

It was hard to imagine persons who flew from heaven to earth with wings, unless . . . unless one thought of gulls. She thought, again, of the gull Lance had startled. She looked up at Martin Kiley. His eyes were bright again. He waited for her answer.

'Yes,' she said, 'I believe in angels.'

Martin sighed.

'I'm glad you came in here to talk with my wife about our insurance,' he said. 'You see what I mean about the good and the bad all happening to me at once? If we were wealthy, and not worried about where our money would be coming from, I might never have met you. I don't think too many people believe in angels anymore. So I know I can tell you this. I know you won't think I'm crazy.

'Have you ever thought you've seen an angel, or known anyone who did?' he asked.

'No – no. I never have. Not an actual being who looked like us,' she answered.

'Have you ever really felt that God, or Jesus, actually spoke to you, or you saw Them?'

Christie believed she had a relationship with God, but she had never actually heard a voice, or seen an image – a person.

'It's hard to explain,' she said. She leaned forward and took Martin's hand again.

'I had a very difficult, lonely time at one period of my life. I began to pray to God. I didn't see anyone, or hear a voice, but changes came, events that took me into a new life.' She paused, watching Martin's face, then added, 'But I have known people who did see someone and who heard a voice.'

She waited for him to speak.

'Well, Christie, you are looking at someone who actually saw either Jesus Himself or one of His angels – right here in this room.' He pointed to a spot by the foot of his bed. 'He stood right *there*.

'He didn't say, "I am Jesus," or "I am an angel." I was just suddenly aware of someone standing at the foot of my bed. I

217

hadn't heard anyone come in. I'd been looking out the window, watching the cars going along that freeway overpass. And I was mourning, I guess. I was alone here, mourning my lost strength, trying to face the fact that I couldn't ever do any constructive work again; probably couldn't ever make love to my wife again. I felt like I had opened a door into a blank wall, or like a jail door had slammed on me. I think I was reaching out in my mind for help, like a man in a dungeon looking up, hoping for a trapdoor to open, hunting for a little crack of light.'

Martin stopped. He had been slowing down as he spoke. He leaned back on the pillows to rest before he continued.

'Did you pray?' Christie asked.

Martin shook his head. His eyes filled again with tears. 'After I had to marry and live with Gretchen outside the Church, I didn't go to confession. I never thought our life together was any sin. But I had been raised a good Catholic. I didn't think I could speak to God anymore or ask for anything.' The tears rolled down his face.

'Were you afraid?'

'No. That's strange, I guess. If you ever see a messenger of God – an angel – you *know* they're from God. You got no doubt. It was like this person was bringing light into a dark place, and – no mistaking it – *love*: real love; a kind of huge safety, like you could never be frightened again. It was like he was telling me all the fear and the confusion and the loss was nothing that could really harm me. I can't say he said it as a voice, or what the words were – but the meaning was "Martin" – he knew who *I* was! – "you are going to be okay. Don't be afraid. Everything's going to be all right." And I believed him. I'm going to lick this cancer.'

Martin Kiley had finally told his story. There was a silence, and in the silence Christie thought she felt, for a moment, some transcendent presence fill the room again. He had dried his eyes, and he looked at her with a vast relief.

'It seems,' said Christie, 'that God can find us anywhere, even outside the Church.'

Martin held her hand and squeezed it. He lay back on his

pillows and closed his eyes.

Christie stood up and walked to the head of the bed. She stroked his forehead and his hair with the palm of her hand. 'You should rest awhile now.'

Martin reached out and grasped her hand. She was surprised by his strength.

'Thank you, Christie,' he said.

'Thank *you*, Martin. You ... you've given me a lot ... you've shared your own gift with me.'

She could feel through his hand that the tension of his body was relaxing. She sat down on the bed again, as silently as she could. She didn't know how many minutes went by. His hand very gradually released its hold. The slight smile on his face gave way to the blank ambiance of sleep. She smoothed the blanket over him, feeling the sense of another strength; a strength she had not come into the room with.

Christie remembered that her next appointment was with Stefan Franciscus. After her last talk with Victor she had decided to call him. She did not know exactly what she would say. But now she felt the meeting was even more important.

Chapter Twelve

Stefan Franciscus had just finished saying the noonday Mass. He was hoping to make his way from the anteroom behind the chancel of St Thomas' to the parking lot, where his car waited, without encountering anyone who would trap him into conversation. He removed his vestments and ran his fingers through his thick grey hair. He checked the pockets of his black suit jacket for his appointment book. He had several patients to see at Broadcliff Hospital. The most urgent case was Martin Kiley. They were to confirm the day and hour of his forthcoming wedding. Franciscus was going to suggest that it be done in the next several days. It was clear that Kiley was a very sick man.

Before he saw Martin, he had an appointment to talk with Christie Wilson. He knew that Christie would do all she could to bend the system in the direction of Martin's needs. Perhaps he could be freed from the pain and side effects of further treatment and be sent home with enough medication to keep him reasonably comfortable.

He reached into a carved wood cabinet and lifted out his black leather case containing the holy oil for the anointing sacrament. It was not called the last rites any more: one of the many Church changes he was grateful for. It had frightened as many people as it had comforted. Franciscus left the ante-chamber and walked down a short hall to a door exiting on the parking lot. Just as he turned the latch, Mrs Bailey, the rectory housekeeper, bustled up to him.

'Lovely homily, Father! I always get so much out of your meditations on obedience! I'm glad I caught you. There is a message that the Sisters at the House of Studies want a date for you to speak to them on hospital chaplainship.'

Mrs Bailey was a stout, fidgety widow, very loyal to her duties as the priests' messenger and housemother. He patted her shoulder.

'Thank you ... thank you, yes. I'm leaving for the hospital just now – have several important calls there. Tell the Sisters I'll be in touch with them tomorrow. I'll be at the hospital the rest of the day.'

Mrs Bailey opened her mouth to say something else, but he had slipped through the door and was heading for his car.

His life at St Thomas' and Broadcliff was exhausting and demanding; filled with people, but lonely – lacking in the sense of community, and without comrades. The college had provided him with both these comforts.

The psychic isolation of his hospital ministry had the interesting effect of making him intuitively sharper. It heightened those senses which perceived the unspoken truths of those around him. He found Christie Wilson an

220

interesting puzzle. Her person had a sometimes disquieting effect on him. He had met her at a time when he had buried, once and for all, the longing to explore further dimensions of life through the love of a woman, and the experience of her body. The death of this longing had been at once sad and freeing. It limited a serious aspect of his ability to suffer. He could still suffer loneliness, and he suffered at one remove with the sick and the dying; but the devouring pain of needing, and never having, a particular human being – an unremitting hunger which gnawed at both body and soul – he had left behind him.

There were moments now, when he sat next to Christie, or when their hands touched in understanding, or gratitude, when echoes of the old pain whispered thinly through the silence in his centre. But it quickly faded. There was about Christie the warmth and sexless sweetness of the best nuns. Something had purged her of that disturbing sexuality which normally glowed from the presence of pretty and voluptuous women. He could, therefore, be quite comfortable with her. In her company, he shared the warmth of that fellowship of the lonely which is akin to love. He was glad she would work with him on the Martin Kiley case.

It was going to be a difficult one. Dr Prince was a man of tremendous personal ego and an iron will. There was no doubt as to his power in the hospital. Kiley had made several references to Prince's determination to achieve further remissions for him with new chemotherapy treatments.

Franciscus himself was sceptical. Since his baptism into the Cancer Unit through Victor Vendetti, he had seen patients benefiting from remissions in the early stages of their disease. Some of them lived for many years, surviving both the disease and the treatments, and gaining precious years of life. But he had also seen patients dying badly from what he felt was prolonged overtreatment. He had seen cases of psychosis where no brain disease had been detected. He wished he knew more about medical terms, and had access to the charts. He depended on what sympathetic nurses would tell him, and on what the patients themselves said. Mostly, he was flying blind in his ministry to the cancer patients, not knowing if their souls were sick from unresolved conflicts and relationships, or if the chemicals had irretrievably twisted and poisoned the systems of their bodies and minds.

He had found patients sitting alone and unreachable, mostly abandoned by the specialists, locked in their delusions.

He had been present with an old man, only days from death, who was tormented by the need to find himself a lawyer, so that he could be defended in his trial before a nameless judge. Christie had held the man in her arms. She had told him he already had the best advocate in the world, because God had appointed a great attorney to plead his cause. It was not the prescribed institutional response.

He had a feeling that Christie's work in the hospital had a precarious future.

Franciscus parked in the Broadcliff ramp and bounded up the inside stairway to the Department of Social Services. The door to Christie's cubicle was open, but there was no sign of her. He walked in and had just taken a seat when she rushed through the door, her lab coat flying behind her. Her cheeks were flushed, and her hair stood out in long wisps where it had escaped from a fastening. She clasped his hand tightly.

'I'm so glad I asked you to meet me today. No one else knows Martin's case in the way you do.' She stopped to catch her breath.

'It's always nice to see you, Christie,' Franciscus said, noticing a new volatility in her.

'Something else has been added to Martin's problems, Father,' Christie told him.

'I'm anxious to hear about it,' he said. He paused a moment. 'Do you want to talk here?'

'Let's go down the hall and see if the chapel is empty,' Christie said.

Going to the chapel to talk with Christie had become a ritual he rather enjoyed. The space and quiet atmosphere were conducive to meditative thought. He hoped it conferred some kind of grace on the problems they went there to confront.

They sat down in the front pew.

'Let's hope we're lucky and get no intrusions,' Franciscus said, taking her hand.

Christie leaned forward and recounted to Franciscus everything that Martin Kiley had told her. Franciscus listened intently. When she had finished, he asked, 'What do you want me to do?'

Christie said, 'When you see him today, you must talk to him about more than the wedding. You must get him to tell you himself about the angel. You see, he believes in the angel, or Jesus, and he believes it was a *promise* that he would lick the cancer. I wish it would be a miraculous cure ... I ... do believe in miracles – but maybe what the angel said was simply that Martin would be all right, no matter what ... even if he died ... that death is not really terrible ... is not what it seems, a black ending to everything.'

Franciscus leaned forward, his arms clasped over his knees, his eyes closed. 'You are afraid that if he continues to go downhill, and the cancer gets worse, it will be harder for him than if he had never seen the angel – or Jesus?'

'It was so real, so absolutely undoubtable. And he is so *sure* of what the message meant.' Christie's voice was shaking. 'What can we do? How can we help him?'

There was a long pause. When Franciscus spoke, his voice was very low. 'We can know how helpless we are to control most of Martin's situation. We can rest in our helplessness and give it to God.' He paused a moment and then took one of Christie's hands in his. 'Now that we both know, we can add to whatever support he needs ... we can give him our understanding. Christie, let me remind you of what you tell the nurses: "Let the patient lead the way." He may reinterpret the message himself. He may even have the miracle of a remission. Victor did.'

Christie had been looking down at her hands. Now she suddenly looked up.

'When I met you in my office, I was very angry,' she said. 'I

223

had just come from the Unit. After I left Martin I stopped in the station to see if any new entries had been made in Martin's chart. There were two entries in the Nurse's Notes. One said Martin had refused to have blood taken, and was acting *"schizophrenic"* and *"paranoid."* The other said he was *"showing schizophrenic behaviour patterns, such as delusions and hallucinations."* I have seen it before, Father; when a patient is labelled this way, the staff begins to treat him as if he is really crazy. Martin is sensitive enough to pick it up.'

Father Franciscus muttered something under his breath which sounded like an oath. For a moment, his eyes narrowed and his mouth closed in a hard line. Then he said, 'I think we will have to lean on whatever angels choose to invade the rooms of Broadcliff, Christie. They can move where we cannot. Humanly, we can support Martin with our perception of his sanity, and our respect – and love. Right now, we will help with the plans for his wedding. It is good to celebrate in the face of adversity. Joy can exorcise many demons.'

Christie looked intently at Stefan Franciscus. There was a wonderful thing about his eyes. They mirrored and contained a tragedy whose origin she could only surmise. But at certain unpredictable moments, flashes of fire came into them; some hint of his delight in secret mischief. That fire was there now. He was taking great pleasure in designing a celebration for Martin, almost in the shadow of his grave.

Christie often thought that the power in Franciscus was fuelled and kept alive not only by prayer, but by those rare occasions when he managed to steal some beauty from the hands of death.

Now he said, 'Before I go to see Martin, let's both of us pray for him, and for sensitivity and guidance.'

It was part of their ritual at the end of the chapel conversations. Christie would say a freestyle prayer aloud, and then Franciscus would say a more priestly one. He waited for Christie to pray first. There was a long silence. He opened his eyes and saw her hands twisting together in her

224

lap. Then he saw thin streaks of tears run down her cheeks.

'Christie.' He put his hands on hers. 'What is the trouble? We mustn't expect all the worst in Martin's case!'

She bit her lip and shook her head slowly. 'It isn't that ... it's that ... You go ahead and pray. I can't ... I don't think I should try to pray ... for Martin ... ' Her whisper was choked off by a stifled sob.

'What is it? Can I help?' He tried to look into her eyes, but she had pulled a tissue from her pocket and held it up to her face. 'Father, I can't pray for anyone now. I – I'm involved in something ... I can't explain ... Maybe God isn't ... with me – anymore.'

Franciscus was astonished into silence. Then his concern took over again. 'Tell me, Christie ... it will help to get it spoken aloud. Perhaps you are overconcerned. God doesn't leave you.'

'I love someone ... I shouldn't love ... someone who is already married.' Her voice was almost inaudible. Franciscus understood Christie's new vibrance.

'To love someone is not a terrible sin. We love if we are human. We die if we do not love – in our souls, we die.'

'But I – I'm doing more than that ... It ... it's physical ... and I'm not sorry. And I'm going to continue ... ' She raised her eyes and looked at him. Her eyes now told him the measure of her jeopardy. He read distances and depths too familiar and too painful: all the old bondage of need.

He bowed his head and folded his hands tightly.

'I understand,' Franciscus said.

'But *you* pray for Martin, Father Franciscus – and for me.'

'I will,' he said, still staring at his hands. He thought for a moment.

'But you can still speak to God. Whatever this relationship consists of, whatever your course, ask God to go with you. Tell Him your fears. Tell Him your needs. Claim his love. You will need it more than ever now.'

He saw that she seemed relieved but still shaky. He sensed her role as a traveller, going into strange terrain. More alone, perhaps, in love than in the old solitude.

'Thank you,' she said. She put her hand on his again.
'Let's pray, Christie.'
They both bowed their heads.

Chapter Thirteen

The weather in Brandenburg had settled into the full heat of
summer. There had been two weeks of high humidity with no
relief from the west wind. The air in the corridors and most
of the rooms of Broadcliff was oppressively heavy. The
prospect of another morning spent in them did nothing to
alleviate the depressed mood in which Virgil Prince had
awakened. He was shaving when his wife called him to the
phone.

'It's Brenda,' she told him. He checked her face with an
elaborately casual glance, being careful to flavour it with a
touch of annoyance. He saw no indication of suspicion. Her
face was bland and innocent. Well, the day had at least
blessed him with continued good luck on the home front. He
dried his hands and picked up the phone.

'Hello,' he said, keeping his voice colourless.

'Hi, lover,' Brenda purred. 'Won't keep you. Just called to
say I'll be in late today. I've had it with the heat and I plan to
spend most of the day cooling off my hot little tail in the club
pool.'

'Very well,' he answered. Damn Brenda. When it was
Dottie who answered the phone, she always managed to load
her messages with insinuating words and phrases, knowing
he was being overheard, perhaps watched, and must remain
unruffled.

'I may drop by the Unit later in the afternoon,' she told
him. He heard the click as she hung up.

Dottie had gone back to the kids, who were eating

breakfast in the kitchen. His mood of depression thickened. It had begun soon after the alarm went off. The first thought in his mind had been the sticky situation he faced that morning with one of his female patients. The woman was full of cancer, but it was essential they do some more unpleasant tests to prove a metastasis to the stomach. If his suspicions were verified, protocol demanded she be treated with another drug combination. Unless her husband blocked his plans, Prince would have the opportunity to collect some of the early data on the performance of a new experimental chemical on advanced disease. There was always the outside chance she might respond with a remission. If she did not, well, she was, in any case, dying.

He knew his depression lay in a growing hostility he had been sensing in her husband. The man was one of those over-protective, suspicious types, more intelligent and better read than average, but of course totally ignorant regarding pathology. Lately he was omnipresent on the Unit, sometimes sounding out other patients and questioning orders on her treatments and tests. Prince had even seen him in conference with a couple of nurses Brenda had tagged as troublemakers. Today, of all days, her support could have eased his own task.

The patient's name was Betty Norman. She had three young children. If he could get to the room early enough to find her alone, he felt he could persuade her the test was necessary. For a moment his mind veered towards the wisdom of waiting for Brenda to arrive. When he faced the patients alone, he felt more vulnerable to their emotional needs and less able to steel himself against irrational appeals.

Virgil Prince had always been proud of his own ego strength. He had built it himself, rock on rock, from the wounds of a childhood and adolescence spent in guilt and shame. This inner power, combined with a genetically strong body and robust health, had given him the stamina he needed for tasks and schedules that would dangerously deplete the average man .

But there had been hours in the past when he had arrived

at the hospital to begin his rounds and had felt dread and failure whispering through his bones like a fatal wind. There had been nights, before the advent of Brenda's constant presence, when the oblivion behind his closed eyelids came alive and pulsed with faces. Each patient who had ever wordlessly begged for him to promise life wavered before his bed with pleading eyes. They repeated the same litany: 'See me!' They chanted, 'Speak to me! Love me!' Only a madman could dare to love them. His role was to stave off death. To try to love the dying was to court destruction.

Prince finished shaving and dressing hurriedly. He drank juice and black coffee as he gathered up some articles he had been reading the night before and stuffed them into his attaché case. He brushed his lips quickly on the side of Dottie's face.

'I'll be home late,' he called as he went out the door. 'Don't wait dinner.'

He slid into the plush seat of his new Continental. Driving Continentals had been one of his self-awarded trophies for the position and affluence he had attained. He turned on the air conditioner, and the big car purred powerfully out of the driveway. The prospect of making morning calls without Brenda evoked her presence all the more vividly in his mind. Always, when he entered the lobby, he knew she was waiting in his office to begin their rounds. Her eyes and her posture were the reflection, the perfect recall, of his best moments. The fear and ache of wispy doubts that had unpredictably invaded his gut had been excised by her presence, and by her confidence and pride in him. The parade of beseeching faces had faded and finally disappeared. His nights on the pillow, before he slept, were now pulsing with erotic images of Brenda: Brenda bending over him, her hair covering his face like a fragrant veil. Brenda striding like a jungle cat about the bedroom at his cottage, grinning at him, her naked body lean and shadowed by the fire. Brenda carelessly tossing her long sable coat on the rough floor before the fire, so that their bodies could be cushioned by its silk.

She had invaded him to advantage, in his work, with her

own strength and arrogance. Some demonic impulse, which it pleased her to indulge, goaded her on to brush him, accidentally, whenever she thought no one could see. These unpredictable contacts, combined with her stubborn refusal to arrange time alone with him as often as he needed it, sometimes made him feel as if his mind and body might simultaneously explode. But in a strange way, it also fuelled his sense of power.

He walked briskly through the lobby now and caught the first elevator going up. Usually there were few visitors on Seven Main at 9 a.m. His prospects for finding Betty Norman alone should be very good. He pushed open the door of her room and Betty looked up. A minor quickening of the hope he used to see on her face when he entered the room played over her features. Then her face became expressionless. She turned her head to the wall. He felt a tightening in his chest. It was a damn shame she had gotten the disease so young. Her body was emaciated, and most of her hair had fallen out during one of the courses of chemotherapy. She had become too ill to manage a wig and now wore a pink paper cap to cover her baldness. He walked over to the bed.

'Not feeling like conversation today, Betty?'

She turned her face from him and faced the ceiling with her eyes closed. She was a rather small girl and had always had a sensational figure, even after three children. When Prince met her she had told him very proudly that she had been a cheerleader in college. She lay motionless. Prince stood by the bed, waiting. Finally he reached out and patted her hand. Some tears spilled beneath her closed eyelids and ran down her cheeks, but she did not move. She remained quiet.

'Feeling rough today, eh?' Prince let his voice slide into a warmer tone than he usually liked to risk. There was more silence. Then a sob shook her chest.

'I can't keep anything down. Not even water,' she whispered hoarsely.

'It's rough,' Prince said. 'I know it's rough, Betty. But I've got a few things in mind I want to try. One is something to help the nausea: a tube that will drain fluid out through your nose.'

'Not another tube!' Betty's face contorted in anguish.

'Now, that shouldn't alarm you,' Prince soothed. 'It doesn't really hurt once it's in place.' He paused a moment and patted her hand again. Then he pulled up an easy chair and sat down beside the bed. Betty opened her eyes and looked at him. Prince leaned back and folded his hands. He conveyed the feeling that he was unhurried.

'If you will give your approval and cooperation, Betty, I have a new treatment that's just become available. It should help, might give us a new remission, provided your big trouble is the kind of tumour I think it is. I want you to let us do another test. It's the only way we can verify the kind of tumour we're fighting.' Prince paused once more. Her eyes had closed again, and she bit her lip.

'You do want to fight this, don't you? You know I'm on your side. What we're both fighting is the tumour. If you begin to fight me, we both lose. The tumour is the winner.'

Betty blinked her eyes slowly and wiped her cheeks with the back of her hand. Prince pulled a tissue from her bedside table and brushed it over her cheeks. They were both silent. Prince waited for her to speak.

'If . . . if I have the kind of cancer you think I do . . . the test would be able to tell?'

Prince smiled and nodded.

'And if it was, you think there's a new drug that might work?'

'Yes. Exactly. Only a few qualifying specialists have access to it. It's a very new drug. You are fortunate to be in a place where the drug can be made available.'

Betty's gaunt face had been changing as they talked to an expression bordering on hope; at least, the despair had lessened.

'What is the test? What do they have to do?' she asked hesitantly.

'Well, it is the same one we tried to do once before – a

gastroscopy. But this time you have so much to gain, you must be brave and let Dr Farnsworth complete the procedure.' Prince had used his most persuasive and reassuring tone. He leaned forward now, to get better eye contact. Betty turned away from him. Her shoulders shook with sobs.

'No,' she whispered hoarsely. 'No! I can't! I'll never let them do that again. They don't give you an anaesthetic . . .' Her voice was choked off by a new flood of tears.

'They can't anaesthetize you, Betty. They need you to be awake . . . They need your cooperation . . . Don't we want to fight this thing through? We don't want to quit now, do we?' Prince waited. She couldn't hear him. Her sobs had become louder. He heard footsteps on the floor behind him.

'What are we fighting with now, Prince?' The voice was dangerously even. Its tone was loaded. Prince turned and saw Paul Norman standing in the doorway. His eyes were narrowed and his face was pale. He took several steps, moving towards the bed. Prince stood up. Betty went on sobbing, her head turning from side to side on the pillow, negating what Prince was forcing her to face.

'I said, "What are we fighting now?"' Paul Norman repeated. He moved over and took his wife's hand, glaring across the bed at Prince.

'Sit down, Paul,' Prince said smoothly. 'I was giving your wife a bit of optimistic news about a new chemical which is very potent against the trouble she's developed.'

Betty's sobs were becoming softer. She clung to her husband's hand. Paul continued to stare at Prince, waiting for him to continue.

'She's just upset over the idea of the procedure we have to do to confirm the stomach problem.' Prince smiled blandly. It was the smile he used to convey the information that a patient was exaggerating some matter in his imagination. A paediatrician dealing with a child who didn't want his diphtheria-immunization shot.

Betty opened her eyes. They were filled with terror. She appealed to Paul.

231

'It's that test ... the one that hurt so much ... the tube down my throat! Please ... I hurt too much already ... Please ... I can't go through with it!'

Prince allowed a brief expression of annoyance to creep around the corners of his mouth. 'Mr Norman, you impressed on me at the outset of this situation that you wanted nothing spared to save your wife. Optimum cancer protocol demands that ... ' The sound of wheels on the vinyl floor interrupted his speech. A young nurse was walking in with a blood-pressure machine. Paul Norman moved towards Prince and took him by the elbow.

'We'll continue this out in the hall, Prince,' he directed. He turned to the nurse, who looked a bit shocked at the sight of Virgil Prince being propelled somewhere. 'Please see what you can do to help my wife until I get back. Don't leave her.'

The two men moved swiftly into the hallway, Prince disengaging his arm from Norman's grasp.

'Norman,' he began, 'you are understandably distraught. It would be unproductive to discuss your wife's treatment until you are calmer. Perhaps I should get a typed report on the reason for the procedure and the purpose and logic of the new chemical I am proposing. You can read it when you and your wife are not upset. I will order a Valium for her.' Prince spoke as he walked, wisely veering their direction away from the nurses' station, where a fascinated audience would witness the discussion. He proceeded as far as a cul-de-sac which ran off the main corridor. Paul Norman cut in front of him and crowded him into it.

'I'm glad I ran into you this morning, Prince.' Norman's hands were shoved into his pockets. He leaned into Prince's face. 'I have had plenty of opportunity to observe my wife's progress and to feel her out on what is most important to her now that we both have faced the fact that she has very little time to live.'

'Oh?' Prince responded. His face was expressionless.

'Yes. I want to take her home and find a doctor who can keep her comfortable there. I heard you urging her on to more "fighting," as if the two of you formed a Green Beret

232

team. My wife has no more strength for agonizing procedures and experimental drugs. What little energy she has left she wants to spend enjoying her children and me in her own home Home is all she talks of anymore.'

Prince digested the news, and a slow smile began to move across his face. He turned, as if to leave. 'You had me fooled, Norman,' he said easily, pulling his gold cigarette case from his pocket. 'I thought if your wife got too confused to fight for her life, you would have the guts to fight for her. Good luck on your decision to take her home. You'll need it.' Prince turned away from him with a graceful movement of his shoulders and started down the hall with an easy, loping tread. Norman overtook him and shoved him against the wall. The hatred in his face astonished Prince. Suddenly he felt real fear. Norman's fingers pressed against his throat.

'I'd kill you with my bare hands if I didn't have four hostages who'd pay for it,' he muttered to Prince between clenched teeth; 'but maybe it's better you live a long time.'

Norman's fingers were a steel noose.

'You've got yourself and your chemicals confused with God, and you've got death confused with the devil – a devil I'll wager you don't believe exists.' He paused. Prince felt a ringing in his ears. The fingers relaxed their hold. 'May God have mercy on your soul,' Norman whispered, and was gone. Prince felt suddenly dizzy. The man was mad. Absolutely mad. He'd come close to throttling a staff doctor thirty feet from a nursing station full of medical personnel. Prince dragged air into his lungs and leaned against the wall for a few minutes. His hand shook as he placed the cigarette case back in his pocket. He waited for his heart to stop pounding. Then he walked to the drinking fountain and swallowed some cold water. He needed to go somewhere and get himself together.

He walked down the stairwell to the ground floor, which brought him out near the chapel. It was just the place to find some privacy, provided no one was there ahead of him. He looked in cautiously and saw that it was blessedly vacant. He closed the heavy door behind him and looked for an inside lock. There was a large sliding bolt near the floor. He slid it into place. He discovered that his knees were weak and made his way to one of the cushioned benches.

Prince had never been in the chapel before. He felt a brief wave of gratitude towards whatever instinct had led him there. It was a perfect refuge in which to get his thoughts together.

He leaned against the back of the bench with his eyes closed, running his hand across his forehead. Some neurological response to shock had brought him close to tears. He sought for some neutral object on which to concentrate his mind and calm himself. He looked around the noncommittal decor of the room and fastened on a wooden cross on a table at the front of the chapel. He supposed people came to this chapel to pray for miracles. He already knew that there were no miracles, no striking into the affairs of man by some supernatural, healing benevolence. The only power one had against fate was knowledge. The stark and empty cross reminded him of the church of his parents; the long, boring hours in hard pews on Sunday; the dreary hymns; and the ignorance of the parishioners. Suffering, they believed, purified them and brought them closer to heaven. Virgil Prince knew that suffering was a thing to be studied, controlled, and hopefully, wiped out. Superstition had never alleviated it, only science. Dedicated men of science had made whatever progress the world could boast of: the control of killing disease, the control of environment. They had done it in spite of superstition.

He was beginning to feel calmer. He saw there was no point in pursuing the hope of treating Betty Norman. Let Paul take her home; he would soon have his hands full, and the two of them would come crawling back to Broadcliff asking for her to be hospitalized again. He took out his handkerchief and wiped some sweat from his face and hands. Well, there were no doctors he knew of who would make house calls. They'd have to make it on private nursing care.

If Brenda had been with him this morning, they would

234

have maintained a united professional front. The wiping of tears, eye contact, touching – they always led to medical chaos. He should not have tried to persuade. He should have simply announced, as if there were not even a question.

The incident had taught him an invaluable lesson. Most of his patients were not eccentrics like Norman. They had respect for the years of technical expertise that medical-scientific research had amassed. My God! Prince told himself: if the progress of the race had depended on men like Paul Norman, bubonic plague would still be rampant.

He could draw strength from the reaffirmed knowledge of his own task. It was the task of a warrior, a foot soldier. He must, if necessary, defoliate a human landscape in order to kill the death that stalked it. That death was cancer. He was at war against death. The weapons he had now could delay it, could cripple it. But always, ahead, lay the chance for a new weapon which would be lethal.

It was becoming stuffy in the chapel now. His legs felt normal again. The time to process things without harassment and interruption was all he had needed. He got up from the bench and unbolted the door. In the corridor he took out his case, lit a cigarette, and inhaled deeply. He decided to check his office on the top floor and see if there was any message from Brenda. Maybe she had changed her mind and was trying to reach him on the Unit.

Chapter Fourteen

Joan Bentley had been waiting to be well enough to leave the hospital for many weeks. When admitted to the Cancer Unit two months before, she had thought it would be for evaluation and treatment. Her husband had brought her in because she had been in a great deal of pain, nauseated, and unable to eat.

When she left her home, she had expected to be returning in no more than a week; but the pain had not abated except when her hypos were working, and the sight of food continued to make her ill.

It was a year ago that Joan had first learned she had cancer. Her gynaecologist had told her after an exploratory operation done to determine the cause of chronic pain. He had discovered uterine cancer and performed a hysterectomy, but the cancer had spread to the bone. He sent her to Dr Edward Nippert, who gave her a series of radiation treatments. Then the gynaecologist referred her to Dr Virgil Prince, who, he said, was a specialist in treating tumours.

She had been Dr Prince's patient ever since. He treated her with chemotherapy. She felt comfortable and confident under his care. Her entire life had been managed and directed by strong, aggressive males – first her father and her brother, then her husband. She felt comfortable and secure in letting them run things. Her power had been in her passivity, which they seemed to dote on and to reward. She was glad to be Dr Prince's patient, almost his pupil; pleased not only for her own sake but for his, when her body responded to the treatments he instituted.

In the beginning, she was afraid of the chemotherapy because of possible side effects. But Dr Prince explained how the chemicals worked, and that they were her only hope for remission and continued life. Her dread had gradually left. She put all her efforts into being a good patient, and she felt reasonably well for some months. Then came the sudden onset of more pain, nausea, and her return to the hospital.

When he admitted her to the hospital in late May, Dr Prince seemed as confident as ever that he could manage and control her symptoms. She waited, optimistically at first, for the illness and pain to lessen, for her strength to return. She had lain in this room through the muggy heat of summer, missing the full bloom of her garden flowers. When they'd moved into their large new home she had planned the garden carefully, and the rooms of her house were never without fresh flowers.

Now, each morning she woke to the sense of days drying and fluttering to the ground like the doomed leaves that filled her garden in the fall. She had begun to lose track of time in the endless procession of metal carts rolling to her bedside, filled with medicines and blood vials and catheters. Pervading everything like a dread fog was the constant spectre of pain, like an old and persistent enemy; sometimes faint and dull, sometimes cruel and grinding.

She stopped exploring her body with her hand to see if the chemicals had diminished her swollen abdomen. She knew it was larger than ever. When she was helped to the bathroom, she averted her glance from the mirror. Her face was yellow and gaunt. The emaciation of her arms and legs reminded her of news photos she had seen of famine victims.

The chemotherapy had many side effects. One of the most demoralizing was that her thick, blonde hair had fallen out except for a few wispy tufts. When she knew her husband and children were coming, she tried to remember to put on the wig they had bought her. It was the same colour as her hair, but stiffer and less manageable. Sometimes, she wore a satin curler bonnet. One of her friends had come in unexpectedly and had seen her without the wig or the bonnet; the woman's expression was almost terrified. One by one, her friends stopped coming. Her daughter, when she came, brought her plants and flowers from the garden. Her two sons sat dutifully on the chair or on the top of the radiator and tried to discuss cheerful topics. She loved to see them all. They were tanned and healthy. They brought, temporarily, air from another world.

Her husband came and sat in the orange vinyl visitor's chair. He tried to make conversation. He was relieved if he could get her a glass of water, or her robe – if he could perform any small act of service. She knew he was uncomfortable and chafing at his unaccustomed role of impotence. Dr Prince was now in charge of her body; Dr Prince and the hospital protocol. Her relationship with her

237

husband had become more and more strained. In his presence she felt a sense of guilt and shame; shame for her ugliness and deterioration, and guilt that she and her body did not respond to the treatment. Her husband had poured hundreds – no, thousands – of dollars into the maintenance and treatments of this now repulsive and recalcitrant body.

Once, recently, their pastor had called on her and reminded her of the edification and glory resulting from the suffering of Christians. He had told her that her reward in heaven would be great.

Just before he departed, he had read her a section of Scripture describing a saved Christian who looked down from his position in Paradise and gazed at the eternal tortures of a damned sinner. Then he had smiled, patted her hand, and left.

She had felt her pain injection wearing off as he proceeded with his attempts to instruct and comfort her. By the time he arrived at the Scripture reading and described the sinner in his perpetual agony, her own pain had mounted and become mixed in a nightmare of confusion with the writhings of the condemned man. Now, often, when the pain became unbearable and the nurses took a while to respond to her call light, the nightmare feeling of hell enveloped her again. She felt the prongs of pitchforks penetrating to her bones. When the hypo came to release her temporarily from the grip of her own pain, she prayed that no one would ever die in sin. Hell had become an overwhelming reality.

One night she had awakened feeling stifled. She knew that it was early August, because her daughter had brought her daisies and zinnias and blue delphiniums. The heat in her room lingered far into the night. She looked down at her arms and saw the tubes coming out of each one. She knew one was an intravenous fluid which was kept going all the time. She had forgotten what the other was. The tubes locked her to the bed through her own flesh.

Suddenly, she had become panicky. She felt that she was suffocating. She tried to cry out, but she could make no sound. She was terribly weak, but some animal need, a

238

desperate, untapped strength, filled her and she dragged herself from the bed, tearing against the tubing. She heard the crash of the bottle and the metal pole. She felt the pain in her arms as the tubes came out. She remembered lying on the floor in the hall. Two nurses and an orderly were lifting her up. She remembered the anger and fear on their faces. They had tied her back in bed with muslin restraints and reinserted all the catheters. They had given her sedatives.

One nurse had come to stay with her. It was Mary. Mary leaned over her, and she saw that her eyes were kind and gentle. Mary bathed her face with cool water, then fanned her lightly with a newspaper. Mary held her hand as she fell asleep.

The next day Joan apologized to the nurses who had been most upset and angry. She had a secret terror that if she did anything to displease them, they would retaliate. They could decide not to come when her call light was on. They could withhold her pain injection, or make her wait until the pain became unbearable. She knew, now, that she was totally helpless and must never anger them. But there were a few nurses whom she trusted, even in her terror. Mary was closest to her. Mary seemed to know simple things to comfort her with: cool cloths, gentle touches. If she could fall asleep this way, listening to Mary's voice, feeling Mary's touch, she seemed to be immune from the nightmares of hell, and from the torture of sinners.

But Mary could not always be there.

Chapter Fifteen

Richard Mulder, resident physician, had begun his month on the Cancer Unit in July. After two weeks he had come to the conclusion that the Unit was a zoo. All his training in medical school had been centred on treatment and cure.

Here he saw dying patients being cared for in the same modality as someone recuperating from an accident or surgery. The ironclad rules that guarded against patient addiction made no sense to him when applied to advanced cancer. He found himself more and more turning to his own sense of human decency.

Joan Bentley was one of the most difficult cases. She was getting worse, in a lot of pain, and subjected to the nagging entrammelment of continued active treatment. He sensed she was bothered by family troubles and fears about dying, in addition to her pain. It was obvious that she had become psychologically dependent upon Dr Prince, her oncologist, and it was also obvious that Dr Prince had stopped making regular calls on her. When he realized this, Dr Mulder made a special effort to spend a little time with her on his rounds and to say something personal in addition to the routine physical check.

Joan always greeted him with a weak 'Hello' and the questions 'Is Dr Prince in the hospital?' or 'Will he be seeing me?' For a while he attempted to cover for Prince. But now it was evident that Prince was avoiding her. When he followed him on rounds, he saw a blatant arrogance and callousness in his asides to the staff, an enormous satisfaction in his power over patients. Mulder's anger accelerated when he heard Prince purring seductively to new patients about 'improving the quality of life,' about his 'star' patients – the ones for whom his chemotherapy had secured long remissions. Mulder knew, as he watched Joan Bentley's hurt and frightened face, that she had once been a star patient.

He wondered if anyone who had dealt with cancer as long as Prince had – more than five years – could bear to love and stand by his failures. Was it unavoidable that a doctor should abandon patients for whom the cause was lost?

These were philosophical questions he wrestled with in the dead of night when he was too tense and tired to sleep. In the daytime he contented himself with muttering expletives under his breath when he was confronted with human wreckage on the Unit. Secretly, or in the presence of other

240

residents he could trust, he referred to Prince as 'that son-of-a-bitch.'

One morning when he went in to see Joan and found her crying and unwilling to speak, he determined to try to get some help for her. He remembered hearing Mary mention that Christie Wilson did counselling on the Unit. She had pointed Christie out to him once. Today he would keep an eye out for her as he made his rounds.

It was nearly noon when he finally caught sight of her sitting at the counter in the nurses' station. She was bent over a chart, making an entry in it.

'Christie Wilson?' He put a hand on her shoulder and she looked up, recognizing the voice and the face. She had been aware of Mulder and impressed with him since his arrival on the Unit. He didn't walk around, like so many of his colleagues, an expressionless robot. His face mirrored his shifting feelings. His eyes, under thick brows, were serious and intelligent. His jaw and chin bristled with a thick red beard.

'Yes,' she smiled, 'and you're Richard Mulder. Mary has told me about you.'

'I hope it was good.' He looked a little self-conscious.

'It was. And Martin Kiley has had some admiring words for you too.'

Mulder laughed. Christie saw that his face was now flushed.

'You're seeing Kiley, then? Martin's a great guy.' He cleared his throat. 'Which brings me to my point. I want to know if you'll see Joan Bentley. She's Prince's patient. The lady's got lots of troubles.'

'Mary's mentioned Joan to me. Now that a doctor's asked me, I can see her.'

Mulder reached up and pulled Joan Bentley's chart from its slot. He paged through it to the Progress and Consultation section. 'Joan's going to need emotional suuport – badly. Things aren't going to get any better for her.' He watched Christie as she scanned the pages and turned them over. She was frowning.

241

'I don't see any entries or initialling by Dr Prince in the last couple of weeks. Is he off the case?'

Dr Mulder lowered his voice, but his words were clipped. 'No. He is not off the case, but he might as well be. Mrs Bentley has been waiting for days to hear from him whether she can be discharged to her home. She is not a candidate for any further treatment. In my opinion, she could die, at the latest, within weeks. She should be close to her family, and be kept as pain-free as possible.'

'Can you call Dr Prince and try to get him to sign a discharge?' Christie asked.

'I can hardly recommend decisions about the case to Dr Prince. I know that her emotional state warrants that a counsellor see her. She has been asking for Prince – she is heavily dependent on him, psychologically – and she has been asking to go home. She seems to be upset since the minister from her church came to see her.'

Christie tapped her closed lips with the barrel of her pen. She saw anger in Dr Mulder's face. What a baptism by fire the residents had! None of them, when they arrived for their month of duty on the Cancer Unit, had any training in the psychology of cancer, or of any slow death process. They were trained to examine, diagnose, treat, and send cured patients home. The sensitive ones saw when treatment was more cruel than kind.

'I understand your predicament,' Christie said. 'I'll go and talk with her, then write my assessment in the Progress and Consultation. Let's hope Dr Prince will come in and see her and agree to a home-care plan. I'll page you and let you know what happened.'

Mulder nodded his head and smiled a wry smile. 'Thanks. I know you're in the same bind I'm in. You get even less communication with these high priests. I hope we can get her home.' Mulder picked his stethoscope off the counter where the charts were spread out and hung it around his neck. 'Good luck,' he said.

Christie put her note pad and pen in her pocket. She shut Joan Bentley's metal-cased hospital chart. There were some factors in this case she wished she knew more about. With Prince incommunicado, many delicate problems presented themselves. She wished she knew who the minister was who had plunged Joan into a deeper depression. She also wished she could include Father Fransciscus in the counselling; but that was impossible, since Joan's clergyman was the minister of her own church. She thought of Martin Kiley and his wedding. It was scheduled a few hours from now. At this moment in time, he and Joan Bentley were the only persons she was counselling in the hospital. More and more, she was being assigned to 'blind' nursing-home referrals.

Suddenly, she felt very tired. A shadow of the old emptiness and solitude enveloped her like a cloud. She sat staring at the open chart in front of her, without seeing it. Finally, she put the chart back in its slot and walked down the corridor towards Joan Bentley's room.

Chapter Sixteen

Father Fransiscus was driving to Victor Vendetti's house on a warm evening in the middle of summer. He had just left the hospital, and his mind was full of Martin Kiley. Martin had talked openly with the priest about his reluctance to be treated anymore with chemotherapy. All he had told Fransciscus confirmed what Christie had related in the chapel. Franciscus always had to struggle with his conscience when he talked with Martin. He felt he could not openly advise him against the new proposal for hepatic infusion. Gretchen trusted Virgil Prince implicitly and believed that each new treatment might cure him, or at least secure an indefinite period of remission. The hospital machinery had ground into action even before Martin's wedding. He was married in his room on Seven Main. He placed a new ring on Gretchen's finger while an electric pump pulsed at his side, keeping the chemicals flowing directly into his hepatic artery.

Today as he watched Martin and listened to him, Franciscus felt he had resigned himself to whatever was decided for him. The memory of the angel and its message had softened and illumined all of his experience. It now guarded him from the dread of whatever pain and diminishment he might have to face in the future.

But Franciscus had come upon a new source of concern for Martin. It was a concern that Martin seemed to feel he needed to handle directly. The problem involved his eldest son. At the time of Martin's divorce, the boy had become very angry, had blamed Martin for the trouble, and had allied himself with his mother. He still lived with her, but had attended his father's wedding as a cold and distant presence. After the ceremony there had been a flurry of kissing and tears and congratulations. Only the son, Josh, stood aloof. Now he had learned that Josh was Martin's favourite son.

The priest's train of thought switched abruptly as he drove into the alley and parked his car. The green of the grass and the colours of the flowers were softened by that special light of the hour before sunset. The earth seemed meditative. The drone of the nearby freeway had changed its tone. It resembled the lazy ambiance of bees gathering nectar.

Franciscus walked up the narrow sidewalk leading to Vendetti's kitchen door. As he went, he noticed that the grapes were ripening nicely. They looked almost ready to pick. The mood of the warm evening filled him with nostalgia. It evoked the summers of his life when he had hurried to meet someone, his heart beating fast, bathed in the aura of a crimson sun.

He heard Victor calling to him from the doorway: 'It's you, Father!' and gently returned his memories to their secret file.

As Victor held the screen door open, the curve of his mouth, the look in his eyes expressed a quiet confidence. There was something in Victor that allayed his own tensions and anxieties. As he entered the door they clasped hands. Victor was shorter than Franciscus and had to look up to see into the face of his friend.

'How about some coffee, or tea?' Victor offered.

'Yes, I'll join you in a cup of coffee. I dashed off to the hospital without it.'

Victor took him by the arm. 'I have a little whiskey here. A touch of that in the coffee is always good.'

Franciscus smiled his assent, and Victor walked over to one of the cabinets and pulled out a bottle. The priest noted that he walked slowly. He was much stronger than he had been at Broadcliff, but it was as if the curve of his remission had levelled off. He had never acquired what Franciscus thought of as normal strength. Victor poured two cups of coffee short of the brims and filled both with whiskey.

'We'll go into the yard,' he said. He led the way to where the chairs always stood, beneath the maple tree. 'The yard is my chapel,' he said.

They settled down in the lounge chairs and sipped their drinks.

'How pleasant it is here,' Franciscus sighed contentedly, and looked around him. A breeze fluttered the thick leaves of the maple, dappling their faces with the filtered sun. 'It's hot and humid in the hospital. I think there are corridors where no fresh air ever reaches.'

Victor bent over his coffee cup and inhaled the aroma. 'I have a neighbour who was in one of the new hospital wings.' He took a sip of his drink. The breeze ruffled his grey hair. 'He told me it was all air-conditioned, but the windows were sealed tight and you couldn't get any outside air. It was cool, but there was never the smell of trees, or the smell of rain, or the smell of gasoline, or the smell of sun. It's hard to get well in a hospital. You can't smell life.'

Franciscus laughed. He loved to hear Vic talk. He always hit the nail squarely on the head. Life did have a smell, he thought. There was the time when the antiseptic smell of a hospital, mixed with faeces and disease, had made his stomach retch. Now he had become immune to it. He moved through it the way certain fish move through polluted water.

'Who are you seeing now?' Vic asked. 'Met any interesting people?'

Franciscus rubbed his chin and gazed at Victor. His concern about Martin Kiley surfaced again. He wondered what Victor would think about the divine visitor who had broken into the strictly controlled structure of Seven Main. He sighed and settled back in his chair.

'I've been seeing an interesting man, Vic. In some ways he reminds me of you. He was always strong and vigorous until he got cancer, and he has great integrity.'

Victor straightened in his chair. He listened as Franciscus carefully recounted the events in Martin Kiley's background, including his problems with the Church over his divorce and second marriage and the sacrament of his recent wedding in the hospital. Franciscus could see that he found it difficult to understand the importance of the wedding. But when he heard about Martin's baulking at more chemotherapy, his interest sharpened.

'He's had chemotherapy before?'

'For at least a year,' Franciscus told him. 'He'd done pretty well on it; then he suddenly got worse. The cancer spread to his liver.'

Victor shook his head. The corners of his mouth turned down. His eyes under the bushy grey brows grew intense, and he leaned forward as he spoke.

'It can't help him if his liver's full of cancer,' he said gruffly. 'I watched Harold. He died with chemicals going into his veins.'

The priest shifted in his chair.

'It wasn't an easy decision for Martin Kiley,' he replied. 'His wife begged him to do whatever Dr Prince prescribed –'

'Martin Kiley!' Vic suddenly interrupted. 'Martin Kiley was one of the men on the ward with me. I remember Prince calling on him and changing his treatment just before he let him go home.'

'Then you know him?'

'Not well,' Vic answered. He stared down at the grass and

seemed to be turning something over in his mind. He sighed, finally, and looked up. 'He seemed to have a lot of confidence in Virgil Prince.'

'Evidently that has changed,' Franciscus told Victor.

'He's between a rock and a hard place,' Victor muttered. His brow furrowed into a deep frown.

'His wife said that if he refused the treatment, it would be like telling her he didn't want to live. It would be a rejection of her. And there are children. She wants him to try everything, to go whatever route the doctors are willing to try.'

Victor shook his head. 'Sometimes there are ways of living that are worse than death.' He sipped his hot drink slowly; then he sighed and eased back in his chair. 'What did it do for Harold to extend his life?'

Franciscus pondered Harold's death. He had watched its progress each time he entered the ward. When he answered Victor, he was trying, in a way, to convince himself.

'Very few people come to their death with their lives resolved. Most people leave unfinished business. I have wondered if the chemotherapy gives them an extension; a longer chance to finish ... things.'

Victor processed this carefully. He thought of his own need to complete his tasks. He was silent a long time. When he spoke, his voice was more passionate than the priest had ever heard it.

'When I asked you to pray for me to get some time to use, and the forgiveness – the absolution, I knew I needed *good* time, time here at home, and to be as much myself as I could be. I didn't want the chemo because it's poison. And the way the doctor acted – he seemed toxic himself. I knew the combination of being locked up in that hospital and him trying to kill the cancer with slow poison could make me crazy, or dull my mind. Somehow, I thought if there *was* a God He could help me better if I was *clear*. And *you*: if you could get to God, if He could hear you, He might want to work with me, use me for some good things.' He paused and watched Franciscus. He went on, his voice almost a whisper now: 'And God *heard* you.

'In the hospital with Prince and the chemotherapy, I would have been a broken, useless tool.'

'You were right, Victor. Your instincts were right, and so was your decision.' Franciscus saw that Victor had more to say about it. He was moving his shoulders restlessly. He put his cup down on the table and clenched his fists, cracking the knuckles.

'I wish I could get the man out of there – haul him out myself.'

Franciscus could see now how Victor must have looked gunning up his motorcycle. He thought again of Gretchen and of the angel. He thought of the angry son. 'Maybe the decision can't be the same for everyone,' he said. 'Martin couldn't make a decision in conflict with his wife. Maybe . . .' The priest's voice trailed off.

'Maybe what?' Victor demanded.

'Maybe the angel will give him his "good time." Maybe the angel can work it out – even in the hospital.'

'The angel?' Victor looked at Franciscus, a bit startled.

'Martin Kiley says he saw an angel, or someone who might even have been Jesus, appear at the foot of his bed when he was waiting for his test results, not long after he'd been admitted. Since then he's had a lot of confidence about his future.'

Victor considered this.

'Was he on a drug then? Some of them make you see things.'

'No. It was before he was put on the new chemical. They had stopped the old one. It wasn't working.' Franciscus thought for a moment and shook his head. 'No, Vic, the patients I've seen who were distorted from treatment drugs saw frightening things. Martin wasn't dreaming. He was awake. He was watching the freeway traffic.'

'The vision – the angel: did it say anything?'

'It told him to be confident that everything was going to be all right with him. It told him there was nothing for him to fear.'

The sun was almost gone. Shadows were lengthening on the lawn. Victor seemed to be in deep thought. Now he smiled suddenly.

'Who knows? Maybe God uses messengers sometimes. Christie told me she'd seen some of his messengers, but I think the ones she's seen are birds and bugs.' He laughed gently. 'I'm willing to believe a lot of things I would have scoffed at before.'

Twilight was closing in, and the air had began to feel a bit damp. Victor got up from his chair and suggested they move inside. The kitchen seemed brighter and more cheerful than Franciscus had remembered it. He remarked that the house looked very attractive and cosy.

'Stella's promotion gave her a chance to fix things up a little,' Victor explained. 'She got some new curtains and those canisters, and she painted the chairs.' He led the way into the living room. 'She made a new cover for the daybed and got some bright pillows.'

Franciscus looked around him and smiled at Vic. 'It matches the newness of your life,' he said. He seated himself in an armchair. The meditative mood of twilight had filled the room. Through the west window they could still see a crimson sky silhouetting the rooftops of Brandenburg.

Victor stretched out on his daybed. It was the hour when his strength was at its ebb. He handed his empty cup to the priest.

'A little more whiskey without the coffee would be good,' he said. 'Would you get me some and help yourself?'

Franciscus went into the kitchen and refilled their cups. They sat inhaling the bouquet of the liquor. Victor spoke again in a quiet voice.

'Father, I hope I'll continue in this remission for a while; but even if I don't, I've had enough time to get Stella into a secure situation. She's got a good job, and she likes herself. She owns this house. It's in her name.' He had been looking at Franciscus. Now he shut his eyes and seemed to be resting. The priest waited, sensing there was more.

'But something has been worrying me. It's about the

"bottoming out" we talked about in the chapel. If the remission doesn't go on indefinitely, if I should get bad again, I don't want to be a burden to Stella, to cause her to quit her job in order to take care of me.' He looked sharply at Franciscus. 'Father, I'm afraid of having to go back to the hospital. I read an article in the paper about a new kind of place called a hospice. It sounds like I'd be okay there and not have to take chemicals – except something for pain. But there isn't anything like that here in Brandenburg.'

'Yes,' Franciscus replied. 'Christie has told me how hospices work. She said she had always wanted to work in one.'

Victor sipped on his whiskey and contemplated the possibilities and ramifications of new beginnings.

Franciscus picked up a coverlet and laid it over Victor's legs. A cool breeze was coming in from the west. He stood and looked down at the thin body on the bed. 'God has done pretty well with you so far,' he said.

'And I'm grateful.' Victor's voice was slow and sleepy. He looked up at his friend. 'Father, don't be long in getting back,' he said. Then he closed his eyes. Franciscus stood beside the daybed for a time watching him as he drifted into sleep; then he let himself out through the kitchen door.

As he walked down the path to his car, the air was sweet with the scent of honeysuckle. He drove slowly down the street towards St Thomas' drinking in the sounds of the summer night. He heard the calls and laughter of children playing under the trees, the sound of music coming from the open doors of houses and cafés. Two lovers passed through the beam of a streetlamp holding each other so closely they seemed a single shape. He turned his thoughts to Victor. All that had happened since he'd left the hospital had been a miracle. The reestablishment of love where love had died, of beauty where there had been decay were miracles. The sadness that drifted around the corners of his mind had the familiarity of an old love song. It always haunted him on nights like this when the earth breathed forth perfume and the air touched his skin like the drift of silk. To shut the door

250

on the night and lie down on his solitary bed was like murdering mystery.

He turned into the alley at St Thomas' and parked his car. As he made his way over the worn bricks of the entrance to the rectory, he reached out and pressed his hand against the cold roughness of the stone wall. He willed away a tightness in his throat and moved on down the passageway. He climbed the long flight of wooden stairs to his room. His window was open, and the fragrant breeze tossed the worn curtains like shafts of soft, young hair. Mortality itself moved through the sweetness of the night. It touched his heart again with its ruinous strength.

He knelt down beside his narrow bed and began to pray. He thanked God for all miracles and brought before Him the questions of Victor's life, of Martin's and his own; and he asked that He use them.

Chapter Seventeen

Brenda Stone sat on one of the stools at the nursing station with Joan Bentley's chart in front of her. She was looking at it, but not seeing it. Virg had discussed the case with her at breakfast. They had agreed that Bentley was taking an impossibly long time to die. There was no explanation for it, really. Many patients in her condition would have died a long time ago. The husband had given Virg instructions to 'pull all the stops – bar no holds – spare no expense' regarding her treatment. None of the chemotherapy had prevailed against her last downhill slide, and all Virg's cases were handled by the latest and most nearly perfect protocols.

Thank God, Brenda thought, she was fencing Virg off from the end pressures of these 'no-win' cases. She could protect him from the pointless drain and waste. He had delegated to her many of the tasks he used to perform himself. She now checked all the patient charts for him, and bothered him only with what was critical: namely, the need of those patients for whom his time and efforts could achieve some payoff – those patients who were still candidates for remission. She had also relieved him of the harassment of his 'beeper'. She now kept it on her own person and screened all calls for him. He had delegated to her the authority to give orders and make decisions when he did not want to be disturbed. The result was that he had more energy. He had escaped from the depression and hypersensitivity she had seen in him before their relationship began. He used to be a brooder – a goddamned Hamlet, in fact.

She smiled to herself. Today was his day off, and he was spending it with his wife and children. Dottie was growing increasingly anxious and neurotic as she registered the changes in Virg. His trips, and his later and later evening hospital calls, had kept him more remote from her. The situation had two aspects, Brenda knew. Dottie's anxiety and her bent for cross-examination harassed him almost as much as the now-absent 'beeper' had previously done.

The second aspect was in Brenda's favour. As Dottie took on, more and more, the character of a suspicious nag, he needed more and more to escape. A structure had been created around Brenda, and Brenda only, which at once sheltered him, excited him, and reflected his power and authority. By tonight he would be mad with cabin fever, bored senseless by Dottie's prattle about the kids' school problems and cavity records, and exasperated by the need for repairs around the house. He would also be seething with need for her. She had managed, so far, to space their rendezvous together with just enough time apart, and just enough erotic subtleties in his exposure to her at work, to keep him in a constant state of restless anticipation.

Something in the thought of Virg's feverish waiting for their meetings brought her back to the chart in front of her. Oh, yes: *Bentley* was waiting; waiting to go home. She scanned the Progress and Consultation section of the chart.

This new resident, Mulder, was really hanging in there – and he was cocky and mouthy. *'Home-care plan must be devised. Patient dying',* with his signature. There was an entry signed by Christie Wilson. *'Dr Prince: Please advise re home-care plan. Kate McGowan must meet with husband to arrange this. Joan Bentley needs to die at home'.*

God, what a nerve! Social workers had no right to advise doctors. Nevertheless, if Joan Bentley got home it would be one less demand out of all the remaining nagging demands on Virg. At this particular time, it was important that he not be distracted by the hospital.

A heavy hand on her arm dragged her back to the moment. It was the hand of Dr Mulder.

'Has Dr Prince given any directives on a referral for Joan Bentley's home-care plan?' he asked. Something in his voice demanded attention.

Brenda gave him a long, level look. Slowly and deliberately, she raised her right knee and hooked her heel over the rung of the high stool she sat on. She arched her neck and pushed back the long, wavy lock of hair, which conveniently delayed or punctuated her speech, as needed.

'As a matter of fact, I was just going to page you,' she said. 'Dr Prince wants Bentley out of here as fast as possible. Get the home-care nurse to contact her husband.' She shut the cover of the chart with a smart crack.

Dr Mulder reached under the counter and drew out a Physician's Referral blank.

'Would you like to initial this for Prince, or will he be in today?' Mulder's blue eyes glittered under his bushy red eyebrows. His voice had a trace of mockery in it. 'Kate McGowan needs a referral from the attending physician before she can contact the family,' Mulder said crisply.

Brenda drew a ball-point pen from her uniform and wrote *'Virgil Prince'* at the bottom of the form, then initialled it herself next to a slash mark.

'Fill out the form, Dr Mulder,' she ordered, 'and see that it gets to McGowan today.' She twisted in her seat, and making a long reach, slid the Bentley chart into its slot. Then she stood up and ran her fingers through her hair.

'So long,' she said.

'Just a minute,' Mulder said. He moved along the counter and placed his rangy frame in the entrance/exit of the station. 'If Prince isn't coming in, you'd better get him the message that Martin Kiley has had some frequent, violent vomiting. The chemo in the infusion has affected him very adversely, worse than the earlier programmes. I think he should be taken off the infusion immediately,' he said firmly.

Brenda lounged back against the counter. 'How long has this been going on?'

'He complained of more nausea and shortness of breath soon after the last infusion was started,' Mulder told her. 'He got through his wedding hanging on by his willpower. I was about to make an entry in the chart that I won't be responsible for the case if the infusion isn't stopped.'

'Wedding?' Brenda looked amused. 'Must be a bit after the fact. He seems to have a bunch of kids hanging around.'

Mulder shifted his stance and folded his arms. 'How soon can you reach Prince?'

'I'll be in touch with him today. We'll check into the alternative protocols.' She frowned slightly and paused. 'It seems I heard something about a consult regarding surgery.'

'Surgery . . .!' Mulder exploded the word through his red beard.

'I'll be in touch. You'll hear something today,' Brenda said. She swept past him, gathering up her stack of portfolios as she went.

Brenda didn't wait for the elevator, but headed down the outside stairwell to the physicians' parking ramp. She slid into her yellow Porsche convertible, lit a cigarette, and roared smoothly through the exit. She headed through the traffic to the expressway. She had a few errands to do before she drove to the lake. Virg was meeting her there at a cottage he had rented. It was thirty miles north of his family cottage, where Dottie and the children had been settled for the summer. This place, plus their joint journeys to medical conferences, had been the setting for their meetings in the last several months. Brenda was glad for this time alone in the car. It was her best thinking time. Today especially, she needed to review her conclusions and her plans, especially her plans for the evening. If it went well, tonight could determine their future.

The wind whipped her hair back as she negotiated the curved entrance ramp. She felt a sense of exhilaration now that she had worked out some tactical problems in her mind. There had been a few occasions lately when Virg's inner conflicts, the pressure of his compartmented life, had cast a shadow on their relationship. These episodes had convinced her that she needed to form a plan of action before things slipped from her control.

Her errands were all in the small resort town near the cottage. One was to pick up a white Charmeuse négligé at her favourite speciality shop. Then she had to pick up groceries for their dinner at the local store. She wanted to get settled in plenty of time to be relaxed when Virg arrived. The drinks must be chilled, the food warmed in the oven, and he must find her out walking along the lakeshore. It should be just before dusk when he got there. It was hot now, and the sky clear, prophesying a perfect evening.

What luck that she had run into Mulder and resolved the Joan Bentley question before he could build up a head of steam! Mulder would bear watching. He was thorough and deliberate. And Brenda had seen, in their encounter today, the evidence of a dangerous persistence. He could mean trouble.

Well, he was placated for the time being, and she had more pressing matters to work on now. She intended to use the hour-long drive to the lake to plan the evening's strategy with Virg. He was difficult to second-guess. He was an extremely complex person, and it was this which most delighted her. Most men were so boringly predictable. To secure them was like snaring rabbits. But even in the moments when she felt Virg was most completely captured, she lived with the knowledge that he could again confound her. Just when she felt comfortably imperious and totally in control, he could bring her down with a sudden gesture. He was treacherous. She had watched and admired his treachery with occasional challengers and opponents at medical meetings. But no matter how much she learned about his mind and his body, there was always a portion of his being which eluded her. He needed a strong woman, and he needed a quick one.

He had been sexually inexperienced, almost naïve, when she first knew him. His marriage with Dottie had occurred when he was still a medical student, and it was doomed from the start. Dottie would never be his equal in any area. Brenda knew that at the moment, Virgil Prince was hers. But nothing, in his case, was impossible. If her strategy was faulty, it was even conceivable that another woman could erupt on the scene and become the permanent recipient of all the talents she had awakened in him. It was this unthinkable possibility which gave strength to her resolve and additional fuel to her passion.

In a curious way, the twelve vapid years with Frank Stone had formed her virtuosity. He had been the unwitting perfector of everything in Brenda that was the opposite of himself. Temperate, cautious and honest on all levels, he had driven her to compensate; had fuelled the fires of all that was fervent, bold, and devious in her personality.

At the outset of her affair with Prince, Brenda had been unconcerned with divorce and remarriage. His response to her, and her obvious power over him, had given her a feeling of freedom regarding decisions and resolutions.

But she knew now that if she was to secure the relationship, there must be divorce. Something in him needed the confirmation and endorsement of marriage. Something she trusted inside herself – something, in fact, that had never failed to give her solid cues – told her that if now, at the peak of his dependence, she did not cut him off, and demand that he divorce his wife, there would be no marriage between them. He would slip back to the old status quo, or find a new woman. And she would be left with the picked-over bones of her old life with Frank.

It was time now for a new tack. Brenda ran her fingers through her hair and took some deep breaths. She was almost to the lake. The air had cooled and freshened. She drove the last few miles imagining possibilities for the evening ahead. She pulled up at a kerb in Shorehaven just after noon.

The Côte d'Azur was her favourite shop. It carried things that she had never been able to turn up even on Michigan Boulevard in Chicago. The shop was dim and air-conditioned, with tiny spotlights placed effectively on the display items. The salesgirls knew her well from many successive summers when she had selected the choicest items from their designer lines. Her favourite greeted her now, with just the right mix of warmth and hauteur.

'Good afternoon, Mrs Stone. Have you come for the négligé?'

'Yes, Germaine.' Brenda turned and toyed with the pink marabou of a chiffon cape on one of the models. She sniffed the air delicately. 'What are you sanitizing the shop with today? It smells delicious.'

Germaine emerged from the back room with Brenda's package. 'Oh, that's "Tortu". It isn't new, but very sexy. Have you tried it?'

'"Tortu"? I don't think so. It seems a bit heavy for August. Maybe I'll try some in the fall.' She tucked the box under her arm.

'The white Charmeuse will be absolutely devastating with your suntan,' Germaine reflected, in the velvet whiskey tenor of the best high-class *vendeuse*.

'I'm counting on that,' Brenda responded, fingering her dependably unruly forelock back behind her ear.

'Will you and your husband be planning a trip to Hawaii again this August?' Germaine inquired politely.

'I think not,' Brenda answered. She curved her mouth in a mock smile of regret. 'This summer I'm just making do with a little beachcombing right here at home.'

She walked out into the street and tossed the box into the back of the car. If the market wasn't crowded, she would have plenty of time to get dinner prepared and still spend a couple of hours deepening her tan. She guided the Porsche through the lazy afternoon traffic of Shorehaven and turned into the lakeshore road towards the Gourmet Grocery Shack and Virgil Prince's cottage number two.

Chapter Eighteen

The day at the family cottage had been a restless one for Virgil Prince. Since his childhood had been spent near water or on it, he felt most relaxed and peaceful at his cottage. Still, he would rather have lived near the ocean. An inland lake was lovely, but did not offer the turbulence and drama of the sea. He would never forget a spring vacation during his college days he had spent wandering the beaches of Florida.

However, the cottage he had bought for his family to summer in was the fulfilment of a dream he had worked hard to achieve. Before he became involved with Brenda, he had commuted from the city to the cottage almost daily. He and his wife had planted a vegetable garden, and the children had helped tend it. His children were very important to him. They combined the best qualities in himself and Dottie. They had her gentleness, leavened with his spirit and curiosity. They were brave and adventurous, but well-mannered. Dottie was an excellent mother and housekeeper, but his life with her had been lonely and unfulfilled after the first novelty of their intimacy wore off. He had buried himself in his work and found in it a way to exercise his need for challenge. He had his first taste of power in experiencing the dependency and need of his patients. But lately he delighted most in pitting his wits against power figures in the organizations and institutions he dealt with.

The family cottage was now a spoiled paradise. He was always eager to get there to see the children, but lately they pouted and whined when it was time for him to leave. Dottie projected an air of suspicion and wounded feelings which made every moment he spent with her tense and guarded. He spent as much time as he could out on the small sailboat with the children. Dottie couldn't sail because of an inner-ear problem which made her prone to motion sickness. As long as he was in the sailboat he enjoyed some freedom of mind. He needed time without pressure, and he needed it badly. He had to find a way to accommodate his diverse needs: his needs as a man, and his needs as a father.

The problem was that Dottie wanted it all. She wanted to be a partner in the whole spectrum of his life, and she was not equipped for it. She should have married a shopkeeper.

Today, when he told her he would not be able to stay beyond 6 p.m. her lip trembled and her eyes filled with tears. If he had not known her IQ from college testing reports, he would have been prone to think of her as mentally inferior. Logic was impossible with her. She began to impress him more as a small, timid animal than as a woman. His way of dealing with her tears was to ignore them. Weakness in people who were close to him turned him off.

When he returned from the sail with the children, he began to sort out the contents of his attaché case, and to change his clothes. He had learned to be careful – to remove dungarees and sneakers, shower, and change into business clothes when he left. It was important since his excuse for leaving was always rounds or meetings at the hospital, or medical conferences out of town. One afternoon a month ago there had been a tricky wind when he was sailing back to the cottage with the kids, and he had been quite late leaving to meet Brenda. In his rush to be gone, he had dashed out of the house in his sailing clothes. Dottie had called him back, and there had been a scene. He was wasting energy these days covering his tracks.

Today the kids were down the beach when the moment came for him to leave. He adjusted his tie, put his stethoscope in his pocket, and walked towards the door, hoping that Dottie would not engage him in a last-minute interrogation.

'So long,' he called in the direction of the kitchen, where he could hear her moving dishes around. She came walking out, wiping her hands on a dish towel and looking at him with an expression of anxious reproach.

'What time will you be home tonight?' she asked. Her voice wavered ever so slightly.

'I may not be home tonight. I may just stay in town. Stan Bracebridge is out of town and I have to see his patients too. I have a meeting with some residents, and it may go on and on.' Prince opened his attaché case and pretended to hunt for something in it.

Dottie looked down at the towel in her hands.

'That's too bad. The Slagers said they wanted us to come over after dinner for a visit. I thought Betty Bracebridge said Stan had to be at the hospital every night this week.' She looked up at him now, her eyes sharp and searching, seeking some sign or expression indicating she had caught him in a lie.

Prince felt the familiar wave of rage sweep over him. He clenched his jaw in an effort not to react with some remark that would lead to a long scene. He pulled a typewritten report out of his case and looked at it.

'Oh, there it is,' he said, with just the right note of casual boredom. 'I need that for one of the residents.'

'Betty said Stan had to be at the hospital every–' Dottie began again. Prince interrupted her.

'He changed his plans,' he said. He looked at Dottie with a level, unblinking stare. 'Tell the Slagers I'm sorry to miss the get-together.'

God. What boredom, he thought. Another evening listening to the Slagers bragging about their retirement plan and the condominium they were buying in West Palm Beach. Dottie had a knack of collecting friends whose backgrounds and conversation were all interchangeable.

He slammed the attaché case shut and went out through the screen door and onto the porch.

'I'll be driving back here tomorrow afternoon if no emergencies turn up,' he said – not bothering to look back;

not wanting to see the confused expression on her face; hating her for her attempts to trap him; hating himself for the bonds that held him.

The Mark VI purred quietly down the gravel driveway and onto the dirt road leading to East Shore Drive. The Drive wound along the lake for hundreds of miles – sometimes following close to the lake, curving along sandy beaches, and sometimes winding through the woods, where tall trees formed shadowy, green-arched tunnels dappled with patterns of yellow sun that filtered through the leaves.

Virgil Prince had long since abandoned the dogma of his family's fundamentalist religious sect. No man who called himself a scientist could in good conscience adhere to a faith that professed the existence of a personal, caring God.

Still, on certain days, in certain seasons, when he drove along the Shore Drive, the old mystical vision came to haunt him and for moments he felt released from the bondage of his own physical blight. Sometimes he had parked along the road, as he was returning to his cottage at sundown, and walked along the deserted stretches of beach that were inhabited by no one, delighting in his anonymity, feeling awe at the red globe of the sun and the infinite variety of fading colours in the water and the sky. At those times he had felt an overwhelming, and totally irrational, sense of power; a power which was not his own, but which he shared.

He had had experiences like this, which he dimly recollected, in his childhood, but mostly in the recent years of his loneliness, before Brenda. His accelerating success in his profession, and his increasing prestige and power, had brought him into Brenda's orbit, and the loneliness had ended. His peace had ended also. Long before Brenda he had learned to handle the physical handicap of his face. Socially, and in his profession, it had become a badge of courage and survival, almost a weapon. It projected the veiled mystery of all masks. But not until Brenda had a beautiful woman been attracted to him physically. Brenda's passionate pursuit of him had ended his sense of sexual inferiority.

The sun was turning red now. It was his favourite time of

day at the lake, the time just before dusk. He picked up
speed on the last two miles before he reached the road to the
new cottage, where Brenda waited. He wanted to get there
before sunset. His heart began to beat heavily, and he felt the
hot, tingling sensation in his groin and thighs that her
proximity always evoked. He wondered how much longer
she could stave off Frank Stone's wounded pride and
outrage. He was more difficult to manage than Dottie.

He coasted down the curved and thickly wooded
driveway. The cottage was built at lake level, and the yard
was all sand, with areas of tall weeds and scrub cedar. He
stopped the car and got out, removing his tie as he walked
towards the cottage. He heard no sound at all. The cottage
was small, but the living room had a fireplace and an open,
beamed ceiling.

'Brenda!' he called, moving through the open rear door.
He walked through the house. All the rooms were empty.
She must be down on the beach. The aroma of chicken, wine,
and garlic floated through the rooms. In the bedroom it was
mingled with Brenda's perfume and body lotion, a floral
scent with musky shadings. Her clothes hung over the back
of a chair. Some taupe lace panties and a tiny matching lace
bra were draped on the arm of the chair. A wet bikini
swimsuit lay on a towel on the windowsill. He walked back
into the living room. An ice bucket with a jar of martinis
chilling in it stood on the coffee table. Lemon twists and
anchovy olives were in a bowl next to it. There were two
glasses waiting to be filled. He poured himself a drink, then
went into the bedroom and took off his clothes. He pulled on
a pair of trunks and walked to the front door. He took a
long sip from his martini and headed down the cracked
concrete path to the edge of the water.

The sky was a breathtaking panorama of dusky lavender
clouds, gilded by the scarlet sun. A breeze rippled the surface
of the lake. He looked down the shoreline and saw a figure
moving towards him. It was Brenda in a long white garment
that blew back from her body in the breeze. In the subdued
light, her skin was as dark as an Indian's. Her long hair

floated away from her face as she moved. There was something in the fluid whiteness of the robe that gave her rather savage beauty a look of purity and fragile grace. He thought of Brenda as having many qualities, but he had never before counted purity or fragility among them. Her tanned thighs appeared and disappeared as she walked in the undulating flutterings of the skirt. As she approached him, she held out her arms, and when he encircled her she curled against him with the softness of a cat. He held her for a few moments and then moved her away from him and looked at her at arm's length. Her eyes were unusually gentle. They had an unaccustomed aspect, almost sad. She smiled suddenly, baring her small, even teeth.

'Did you bring me a drink?' she asked.

'I'll get it now. I went looking for you first.'

Brenda sank slowly down on the lavender sand, the white skirt spilling around her like foam. It parted to reveal one lean tanned thigh, and then the other. She pushed her hair back from her face.

'Please, baby, bring my drink. Let's stay out here until the sun goes.'

Virgil was taking in her whole aura, the subtle difference in her air. She was capable of infinite changes, some of them confounding. She smiled at him again. Her hands rested lightly on her knees. Her thighs moved slowly, closing and opening. Her eyes were dreamy and half-closed.

'Have a sip of mine,' he said. He handed her the glass. She took a drink and ran the tip of her tongue slowly over her lips. She stretched one long leg in the sand and then the other. She put the glass down beside her, then slowly studied his body with her eyes.

Prince dropped down on the sand and pinned her shoulders to the ground. He covered her mouth with thrusting, almost angry pressure. Her body writhed under him; her thighs lifted against his own with incredible strength, almost forcing him away. Her sharp nails caressed his shoulders and then cut into his back like tiny knives. She sometimes used her nails and her teeth in alternating caresses and lacerations until he was rocked between feverish heat and quick flashes of pain. Now she was moving her thighs so that he could not enter her without being brutal. He shuddered, then rolled over on his side and groaned.

Brenda opened her eyes and looked at him. The bad side of his face was turned to her, an aspect he managed to avoid in most encounters.

Now she gazed at his face and softened. The full curve of his mouth, the line of his forehead, nose, and chin were clean and intact, but the red glow of the sinking sun deepened the stain of the mark. It looked like a ragged wound which had ceased bleeding, but had never healed. She raised her body and rested on one hip. She leaned towards him and caressed his head gently with her hands. Her mouth travelled over the sad terrain of his ruined face, lingering on his eyes and his brow. Finally she pressed her lips on the discoloured side of his mouth. Something she had not planned was happening. Up to this point everything had gone as she intended, but now she had lost her way.

There was a long silence; then he said, 'Brenda ...'

She could not answer.

'Brenda,' he repeated. He turned her face towards him with the tips of his fingers. Her cheeks were wet.

'Brenda – I've never seen you cry ... What is it? What's wrong?'

He was looking at her with his full face now. She saw the strength of his perfection balanced against his vulnerability. She remembered the problem – and the plan.

'It's getting cool,' she said. 'The sun is down.'

'Do you want to go inside?'

'Let's get my drink,' she said. She stood up, shaking the sand from her skirt, and walked up the path to the cottage ahead of him, the white négligé moving and luminous against her dark arms and shoulders.

When they were inside the door, he took her in his arms, more gently than he had ever done before. Brenda returned his kisses, briefly; then she turned away.

'There are some things we must talk about, Virg. We

264

should talk now. If we make love I won't be able to say them.'

Prince looked at her questioningly for a moment. She met his gaze steadily and said nothing. He turned and walked over to the table and poured a martini into her glass. He refilled his own. They touched glasses.

'The food smells fantastic. Chicken in wine?'

'. . . over wild rice, with snow peas,' Brenda said.

Prince went over to the sofa and sat down. She was impressed again with the singular grace of his body and his strength. She decided not to sit on the sofa with him. She sat in a large chair facing him and crossed her legs. The front of her skirt parted, exposing her legs to the tops of her thighs.

'There are two messages from the hospital. The Joan Bentley situation is getting worse. Dr Mulder was uptight about getting a home-care order.'

'Did you tell him to go ahead?' Prince asked.

'Yes. Number two: Kiley is worse also. More vomiting, more shortness of breath, since the new treatment. Mulder wants to know if he can take him off the infusion.' Brenda recrossed her legs slowly, then reached over and picked a cigarette off the table.

'I talked to Schwab about doing surgery. He won't last more than a couple of weeks if nothing is done. If the surgery works, and he lives through it, it could delay things some.'

'Are you going in tomorrow?' she asked.

'Yes. I'll talk to Kiley and tell Schwab to schedule the surgery,' Prince answered.

'Well, his wife will go along with whatever you suggest. Do you think he can take the surgery?'

'We'll see,' said Prince. 'It's worth the gamble. He can't get worse.'

Brenda lit her cigarette and inhaled deeply. She lifted her hips and tucked one leg under her.

'Is that all?' Prince asked.

'No,' Brenda said. 'I have to tell you some decisions I've made. They will affect our relationship.'

Prince felt slightly annoyed. He didn't feel in a mood for heavy decisions. His day with Dottie had been strain

265

enough. He wanted to discharge the pent-up sexual needs Brenda had evoked. Then he wanted to build a fire and have dinner beside it.

'Decisions?' he echoed.

'I have had to make some decisions, very difficult decisions ... and if you want to continue seeing me, other than at work, I'm afraid you'll have to make some too.'

'And what decisions have you made?' he asked. He watched her carefully. She mashed out her cigarette in the ashtray and walked over and stood in the open doorway. She looked out at the water. He couldn't see her face.

'Our relationship is going to suffer – it hasn't yet, but it will – from all the pressures you're going through – and I'm going through – to cover our tracks at home,' she said.

'Is Frank cracking down on you? Has there been more trouble?' Prince wanted to know.

'He knows. There's no point in trying to pretend to him anymore. He won't take any decisive moves. He won't do anything big. He'll just continue to create minor hells for me.'

Prince was silent. He had been through a few of his own.

'I guess I've admired your ability to handle things without whining. I assumed you were handling Frank,' Prince said.

Brenda turned from the door and stood facing him directly. The light of the horizon was behind her. The room was almost in darkness. He still could not see her face, just the shape of her body through the sheer négligé.

'I *handle* him. But it costs. Is everything fine between you and Dottie? Is she buying your heavy work schedule?'

Prince heaved a long sigh. 'No,' he said, 'she's not. She's at me every minute I'm in the house. And when she's quiet, you could cut the air with a knife.'

Brenda crossed the room and stretched out on the end of the sofa facing Virgil. He could see her expression now. It was dispassionate and smooth.

'Virg, I've decided not to see you anymore, unless you get a divorce. If you want a casual screw, there is plenty of material for that around. If we go on seeing each other,

Dottie will eventually blow, and create a mess, anyway.' She was staring at him with a level, unblinking look. Her voice was cool. He knew she was right.

He shifted around in his seat until he was looking at her with his tentative, three-quarter effect. He managed a controlled half-joking tone.

'Is that an ultimatum?' he asked casually. He was proud of his voice. It contained a tinge of boredom. He had always had a hunch that he would be dead with Brenda if he lost control.

'Yes,' she answered.

'Are there time limits, madame? What are the terms?' He lowered his voice to the soft, teasing tone that had always turned her on.

'This is the last night, Virg. After that, let me know if you've started a divorce. Let me know when you've moved out.' She saw a sudden blankness in his expression, and knew he was stunned by the clean cut she had made. She waited for him to respond. When he remained silent, she stood up.

'Everything is ready in the oven. Do you want to eat now, or shall we have another drink?'

Prince got up and walked over to the ice bucket. He put two cubes in his glass and poured gin over them. He had known that he would have to make a decision soon. The pressure from Dottie was getting unbearable. But he had felt that whether the decision to leave was made by him or Dottie herself spoke of divorce, Brenda would remain a constant factor through it all. He wondered how he would handle the sexual deprivation, if Brenda really meant her ultimatum. How would he be able to take seeing her all the time at the hospital, knowing they could not have each other later? He took several large gulps of the martini. Maybe Brenda was right. Good strategy involved initiating the moves. If he waited for Dottie to make the first move he would be forced into a defensive position, just as he was with Brenda now.

She walked over and stood beside him. She held out her glass and smiled.

He lifted the carafe of martinis and poured some in her glass. He was aware his hand was unsteady.

'I'm going to take a couple of weeks off, starting tomorrow,' Brenda said. 'A friend in Chicago has been wanting me to visit. I'll need a little distance – and you'll have time to think: some time for hospital problems and for Dottie.'

God. Now she was going away!

'You run a tight ship, baby,' he said wryly. His voice sounded unsteady now. 'So it's going to be cold turkey . . . or haven't *you* felt any addiction yet?'

Brenda heard the slight catch in his voice. It was time to let down the bars, briefly. Virg needed a fresh – indeed, a raw – memory to carry with him when they separated. She walked over to the sofa and stretched out with her arm along the back. She took small sips of her drink for a few minutes, looking at him over the rim of the glass. Then she put the glass on the table.

He watched her with his eyes half shut. He stood motionless, but she noted that the muscles in his legs were flexing, as if he were restraining some power in them. She admired his control. She raised one knee up to her chin to part the long skirt. Her legs were exposed now. She slowly undid the top buttons of the bodice until it opened to her waist. Her small breasts gleamed whitely against the dark skin of her arms and rib cage. She unbuttoned the négligé completely and let it fall from her shoulders. She leaned back and stroked her breasts with her fingertips.

He stood quietly for a few seconds before he surrounded her. He ripped the négligé from under her hips and fell on her body with a ragged sigh of relief. His shoulders and arms shook as he held her. She had perfected the art of teasing him until he took her in a rage. The strength of his sexual onslaughts was a gauge of her power. This time she would carry bruises to Chicago.

At the moment of his release she buried her sharp teeth in his shoulder, pressing slowly until she could feel the warm, salty taste of blood on her tongue. He would bear her mark while he worked out his future freedom, or his bondage. When she felt the familiar spasm of his whole frame, she let herself be lost, drawing in heat from him until control was no longer possible. Her frenzies in his arms frightened her. But she had managed to decide when she would allow them. Tonight she could celebrate,

With one minor deviation, she had successfully followed the inner protocol of her own wisdom.

Chapter Nineteen

As the summer progressed, Christie and Lance had a series of rendezvous. Lance suggested he and Christie meet every other weekend. The foundry in Chicago and his business travel, plus his wife's presence at Pacifica most weekends, caused a logistics problem. He would designate some location midway between Brandenburg and Chicago, or Brandenburg and Pacifica, and they would drive to meet each other. They met in small-town motels. Lance had been talking to Christie about taking her to Mexico for a long vacation. He said he was going to plan ahead to leave the foundry. She told him she could not leave the hospital now. She had been seeing Joan Bentley, who was still depressed, and Martin was in a critical stage. He made no comment when she spoke about her work, but she sensed a withdrawal whenever she mentioned it. She had learned to mention it less and less. He insisted they must plan at least a week to be together before the summer ended. They would make a quick trip to Mexico or he would find a cottage at the dunes, a place far enough from Pacifica to insure against their running into his wife, and her friends.

Each time they met, he fell upon Christie with the ravenous plunge of a starving man attacking his first food.

He told her he knew he would die if he could not see her. The intensity of his sexual aggression always contrasted stunningly with the poetic quality of his other moods. They often drove into the country, where they could make love under the trees. He made blanket nests for her in vine-covered arbours and under willow trees and groves of oak. He made love to her until they were both exhausted; then he lay holding her feet in his hands and kissing them, telling her the ways in which she was unique, different from all the other women he had ever known. He said she had the grace of a dancer, the mystery of a witch. He told her he continually dreamed of having a child by her, and drew word pictures of the child. It would be a girl, and because she was its mother it would be a magical child, a kind of changeling, full of gifts and indescribable graces. He held Christie close as he spoke. She turned her face into his sleeve and wept.

His manners were often crude. After they had been making love for several hours he would eat like an animal, picking up most of a steak and gnawing it from around the bones. He would tear a loaf of bread apart with his hands and talk to her with his mouth full. He could consume great amounts of liquor without appearing drunk. And yet he would hold her in his arms during the night and describe to her the music he had loved. He would sing to her the phrases in it that could break his heart. He would close his eyes, sitting cross-legged in the bed, and move an invisible baton through a symphonic excerpt he had long ago committed to memory.

Christie sometimes lay awake and watched him as he slept, awash in the shocks and surprises of his nature, weak with exhaustion and tenderness. In the beginning, she had returned from their meetings with her body aching and her knees weak. But after a while she became used to it and knew she was gaining strength and stamina. She told herself that Lance was her private boot-camp training. Soon she would be able to fly up the long stairwells of Broadcliff without getting breathless at all.

Sometimes she perceived herself as balancing on a

pendulum that swung between Lance's massive energy and the dark, inexorable wasting away of life on the Cancer Unit. She hoped (she did not dare to pray) that somehow God could redeem her violation of law with another law; that he could effect a silent transfer of life and energy so that her happiness and strength could make her a 'carrier'. She wanted to become a carrier of life and healing in the way that there were carriers of disease.

On the weekends when Lance could not meet her, Christie went to see Victor. They sat in the quiet shade of his maple tree and shared their thoughts. She did not speak much about Lance other than to say that she was still seeing·him.

Victor privately worried about her situation, but Christie continued to look lean and healthy and buoyant. The rosy tan of her skin attested to weekends outdoors. She was quick to laugh, and alive to every nuance of their conversations. For her, this time with Victor under his tree was a quiet blessing. He was eager to hear news of the patients, particularly Martin. All the feelings and concerns, all the events she had learned to suppress when she was with Lance were received by Victor as treasures.

She sat with Victor in the grass beside his lounge chair one Saturday afternoon.

Victor reached out and took her hand.

'You have to be brave, Christie. You have to have confidence in yourself and in your instincts about people.' He looked away from her and up into the maple leaves.

'When I rode the wall in the carnival, you know, there were high stakes I was playing for, and only my wits and my knowledge of the cycle between me and disaster.' He paused before he went on. The muscle in his jaw tightened, and Christie knew he was thinking of Renée. 'When I was on the Cancer Unit I was there long enough to learn they got stiff rules and what the patients need doesn't always match up with the rules. It's like working there with people who are dying, doing what you're trying to do, is like riding a wall too. You're balancing between your instincts – your *feel* of things – and that hard wall of the law, the institution. . . .' He waited before he went on, searching her eyes, and she saw in him that profound sadness which is always the price for true knowledge. She tried to blink away tears, but they came anyway. She felt his rough hand against her cheek, brushing them away. His fingers tipped her chin, forcing her to look at him again.

'I want you to trust yourself, Christie,' he said. 'Do with those patients what you did with me. Find a way to give them back them*selves*.'

Christie absorbed his words, knowing they would be a bulwark against all that would ever be demanded of her.

'I will, Vic,' she answered.

He smiled at her and squared his shoulders, rubbing his hands together briskly.

'Now tell me what's going on with Martin Kiley.'

'He isn't doing very well physically, but he still believes the angel is going to protect him. The thing that he's most anxious about is that his oldest son has been angry with him ever since his mother and Martin were divorced. The only time he came to see Martin was to be present at his wedding. Martin loves the boy a lot. He wants to reach out to him, to mend things, but the boy just stays away.'

'His oldest son, eh?' Victor sat back in his chair and rubbed his forehead.

'I talked with him for a few minutes after the wedding,' Christie explained. 'This son is proud and stubborn, and you can see he's been hurt a lot by his father's second marriage.'

Victor thought about this and was silent for a few minutes. 'Do you think Martin Kiley is going to die?'

'The cancer has spread to his liver. The new chemicals have caused new troubles.'

Vic frowned. 'Someone has got to get them talking,' he said. Christie was remembering the remote look on Josh's face, the look of betrayal in his eyes, the day of the wedding. Suddenly Christie seized Victor's hand.

'Vic! I just thought of something! It might be the key. Gretchen, Martin's wife, told me that Josh is crazy about motorcycles. He's saving up to buy one. She says his room is full of posters of motorcycles and riders!'

Victor's eyes began to glitter. 'Do you think he'd like to meet an old death driver?'

Christie stood up. 'I can ask him. I can get his phone number from Gretchen. He lives with his mother.' The excitement in her face blurred slightly. 'I hope he'll come to see you. . . .'

'He'll come,' Victor said, cutting into her doubt. 'He's crazy about motorcycles, isn't he? What's his name?'

'Josh,' Christie replied. 'Joshua Kiley. And he's seventeen years old.'

Victor raised himself from his chair a bit unsteadily. Christie took his arm to let him lean on her. She noticed that he winced with pain as he stood on his feet.

'Are you okay, Vic?' she whispered.

He patted her hand. 'Let's go find my pain pills. I'll ask Stella to fix the three of us some drinks.' He smiled and winked at Christie. 'We should toast to the success of our plan.'

They walked across the grass to the kitchen door. For the first time since Vic's return from the hospital, Christie watched his face and felt a shadow of foreboding. It chilled her heart, and she shivered slightly in the afternoon sun. Victor put his arm around her waist.

'We both could use a little warm-up,' he said. He opened the door and they walked into the kitchen.

'Stella?' he called. They heard her voice answering from the bedroom.

'Coming!'

Christie noticed again the confidence in her voice and in her step as she came into the room. She had tied a pink silk scarf around her neck and wore a printed summer skirt. She smiled at Christie. Victor patted her on the cheek.

'How about a drink for us, Stella? It's about that time.' He walked over to the counter and dropped some pills into his hand from a plastic bottle.

Stella reached into the cupboard and pulled out two bottles and three glasses. 'How about Manhattans?' she

273

offered. 'That's my favourite – okay, Christie?'

Christie smiled her agreement and watched Stella measure out the drinks while Victor removed ice from the trays. Victor went into the living room and stretched out on his daybed. Christie carried in their Manhattans and arranged the knitted afghan over his legs. They heard Stella talking from the kitchen.

'Ask Christie to stay for dinner, Vic. We're having chuck roast and fresh corn and tomatoes.'

'She'll stay!' he called back. 'Won't you, Christie?'

Christie nodded. She was glad to spend part of the evening with Victor and Stella. They had become a bit like foster parents, but more like friends. She would not see Lance until the next weekend, and she missed him a great deal in her small, empty apartment.

Chapter Twenty

Jack Bentley's sister, Lorraine, had spent a lot of time on the phone that morning. First with her brother, and then with his older son's fiancée. Since her sister-in-law had been ill, she had been forced to assume the role of surrogate mother to her brother's three children. It took up a lot of her time, and just when her own children were on their own and she had been ready to enjoy some freedom.

Tonight she was hostessing a party at Jack's house to introduce Tim's fiancée to her brother's – and Joan's – friends. Now she had to call the florist. There wasn't time to fool around trying to pick flowers from Joan's garden, as Tim had wanted her to do. Besides, the garden was a little scrubby. Nobody had time to weed it, or organize the boys to keep it up. Lorraine had Jack and the 'children' over quite often, and his maid and cook kept the house presentable, but the garden was a casualty she just couldn't worry about. She did want to preserve the decencies and amenities as much as possible, for Jack's sake, in spite of the tragedy. Joan's long illness had exacted an emotional and physical toll on everyone. Lorraine had planned the party tonight knowing it was something Joan would have done, if she were still a functioning person.

This – illness – had seemed to drag on for months after Joan's last remission ended and she took a turn for the worse. The constant trips to the hospital were a terrible drain on everyone, and of course she couldn't be taken care of at home in her condition – pumps and tubes all over the place, not to mention the fact that she needed assistance even to move. Now, in the midst of last-minute preparations for a party involving a hundred people, Jack had told her he'd been called to the hospital for some meeting about Joan's problems, and he had asked that she go with him. Well, she could understand that. She was the only one he could turn to in the midst of the pressures and decisions he must live with. It just couldn't have come at a worse time.

She dialled the florist and ordered six informal arrangements in vases to be delivered. Then she dialled Jack's house and spoke with the cook and the maid, explaining where to place the flowers and when the caterers would arrive. Hopefully, she and Jack would finish their errand at the hospital in plenty of time to freshen up and get ready for the receiving line.

Thank God she had gone to the beauty salon yesterday, or her hair and nails would have been a mess. Jack was due to pick her up any minute. They were going to have lunch at the Seville and then go on up to Broadcliff Hospital. She wondered if Joan had taken a turn for the worse. Well, one couldn't imagine how she could get any worse. Her condition had been unspeakable the last time Lorraine had been there to visit. Her body was grossly distorted, and she didn't even bother to wear the wig anymore. Lorraine had taken her a curler bonnet to wear in lieu of the wig, but the nurses didn't always put it on her. It would be a blessing if

God would just take her. Her life had become a burden to herself and to everyone else.

For a moment, a rare philosophical thought disturbed the smooth flow of her rational mind. She pushed the French phone back into its corner on the carved walnut desk and mused for a moment. What an irony it was that death should be such a disorderly thing! It was as chaotic as childbirth, not to mention the messy and grotesque act of sexual union. Everything that had to do with the creating and ending of life was somehow violent, grotesque, or messy. Really, it was only those precious spaces in between that one could control and organize into any semblance of grace.

She stood up, adjusted her pale-shell-rimmed glasses, and smoothed her skirt. She sighed deeply. Then her mind came back to matters at hand. She heard poor Jack's car in the driveway. She gathered up her handbag and hoped he had remembered to reserve a table at the Seville. They both detested standing about in the entrance.

She saw him through the window in the foyer walking towards the door. He had beautiful manners. Jack was an elegant man, very ascetic. She wished her own husband had his habits. Jack never tooted a horn, or let a woman climb into his car while he sat, inert, in the driver's seat. She opened the door and welcomed him.

'All ready, Jackie boy.' She embraced him and kissed his cheek. 'It was so dear of you to take me to lunch.'

He smiled, his handsome face dimpling at the chin.

'Everything all set for Tim's party?' he asked.

'Absolutely. It's all going as smooth as glass. It should be lovely, something they will always remember. Memories are so important! Young people should have *fun*, Jack. Things to look back on. *Gay* things. We have to see that ... this thing doesn't spoil the best years of their lives.'

Jack started the car. He was very proud of the Mercedes. It ran like a German clock, eminently predictable. They purred along past the rolling green lawns, shrubbery, and flowers of West Avondale towards the freeway and downtown Brandenburg.

276

Kate and Christie were finishing lunch in the hospital cafeteria. They had been going over the facts of Joan Bentley's case, and Kate had worked out a home-care plan involving visiting nurses and any emergency equipment such as oxygen that might be needed. Everything now depended on the willingness, or *will*, of Joan's family to help her die at home.

'Could you tell anything about Mr Bentley when you talked to him over the phone?' Christie asked.

'Well, he sounded educated and – cultivated, and a little annoyed at being asked to meet with us,' Kate answered. 'I don't think money will be any problem.'

'Did you tell him you were the home-care planner, and that it was about her going home?'

'I said the doctor was ready to discharge her; that I would like to talk to him about a home-care plan for her. Once they get her off the chemo and tubes, she'll just need good nursing care and medications for pain. She may need oxygen at home – but I don't think she can live very long, Christie.'

They sat and thought for a few minutes. They had finished lunch now, and were putting their trays back on the tray racks.

'I really think she's waiting to die until she's back in her own home with her husband and kids around her,' Christie said.

They weaved through the crowded exit of the cafeteria and pressed the Down button on the elevator.

The elevator doors opened suddenly, revealing Virgil Prince. He walked out and went swiftly down the hall.

After the elevator doors closed, Kate said, 'He looks uptight. Wonder what happened to his nurse-guardian?'

'Someone on the Unit told me she was on a vacation,' Christie answered.

'Without *him*? Weird, Christie, decidedly weird.'

'I thought so,' Christie said. 'Maybe he'll actually see Joan Bentley before she leaves, now.'

They walked out of the elevator and turned down the hall to the Social Services Department.

'You know one more thing Joan needs before she dies, Christie? She needs to see her garden. When I went up to talk with her once, she told me how she couldn't wait to see her garden again.' Kate stood in the doorway of her office and looked at Christie. Christie loved the way Kate had of finding the key to what people cared about and needed, even in brief encounters. She leaned over and gave her a hug.

'Where do you want to talk with Mr Bentley?' she asked.

'Here in my office. It's bigger than yours. He ought to be here any minute,' she said.

'Do you think he realizes that Joan is dying?' Christie had some apprehensions about this meeting.

'He has to know. He sees her.' Kate's eyes took on a determined clarity.

Suddenly there were voices in the reception area. They heard the secretary say, 'Mrs McGowan is in her office. Go right on in, Mr Bentley: second door on your right.'

A drift of some expensive floral scent preceded Mr Bentley down the hallway. Kate and Christie exchanged puzzled glances, then saw that he had a female companion.

Jack Bentley was as attractive as the photo of himself that Christie had seen in Joan's room. He was tanned and smooth-looking in a well-tailored summer suit. The lady he ushered into Kate's office exuded well-bred assurance. She looked to be Jack's female counterpart, but her manner was less warm and open, her features finer and a bit pinched.

'This is my sister, Lorraine Krause,' he explained. 'I took the liberty of bringing her with me since she has been helping with my family situation while Joan has been ill.' He paused and smiled engagingly. 'I'm not too expert in being a bachelor father.'

'It's nice to know both of you,' Kate said, returning his smile. 'I am Kate McGowan, Home Care Coordinator, and this is Christie Wilson, who works on the Unit with cancer patients.'

Kate indicated two chairs. 'Won't you sit down?'

Kate sat down at her desk.

'Christie has seen Joan several times lately, so I wanted her

278

to be in on our meeting to give you her impression of Joan's needs.'

'Her needs?' Lorraine asked. Her voice was cool and daintily puzzled. She leaned forward to study the plastic badges pinned on the chests of Kate's and Christie's lab coats.

'"MEDICAL SOCIAL WORKER",' she read. 'I'm afraid I don't understand why social workers would be involved in my sister-in-law's medical situation.' She said it quietly. Kate had heard Saran Wrapped voices before and braced herself for what was to come. She exchanged glances with Christie.

'As Kate said, it is her job to make plans for the care of patients when they are able to go home. The reason I've been seeing Joan is that I am a counsellor,' Christie said gently. 'The hospital is a complicated organization,' she added; 'it has decided that to accommodate things, we must work out of the Social Services Department.'

Lorraine drew back in her chair. 'You're a counsellor?' she asked.

'Yes,' Christie answered.

Lorraine shot a heavy look at Jack. He cleared his throat.

'You have been counselling with Joan?' he asked, politely but with a note of suppressed shock in his voice.

Lorraine didn't wait for an answer. 'My brother engaged a specialist, an oncologist, to direct Joan's treatments. He did not engage a counsellor to treat her disease. Her problem is medical.'

Christie had a feeling 'nurse' might threaten Lorraine far less than 'counsellor'. She was relieved when Kate grabbed the ball and moved with it. Kate shifted in her chair and leaned towards Bentley and his sister. She spoke in a clear, soft voice.

'Cancer patients who are hospitalized for long periods of time are in a great deal of pain. They are isolated from normal events and from those close to them. Hospital environment is very impersonal. They all get depressed. Sometimes they feel guilty for the trouble their illness causes their families. Joan has suffered from all these things. We find it helps to let patients talk with a sympathetic, trained, neutral person.'

There was a brief silence. Then Jack Bentley spoke.

'When you called me, you stated that we must have this meeting because Dr Prince was ready to discharge my wife. I wish he had called me and discussed it first. I have tried to reach him, but it is impossible to get calls through to him, or to have him return them.' It was clear by his tone of voice that Bentley was a man unaccustomed to being ignored.

'Yes,' Kate said. 'I understand your frustration. Actually, we have not been able to talk personally with Dr Prince either. He left a written order on her chart, through his nurse, for us to go ahead and talk with you about a home-care plan.'

Christie decided to speak again. 'We need to get your feelings about your wife's returning home. If you want her to be at home, then we want to do all we can to help you work out a plan for her care there.' She looked from Jack Bentley to his sister, waiting for their response. Bentley looked at Lorraine, who nodded her head to him, then settled back, her lips pursed in a thin line, to listen to his response.

'I am astounded that Dr Prince is thinking of sending her home,' Jack Bentley said. 'Joan is in worse condition now, and needs more nursing care than when she came into the hospital because she felt too ill to cope at home. I would assume he would not separate her from professional medical care under such conditions.'

Kate looked at the couple steadily for a moment before speaking.

Her voice was very kind.

'Mr Bentley and Mrs Krause, may I ask you what your perception is of Joan's present condition?'

Lorraine spoke now. 'Joan is a terribly sick woman – so sick and unable to cope with her own rudimentary personal hygiene that she belongs in a hospital, not a home situation.'

'You are right in your first observation,' Kate responded. 'Joan is as sick as anyone can be and still continue to live. As to your second observation – or conclusion: that, of course, depends on Mr Bentley's feelings about how his wife should spend the last weeks of her life.'

Both Jack and Lorraine shifted in their seats and fussed with their various clothing accessories. Jack cleared his throat nervously.

'You are saying that my wife is near death – dying?'

'Yes,' Kate said softly. She looked at both of them with a level, gentle gaze. 'I believe, from what you have both said, that you are aware of her condition. As to treatment, all Dr Prince's new chemotherapy protocols have not been able to secure a remission.'

Jack Bentley leaned forward and bowed his head. He studied his hands, opening and closing them and cracking his knuckles. Lorraine crossed her legs and pulled a lace hanky from her handbag. She patted it delicately over her upper lip and chin. It was, as usual, hot and stuffy in the office. Everyone was perspiring.

Lorraine now spoke in her precise, half-polite, half-patronizing tone: 'Are we to understand that you are calling this meeting to arrange for a dying woman to be discharged from a hospital and into her home? Away from medical care?'

'There comes a certain point when people are dying,' Kate began, 'when vigorous treatment and continuing tests cause more suffering than a course of simply keeping them out of pain. Almost all the patients I have known, have wanted to spend their last days at home with their families. There are ways to give them good care at home. There are Health Department nurses who make calls at home. If the family is not poor, private-duty nurses can be obtained. The doctor sees that the patient has enough of the right pain-control medications. This is where I come in. I can get in touch with the right people who can help take care of Joan. I can help you plan it all, so it will be as good an experience as possible. But the first thing we have to know is whether Mr Bentley and the family really *want* Joan to be home.' Kate had now laid out all the facts. She waited for their next response.

'Do you think my wife knows she is . . . is going to . . . pass away?' Jack Bentley asked.

Christie had been watching the exchange, waiting for Kate to explain the home-care options, absorbing the feelings projected by Jack Bentley and his sister. Now she spoke:

'We are quite sure that Joan knows she has very little time left. The nurses who have been close to her; Dr Mulder, who sees her every day; and I, who have talked to her at length, are all aware that what Joan wants, and needs, most is to go home. We even feel that she is hanging on to her life, as painful as it is, only to hope to live long enough to see her home once more and to die with her family round her. The solitary time in her room tends to distort reality: there is no punctuation in time; every day, in the hospital, is the same. She has begun to have nightmares. I feel this would all be alleviated if she could be in her own personal environment.' As she spoke, she watched their eyes, trying to know if they were understanding and responding. Both Joan's husband and her sister-in-law were looking, now, at the floor. Christie went on.

'Even though you visit her here, it is an awkward and unnatural environment. All the institutional routine dominates the scene.'

Lorraine removed her glance from the floor and directed it at her brother. She reached over and put her hand on his knee. He cleared his throat and ran his finger around his neck beneath his shirt collar.

'You realize, of course, that I have two sons, one about to be married, and a teen-age daughter. My sister has spent a great deal of time planning a party to introduce Tim's fiancée to our friends. Having seen my wife's physical deterioration and the amount of care she needs, you must be aware that to take her home would be to turn our home into a virtual infirmary.'

Both Kate and Christie watched him in fascination. Then Lorraine spoke.

'Tim and Gwen's wedding will be in two weeks. It is depressing enough for them to have this . . . illness, marring

what should be the happiest time of their lives, without ...
without ...' Her voice trailed off.

'Without what, Mrs Krause?' Kate asked, softly.

'Without turning their home environment into the scene of a deathwatch,' Lorraine said. Her face had become flushed. Her nose was pinched. Her lips curled slightly over her teeth. She fanned herself with her white lace hanky. It looked as if she were suppressing tears. She shifted and blinked her eyes.

Jack reached over and patted her hand. He leaned forward and spoke in a quiet but severe tone, looking straight at Kate and Christie.

'I have been with my wife enough in her present condition to know that her helplessness presents certain gross indelicacies which I do not want my sons exposed to, nor my teen-age daughter. I would like to shield them from the raw side of life as long as possible.'

'I see,' Kate answered.

'Have you discussed Joan's feelings with *her*? Has she mentioned coming home to you?' Christie asked.

There was a pause; then Bentley spoke.

'Yes, she has mentioned it – always in the context that she hopes she'll soon be improved enough for Dr Prince to let her go home. ...'

Lorraine interrupted. She had overcome her suppressed tears.

'Incidentally – if you will think for a moment – what Jack just *said* is the key to this whole messy predicament: "improved enough for Dr Prince to let her go home"! You see, if she mentions, or asks, to go home, the solution is for Dr Prince simply to tell her she is not *well* enough to make it at home. After all, that is the truth, as far as Jack and I are concerned. In fact, if Joan were not so far removed from her own ability to reason in a rational way, so far from being herself, the last thing she would want would be to spoil the home life of her children at such a crucial time in their lives.'

There was a long silence. Jack settled back again in his chair. He brushed some lint from his jacket cuff and sighed.

'Do I understand that you would like to have Dr Prince interpret to Joan your wish for her to stay here in the guise of a decision on his part that she must be more well before she goes home?' Christie asked politely.

'Exactly,' said Lorraine. 'It is the most rational way to deal with the dilemma. Joan is not herself. We must think of the best interests of Jack and the children – who, after all hopefully, will survive all this. They still have their lives to live.'

Jack Bentley spoke again: 'Is there any way a patient's family can manage to get in touch with Dr Prince? As long as we are here, we should try to tie up all the loose ends and settle this affair.'

'We saw him in the building this noon. I think I might be able to locate him,' Christie told Bentley.

She walked out of the room, reaching up to secure a loose strand of hair.

Jack Bentley stood up. 'It's very stuffy in here. If you locate Dr Prince, tell him we'll be waiting to speak to him in the snack shop. It's air-conditioned. If he is unavailable, I will trust you and your co-worker to give him my message.'

Lorraine stood up and smoothed her skirt. 'We wish to thank you for your time and efforts on behalf of my sister-in-law. It is a tragic situation. We will just have to leave it up to God. I hope He takes her before she has to suffer more.'

'Yes,' Kate answered.

Jack Bentley reached out to shake Kate's hand just as the phone rang.

It was Christie, at the nurses' station on the Seven Main Unit.

'I found Dr Prince,' she said, in a cool voice. 'He said he would speak with Mr Bentley up here in the lounge. He's making rounds now.'

'Good girl,' Kate said. 'I'll send them right up.' She paused a moment. 'Christie, get back to me as soon as you can.'

There was a silence on the other end of the line. Then Kate heard a catch in Christie's voice; it dropped to a whisper.

'Dr Mulder told Joan he had the order to arrange her

284

home care. He's up here too. He just told me. She's having Mary pack her suitcase.'

Kate was chewing her pencil. 'See you,' she said, and hung up the phone. She broke the pencil in half and tossed it onto the desk. She turned to Bentley and Lorraine.

'Dr Prince will see you on Seven Main right now. Take the elevator in the main areaway to the left.'

'Thank you,' Lorraine said. They were walking out the door. They both looked revived and purposeful.

'You're very welcome,' Kate said. 'It's part of our job to get people to people.'

The sound of their footsteps grew fainter and then was gone. Kate shut her door and kicked the wastebasket across the room. It crashed against the wall.

Then she sat down at her desk, put her head down on her arms, and wept.

Chapter Twenty-One

Virgil Prince handled his interview with Jack Bentley and Lorraine smoothly and with little comment. He then delegated the task of telling Joan she could not go home to Richard Mulder. Mulder spent a long time with Joan after he broke the news. He reported to Christie that she had not been hysterical as they had anticipated, but rather, 'frozen'. She had sat quietly, twisting the bed sheet in her fingers. Only a few tears had run down her cheeks.

Christie had been stopping in to talk with her every day and had gained her trust and confidence. Joan had finally given word to the staff that her own minister was not to be admitted. His attempts to instruct her only reduced her to tears or brought on nightmares. With Joan's permission,

Christie had taken Father Franciscus in to meet her. He sat and chatted with her quietly, allowing her to introduce any questions that concerned her. Life' had taught him that unless he could reach her as a person, he could not reach her as a priest.

Now that the blow had fallen and she knew she could not go home, the members of the staff who were closest to her, and even Franciscus, experienced in her the withdrawal Mulder had seen when he broke the news. Joan was disturbingly quiet. She had even ceased to weep.

The day Jack Bentley and Lorraine came in for their conference, Joan had asked Christie to shop for some cool night-gowns for her. She hated the string-tied regulation gowns, and her nighties were quickly soiled and blood-stained. Christie had shopped for the gowns and taken them to Joan, but they had lain open on a table in her room ever since, unworn and untouched.

One morning several days later, Christie was sitting at her desk organizing her schedule. Her mind was divided between Martin Kiley and Joan when her phone rang.

'Christie?' It was Mary's voice on the line, talking very low and fast. 'Can you come up to the Unit soon? Right now? Joan is real bad. The student who's been with her today came to me about it. I want you to talk to her. I told her to wait for us in the nurses' conference room. I don't think we should discuss it in the station.'

Christie looked at the two nursing-home-placement requests in front of her. She filed them in the corner of her desk under a stapler.

'I'll be right up,' she said.

Mary was watching for her when she stepped out of the elevator. They walked down the hall towards the conference room.

'I want you to hear this before we try to do anything more. Actually, we're stalled ...' Mary broke off, and they went into the conference room.

'How is she?' Christie asked as soon as they had closed the door. The student was very young, a nice-looking blonde girl with a long ponytail.

'She's real bad.' The student's eyes were excited and frightened. 'One of the nurses thinks she should be watched around the clock: constant in-room nursing care. I agree. We think she might kill herself – jump out the window, maybe.'

Christie spoke quietly. 'How long have you been with her?'

'On and off since I came on duty at 7 a.m. When I went in to check on her the first time, she was sitting with her head between her knees, crying and incoherent.'

'She tried to pull out her catheters,' Mary said. It was the first time Christie had seen her look frightened. 'She's asking for more pain medication. The new resident can't give her more without Prince's approval.'

'The night duty nurse said she hasn't had much sleep,' the student offered.

'She's built up a terrific tolerance to the pain medication.' Mary's voice was strained. She looked like someone who had seen the ultimate human trap.

'Is someone trying to reach Prince?' Christie asked.

'Yes. Lois is. The office nurse says Prince is out of town today and Bracebridge is taking his calls. Bracebridge's nurse just takes the messages and says she'll give them to him. We're paging him here in the hospital. No luck so far.'

'Is anyone with her now?' Christie asked.

'Randy's in there till I get back,' Mary said. 'Dr Mulder was with her for a while, but he's been called down to Emergency. Ever since she heard she can't go home she seems to have more pain. She's either asking for hypos or trying to climb out of bed and remove the tubes.'

The student spoke again, still highly agitated. 'Well, somebody better order constant supervision. She could jump out the window.' The girl was looking at them strangely now. 'Besides,' she said, 'she's been a mental case. She had a breakdown. It's recorded in her chart.' She raised her eyebrows and wrinkled her nose.

'Look,' Mary said to the student, 'I agree Joan's in a bad state, but I can't order round-the-clock supervision. The only persons who are authorized to recommend round-the-clock supervision to a family are the physician and the Unit supervisor. We can't do it. We could get in big trouble. We've got to get hold of Mildred Schultz.'

Christie looked suddenly blocked.

'I'll go see if I can find her,' Mary said quickly.

Christie was staring at the floor now, frowning. She looked up at Mary.

'See what Mildred says; but I just don't see Joan trying to kill herself. She's probably too weak to climb out a window. I'm going to try something, if I can get Joan to cooperate. . . . It can't hurt anything . . . and it might help.'

She turned and left the room. Mary and the student looked at each other.

'I'll check with Mildred Schultz,' Mary said. 'Come with me.'

They found Mildred's office door open. When they walked in, the room was empty. Roberta Smith looked in the door.

'Where's Mildred?' Mary asked her.

'She's off today. Why?'

'Who's subbing for her?'

'Sylvia Lodge,' Roberta answered.

'Where can I find her?'

Roberta glanced down the hall. 'I think she's in the utility room.' She stared at Mary suspiciously. Mary often thought Roberta's face looked as if she'd just caught the scent of something rancid. Right now she had the urge to slap her.

Sylvia Lodge appeared in the hallway. Mary put her hand on the student's arm. 'Just tell Mrs Lodge exactly what you told me,' she said. 'I'm going to check on Christie.'

Mary walked down the hall taking slow, deep breaths. She had a terrible dread of seeing Joan trapped in this morass of misery and panic. Seeing her when she was calm from the hypos and tranquillizers was bad enough. She remembered how she had looked when she came onto the Unit in early May. She had been a beautiful woman. She had expected to go home in a week.

Mary stood outside Joan's door with sweaty palms, trying to get her mind together. The door was slightly ajar. Randy must be in the room with Christie. She heard her voice.

'Just let us lift you *real* easy.'

'We're going to help you into bed,' Christie said.

'No ... no! ... I'll hurt more! I lay there all night with nothing but pain ... no *sleep*! Please ... *please* give me my shot.' She was sobbing ragged sobs. 'Please put me to sleep ... give me my shot!'

Mary looked in through the partly open door. Christie and Randy were lifting her, and she was half off the footstool. Her thin shoulders were shaking. The wig of blonde curls, not so soft and long as her own hair had been, was tipped over on one side of her forehead.

But they were getting her to move.

'I promise, Joan, I promise, it won't hurt any more in bed than on this footstool,' Christie persuaded.

'Dr Prince ought to be here before long,' Randy said in a silky, soothing voice – white-lying her way through to the next hope. Joan was leaning over, almost in the bed. The hospital gown was wet and wrinkled with perspiration. There was a sweet spill of orange and lavender silk on a table by the wall – the new nighties Christie had brought, with the tags still on them.

Now they were easing her down on the bed.

'That's the girl ... now you're in your bed!' Randy soothed. 'I'm getting you a cool wet towel and I'm going to wipe your face.' She went into the bathroom, and Mary heard water running. Joan was sobbing, but a little more quietly.

'Please get me my hypo,' she moaned.

Christie bent over her. Randy came with the wet cloth and began to wipe it gently over Joan's face. She straightened the wig.

'That's better. . . . It's going to be all better,' she whispered.

Christie sat down on the bed.

'Joan, you've let me rub your legs before. Would you just roll on your side as much as you can, and I'll try to relax you. It'll help the pain.'

She ran her fingertips over Joan's shoulders and down her arm. Joan stopped sobbing for a moment and listened. Mary

289

moved just inside the door.

'My dad taught me to do this ... when I was a little girl. ...'
Christie's voice got slower as she stroked Joan's back. 'He
used to do it for Mom and me when we were sick or tired ...
or hurt. ... You have to get on your tummy as much as you
can and I'll just ... very gently ... massage you ... and we'll
talk real slow. ...'

'Your *dad*?' There was a tiny spark of interest mingled
with the pain in Joan's voice. She had worshipped her own
father. Christie was going on with the fingertip stroking.
Randy was pulling out the sheet that had twisted between
Joan's legs.

'Yes ... my *dad*! Now, you tell me if I'm pressing too hard.
I'm going to go very gently,' Christie said.

Randy slipped around the bed and tiptoed to the door.
She saw Mary and put her finger to her lips for her to be
quiet.

Christie looked back at Randy and motioned to her to
raise the bed up higher. As it moved up, Christie slid slowly
off the edge; then she stood by the bed, rubbing Joan's arms.
For several seconds she said nothing; then she began to talk
again. She was putting some light pressure into her rubbing –
not with her fingers now, but with the palms of her hands.

'Joan,' she said, 'can you tell me some more about the trip
you took – with your husband ... the second honeymoon. ...'

Joan's moans were getting farther apart. 'The beach?' she
said. There was still pain in her voice, and weariness, but
more weariness than pain.

'Tell me how it was,' Christie said. She was working on her
neck and shoulders.

'Water' ... a long silence ... 'Sky ...' Joan's voice was
beginning to match the rhythm of the pressure – release,
pressure – release of Christie's hands.

'The colours ... tell me the colours.'

'Dark blue ... green ... *pale* green ... white foam ... and
sky ... pink ... lavender ... at sunset ... and sand ...
lavender flowers ... all colours ... gold ...'

'Do you remember sounds?' Christie had moved down her

back. Joan was lying half on her side; because of the swollen abdomen, she couldn't lie on her stomach. Christie worked around the parts she couldn't reach. One leg crossed over the other. She moved slowly, slowly, down her legs, pressing, releasing ... pressing, releasing. Everything was quiet.

A breeze from the window ruffled the unworn silk gowns. Christie pushed back some hair that had fallen in her eyes with one hand. She never stopped the beat of the slow massage.

'Sounds ...?' Christie asked, whispering.

Joan sighed. 'Sounds were ... ssshhh, water, ssshhh ... waves ... on stones ... and ... ssshhh ... on sand ... waves ... winds.'

'Ssshh ...' said Christie. 'Wind ... in pines ... ssshh ...' Her voice faded out. Joan sighed again and was quiet.

Christie kept rubbing her legs, repeating the hushing sound in a whisper like a litany until she heard Joan breathing evenly. She gradually lessened her touch to a light stroking; then she lifted her eyes to look at Joan. Her face had the pallor and frailty of a spectre, its bones protruding under a thin film of flesh. Beads of sweat covered her brow, but she slept. She slept.

Mary looked over at Randy. Her eyes were full of tears, but her face was as bright as Christmas morning. Then there were voices behind them, and the noise of feet. Randy started up like a deer in the cedars. Mary backed out the door, pulling Randy with her by the seat of her uniform. Standing behind them in the hall were Roberta Smith and an LPN with a blood-pressure apparatus on wheels.

'Shit,' Mary said under her breath. '*Shit!*'

'Don't go in,' Randy whispered. 'Christie's putting her to sleep.'

Roberta Smith drew herself up and gave each of them a glance of icy contempt. 'With what?' she demanded.

'Have they ever located Bracebridge?' Mary countered, in what she hoped was a tone of exquisite politeness.

'The nurse has given him the message to call back,' Roberta said, smoothly.

The LPN with the blood-pressure machine had started to

turn away. Her face was confused and frightened. Everyone on the floor knew there was talk that Joan was in a suicidal state. Roberta didn't call her back to do the blood pressure. She was busy processing the interesting news that Christie was putting somebody to sleep.

'With *what* is she putting her to sleep, since Bentley can't have more medication for two hours and since Mrs Wilson cannot do treatments?' Her tone was icy, but reptiles slithered over the stones in it.

Randy leaned over until her eyes were very close to Roberta's and levelled into them. She spoke evenly and slowly enunciated every word with an awesome precision.

'She is giving Joan a slow, gentle massage, and Joan is drifting off to sleep *without meds*, and she has stopped sobbing and has stopped begging for a hypo.'

There was a heavy silence. Then Roberta Smith's face was a sight to watch. Emotions swept over it like a storm. First triumph, then contempt, then cunning. It settled at last into outrage.

Mary almost lost sight of the hell Roberta was bound to raise. It was such a field day to watch the uptight, sterile self-possession drain out of her. It would take her a good half-hour to get her face in order. Then she would have to find Mildred, who was not around, to file her complaint. It wasn't protocol for an RN to go directly to the Chief Administrator, Calvin DeHogue, or Margot.

Mary could see DeHogue when he got the bulletin that Christie Wilson was delivering body massages on the Unit. What a crime! Touching bodies without a licence; putting a person in pain to sleep without medical orders. At least, he would dispatch an 'incident report'.

Roberta Smith spun on her heel and marched down the hall to the station. Randy backed up against Joan's closed door. Behind her head was a plastic plaque:

JOAN BENTLEY
VIRGIL PRINCE, M.D.

292

She folded her arms over her chest.

'What can she do?' Mary whispered.

'Everything,' said Randy. 'I'll hang around here until Christie leaves, or signals.'

Mary looked at her watch. It was 1 p.m.

'I'm going to get some sandwiches from the vending machine,' she said. 'We've missed our lunch break. If she's still in there when I get back, I'll stand guard while you eat.'

Randy nodded. Mary turned to go and then remembered something.

'Do you want ham and cheese or a pizza combination?'

Randy's fierce vigilance melted a cubic centimetre. 'Ham and cheese.' She smiled and waved Mary off. Then she planted her feet apart and squared her elbows again.

Mary ran into Hugh in the vending-machine room and told him about Christie's putting Joan to sleep with a massage.

'Does anyone know about it?' Hugh looked grim.

'Roberta Smith.' Mary's eyes were anxious.

'We better get back up there.' He shoved some change he'd been playing with into his pocket. 'Roberta could have made trouble already.'

They both started walking fast, Mary bringing up the rear with the sandwich tray.

'I'm going straight to the station and see what I can hear,' Hugh said, over his shoulder.

When they arrived on Seven Main, they saw two things at once. Roberta Smith was emerging from Mildred's office, wearing an expression of smug impassivity. Stanford Bracebridge was talking with some students, some nurses, and the ward clerk in the station. His white hair stood out in all directions, like a ratty nimbus encircling his head. The corners of his mouth dimpled in what looked like a suppressed grin. Mary never let it fool her. He could be lethal when crossed, or if someone fouled up on his orders. She had seen his victims licking their wounds.

She ran into the utility room and stuck the tray into the refrigerator. When she returned to the station, Roberta was entering Bracebridge's aura, smoothly and quietly, with her best professional face. Bracebridge hadn't noticed her. He was questioning the group around him.

'What's the crisis with Joan Bentley?' he asked.

Roberta Smith spoke up. 'She had her usual insomnia last night. She wouldn't stay in bed and was keeping the other patients awake all night, crying and walking out of her room. This morning she was hysterical and paranoid. She pulled out her catheters.' Roberta was clocking off the facts and accusations like a prosecuting attorney.

Bracebridge had been piling his metal charts onto a cart. He pulled out Joan's chart and paged through it.

'Yeah . . . she's sure got a lot of problems.' He stretched his large frame elaborately, and sat down in a swivel chair. He pulled out his pen and wrote some orders. Then he looked around at everyone.

'Dilaudid PRN and Valium every three hours. A sleeping pill if she needs it,' he recited aloud. 'I'll go take a look at her.'

Roberta had opened her mouth to say one more thing to Bracebridge when Sylvia Lodge appeared, the student trailing behind her. The resident who had been subbing for Mulder was coming, at a swift pace, down the hall from the other wing. Everybody was converging on the station. The word was out that Bracebridge had appeared.

Sylvia walked around in front of him and spoke.

'Dr Bracebridge?'

'Yes?' He looked up at her with an appraising glance. Her demeanour was soft but impeccable.

'I think you should know that the student who has been with Joan Bentley all morning reported that she felt Joan was suicidal.' She paused for a moment, looking at Bracebridge with a cool, professional stare. He was listening to her with his *Mona Lisa* smile.

'I have just come from Joan's room. She now appears to be sleeping peacefully. One of the medical social workers is sitting beside her, in case she wakes up. The reports of her condition must have been exaggerated.' She delivered this statement in a dry, clinical voice.

Everyone at the station, including the resident who had seen Joan hysterical and falling in the hall, reacted with stunned silence. Roberta's face became flushed. Her eyes glittered, and her mouth twitched. Then the flush receded. She lifted her eyebrows and walked towards the cabinets, evidently preparing to deliver the next round of medications.

Mary walked over to Bracebridge. 'Excuse me, Doctor,' she said. 'With your permission, I feel that if Joan Bentley is now sleeping, she shouldn't be disturbed. She will need medication soon enough after she wakes up.'

'We-e-ell . . .' Bracebridge heaved up out of the rolling office chair he'd been in. 'I guess I'll just mosey down there and take a peek in,' he drawled. 'Ye gods, it's hot in this damn hole.' He loosened his polka-dot tie and unknotted it. His shirt collar stood on end.

'I'll go with you, if you don't mind,' Mary said.

'Swell.' Bracebridge grinned. He reached over and gave Mary's arm a pinch as they walked out of the station. 'Hey, you're losing a little weight, there. Better watch that. Is the stress Unit getting to you?'

Mary laughed. 'Well, the heat is. This place is better than a steam bath the last week or two.'

As they approached Joan's room, they saw Randy at her post by the door. When they got even with her, Mary whispered in her ear: 'Sandwich is in the refrigerator. Everything's cool, so far.'

Bracebridge wrapped his long fingers around Joan's door-knob.

'She's sleeping,' Randy said to Bracebridge. 'Someone's with her.' She put her hand to her lips, and looked at Mary anxiously.

'Who's with her?' asked Bracebridge, looking at both of them.

'Christie Wilson,' Mary said. He turned the knob slowly and pushed the door open about a foot and a half.

Christie had evidently closed the upper row of shutters to cut the glare. The room was in a cool kind of twilight. Joan had turned over on her back and was covered only with a sheet. Her face had the kind of peace one sees on the face of a child who has been ill. The fever breaks and the child falls asleep: that unguarded, vulnerable peace. Her wig was on straight. Christie was sitting in the big chair by the window with her eyes shut. Her face was serene, with a faint smile. Her hands were loose on the arms of the chair. She appeared to have fallen asleep too. The breeze had picked up, and the tails of the nighties were billowing up like an orange-and-lavender spinnaker. Christie had weighted the tops down with something.

Bracebridge stood motionless, filling the doorway. He stood there for a long time without making a sound. Then he backed out and carefully shut the door. He left his chart cart there and walked down the hall. He had Randy and Mary by the elbows. At the end of the wing was a long window. He stopped there and they stood in the west wind, letting it flap through their sticky clothing.

'So she was really ba-ad, eh?' he said.

They both nodded. Randy's face was a road map of the morning. Mary had never been in a face-to-face encounter with the great Stanford Bracebridge. He was like a mythical figure escaped from a legend. She took a good look at him. His eyes were wet. He blinked them.

'Pore li'l thing,' he said. 'It's gonna be rough before it's through.' He pulled out his handkerchief and wiped perspiration off his face. 'They both look all tuckered out,' he went on. He looked from Mary to Randy. 'Hey! Anybody know what zonked her? She's got the damnedest addiction level *I* ever saw.'

Randy and Mary looked at each other like cornered rats, racing through the same fast debate in their heads.

Mary took a deep breath. 'Nobody knew what to do with her. She was exhausted,' she explained.

'She was hysterical,' Randy added.

'The new resident wouldn't order anything because of the OD record,' Mary told him.

'So what knocked her out?' He waved his hands in the air.

'Christie!' Randy said, her face beaming with satisfaction.

Bracebridge looked confused. 'What – how . . .?'

'She knows how to do a slow, gentle massage,' Randy said. 'Her daddy taught her.'

'Cheee-eeeze,' Bracebridge hissed in a long, low whisper. 'I'll be goddamned.' He looked at them for a moment, rubbing his chin. His eyes were blinking. Then he said, 'Anybody *see* it?'

Randy and Mary looked at each other. 'Just us,' they said.

'Anybody know about it?'

Mary thought a minute. 'That we know of, only Hugh Belding, and . . . and Roberta Smith.'

'Well,' cracked Bracebridge, 'tomorrow, the hospital!'

He turned back down the hallway. Randy remained at the door. Mary followed behind him. When they arrived at the station, everyone was still there but Hugh. Bracebridge walked up to the counter and planted both his elbows on it.

'Now hear this!' he intoned in a voice that made them all look up at once. 'Nobody goes in Joan Bentley's room to take any blood, measure any blood pressure, give any meds; *nobody* does *nothing* until Mrs Wilson comes back down here and says she's awake.'

Mary wanted to get down on the floor and kiss his feet. What a payoff! She didn't wait around for any more grace to fall. She started to leave for the utility room, to see if the sandwiches were still there, when she felt a heavy hand on her shoulder. Bracebridge pushed her down the hall ahead of him, at the same time speaking *sotto voce* in her ear.

'Somebody's always gonna blow the whistle and stop the music,' he said. 'That's life. But nobody says you can't keep dancing till they do.'

She stopped dead in her tracks. She stood there watching him sail down the hall to his chart cart, his checked coattails flapping in the draughts from the west wind.

Chapter Twenty-Two

Josh Kiley was following at a safe distance behind Christie. His car was an old Valiant, and paint was missing here and there on the fenders. The bottom of the car under the doors was rusted out from the salted roads of winter, but the fenders had been bent by his tendency to drive too fast. He was driving very carefully now in an effort not to plough into Christie at some stop sign. He had been excited when he heard she knew a former stunt driver, and had made a date with her to meet Victor Vendetti. She'd said he was actually a 'death driver' and had spent a lot of years in carnivals and even had his own show. Josh had never dreamed he would be able to meet a professional stunt driver.

Josh liked the guy's name a lot. He had thought about it ever since Christie's call and had repeated it aloud to himself. *Victor Vendetti*. It made him think of power and big risk and triumph. He imagined a man with broad shoulders and a small waist in a silver-studded black leather jacket and boots and a silver crash helmet, like some of the big rock stars on his album covers.

Jeez. Christie sure was leading him into a crummy neighbourhood. He saw cheap cafés and old clapboard houses, grey with age and no paint, lining the streets. The screens on the porches were torn, and weasely-looking dogs and dirty little kids stood around in the yards. Christie slowed down now. She stopped at a house in the middle of the third block. It too was grey and weathered, but someone had begun to put aluminium siding on it. You could see where he was half done with one wall.

He climbed out of his car and walked up to Christie, who was standing on the kerb. She smiled at him and said, 'Let's go.' He followed her down the cracked sidewalk, a small fox terrier barking at their heels. The walkway wound around the small house, and Josh saw that the backyard was an incongruous oasis of green grass, shrubs, and flowers. Grapevines heavy with purple grapes reached up and over an arbour as far as the roof of a small shed.

'There he is,' Christie whispered. 'There's Victor. He spends most of the day in his yard.'

Josh saw the slight body of an old man lying on a mattress-padded lawn chair. He wore a long-sleeved shirt, but you could see that his arms underneath the cloth were painfully thin. His chest looked sunken. He was *really* old, Josh thought with shock; probably even older than his father; maybe sixty. Well, Christie had told him the guy had been real sick. He looked at her uncertainly. She was walking across the grass to his chair, calling softly.

'Vic ... Vic ...? You have a visitor.'

The old man woke up and looked at them. Josh was startled by his eyes. They were alive with curiosity and an alertness Josh had never connected with age.

'Hi!' Victor stood up now, leaning on the chair arm for support.

Christie introduced them.

Victor clasped Josh's extended hand. Josh was again surprised. The grasp was firm and strong. He really liked the old guy's eyes. They made you want to know some of the things he'd seen.

'So you're the motorcycle buff, eh?' Vic said. 'Well, it's nice to meet you. I've been looking forward to a long talk.'

Josh grinned and pressed his hand in return. He looked over at Christie. She was glancing at her watch.

'If you can find your way back, Josh, I'm going to be leaving. I explained to Vic that I have to get back to work.'

'Sure,' Josh answered. 'Sure, Christie.' She waved to them and walked away. Josh looked around, searching for a place to sit.

299

'Here,' Victor said, turning towards a chair that was folded up against the tree. 'Let me open up this chair.'

'No – that's okay, Mr Vendetti. I like sitting in the grass.' He smiled and added, 'You got a nice yard here. Lots of flowers.' He folded up his long, slim legs and seated himself cross-legged on the ground beside Victor's chair.

Victor stretched out again and studied Josh. The boy had a sensitive face and grey eyes like his father's. He wondered if Josh's slim frame would ever grow into the wrestler's body which had been impressive in his father. He was at that awkward, slippery age when a boy's features are changing. There was something still vulnerable and childlike about his face.

'Ever ridden a motorcycle?' Vic asked him.

'Yeah. Well, I rode my friend's bike a couple of times. I really like it. You really get a feel for the road. I like all the smells coming up at me.' The expression on Vic's face made him warm up to his own thoughts. 'I like the speed and the sensation that I'm driving by the seat of my pants.'

Vic lay back and laughed. The boy's voice was eager and gentle. It cracked occasionally.

'You got the bug, all right,' he told Josh. 'If I still had my cycle, I'd like to take you out in a field and show you some fancy stuff.'

Josh leaned towards Victor. His voice was hushed and respectful. 'Christie said you were a death driver way before Evel Knievel.'

Victor smiled and looked up into the leaves of the tree. 'I rode the cycle for seven years,' he said. 'I was a roustabout in the carnival for a couple of years before I worked up my act. I had been saving up a long time to buy my cycle.'

Josh's expression was very serious. 'I been saving up to buy me a cycle too. It'll take me another six months and I'll have the down payment.' He looked down at his hands and frowned. 'My mom – she isn't so hot about me riding a bike. I've had a few fender-benders with my car.'

Vic's expression became very intense. Josh now saw silver studs and black leather in the old man's eyes.

'You've got to remember that real drivers know when to unleash the power and when to hold it in. Punks don't know that. Punks bottom out against telephone poles and gas pumps. Punks stunt in the wrong places.'

Josh looked at Vic respectfully.

Vic went on. 'Virtuosos are never reckless,' he said.

'You must've been a real virtuoso,' Josh replied. 'What kind of stunts did you do?'

'They called me a death driver because I rode the Wall of Death,' Vic answered.

'The Wall of *Death*? Jeez! What kind of wall was that?'

Vic explained it to him. 'It took hours of practice to get the act perfect. The steering had to be precise and geared to the speed, or I'd go over the top, or crash to the ground.'

'Jeez!' Josh's eyes were wide with awe and incredulity. 'Jeez!' he said again, emitting a long whistle. 'I don't think I could ever practise enough to succeed at doing that! You did it for seven years? Why did you quit?'

Victor had slumped a little after the tense description of his feat. He sighed and relaxed against the chair. His mouth curved in a smile and he closed his eyes.

'You always have to know how and when to quit. I guess I should have quit it sooner. I kept at it until ... there was a tragedy.'

'You ... you weren't in an accident?' Josh's face was stricken.

'No ... no. Not me. It was my partner. She was newer at it than me. I – well, I lost the heart for it after that. After she died I never went back to the wall.'

'Gosh! That's terrible! I'm sorry about your partner.' Josh sat quietly now, looking at Vic and trying to imagine him at his peak. He wondered about the intervening years and what had brought him to this house in a run-down neighbourhood in Brandenburg.

'Where did you ride the Wall of Death, Mr Vendetti?'

Vic reached over and patted Josh's knee. 'Call me Vic, won't you?' he smiled. 'I worked out West, around Phoenix and Reno and up and down the California coast.'

301

'How did you get back here ... Vic?'

'Wandering. Bumming it out. Working as a shill and as a roustabout again. Life is a spiral – like the wall. There's peaking and holding and bottoming out.'

'Bottoming out ...?' Josh thought he understood about the peaking and the holding.

'Bottoming out: it's more important than you think. If you know how to come down off the wall, you avoid disaster. Life's like that. You'll find out.'

Josh sat looking down at his clasped hands. He unfolded his legs and stretched out on the grass, leaning on his elbow.

'Christie said she met you in the hospital, that you were pretty sick. How are you doing now?'

Victor tapped his chest over his heart. 'I feel good here,' he said. 'And I feel good here.' He tapped his forehead. '*That's* the real important part. But my body, well, I guess it's dying.'

Josh sat up straight. His voice was deep and husky, but it cracked again as he spoke.

'Your body ... is *dying*? Are you sure?'

Victor nodded his head. He smiled at Josh. 'I'm sure. I just don't know how long it's going to take, and I want to ride it out the best way I can.' He sat up straight and swung his legs over the side of the chair. Josh knew he was about to say something important. Maybe the most important thing of all.

'A funny thing happened to me, Josh, while I was in the hospital – and afterward, here at home. I met Christie, and a priest ...'

'Father Franciscus?' Josh asked.

'That's right. And I began to understand some things, a lot of things, about my life. Now it's like all the time I can see my body dying, something else – whatever it is that's really *me* – is getting stronger, reaching its peak.' He tapped his chest again. 'I'm in a holding pattern, Josh. My body can bottom out when *I* know I'm ready.'

Josh looked at his wasted body and sunken cheeks and knew he saw the worn-out garment of a great virtuoso. Tears stung his eyes, and he felt suddenly embarrassed. He had cried into his pillow when he was a kid and his mom and his dad got divorced. But he had never felt before like crying over a stranger. He swallowed hard and waited until he knew he could talk with a steady voice.

'My dad has cancer.' He was surprised at the even, disconnected way he had managed to say it.

'That's what Christie says.'

The corners of Josh's mouth turned down and he clenched his jaw.

'I don't know if he's dying. I saw Gretchen crying one time. And my mom's been crying at night when she thinks I'm sleeping. My mom says he's getting worse.'

Victor cleared his throat and spoke casually. 'I think I might have met your dad up on the five-bed ward, when I was at Broadcliff.'

Josh looked up, his attention quickened.

'You met my dad?'

'Well, I didn't exactly meet him. I was, well – out of it, and a little crazy. Me and institutions don't hit it off too well. They have too many rules. Anyway, I saw him – and I heard him. Is he a big, muscular guy with grey hair and grey eyes?'

'Yeah!' Josh said. 'That's my dad.' His voice was proud and tender for a moment; then it grew hard, along with his face. 'I don't see my dad much anymore,' he said. 'I didn't see him at all before he got sick, and then only a couple of times and at his dumb *wedding*. I don't know what to say to him.' Josh pushed some hair off his forehead and looked self-conscious.

'What's the matter between you and your dad?' Victor asked bluntly.

Josh moved his long legs restlessly, rearranging them, then wound up sitting tailor fashion. He pulled up some long blades of grass and began to weave them into each other in a kind of braid. He blinked his eyes as he spoke. Victor saw that he had probably never before spoken aloud about his feelings about his father.

'It's his fault they got divorced. I know it's his fault. Long before they got divorced I used to hear her crying in the

303

night. *He* never heard her. *He* was sleeping like a log.' As he spoke, the bitterness in his voice attained a finer edge. 'She still cries, now, when she hears he's getting worse. *She* never got married again. *He* did.' He became silent now, looking into Victor's eyes for vindication. He saw no dispute in them. He knew that Victor understood his rage.

'I *see*,' Victor said, looking steadily at the boy.

Josh thought that the old man had the fiercest and the kindest eyes he had ever seen except ... except for his father's. The memory of his father's face intruded into Josh's heart like the sudden cut of a knife.

'I loved ... my father,' he said. As he said the words, he felt a tension within him breaking. It was the tension that the energy of his anger had sustained. Until now, it had given him the hardness of spirit to remain aloof from his father, to punish him with his absence. The release of the tension made him feel suddenly naked, vulnerable, and frightened. The power in his anger had protected him from the wounds of love. What would protect him now?

He felt Victor's hand on his shoulder. 'Josh?'

The boy bit his lip and looked at Victor. Tears spilled from his eyes. He could not stop them. He buried his head in his arms, and his shoulders shook with sobs. Victor squeezed Josh's shoulder with his hand. He said nothing for a long time, waiting for him to discharge some of his pent-up sorrow. After a while the weeping stopped and Josh breathed a deep sigh. He pulled out a handkerchief and blew his nose.

'I guess you think I'm some kind of punk now,' he said hoarsely.

'No,' Victor replied. 'I guess I'd think you were a punk if you *didn't* cry about your father. I know what it's like to think you've lost someone you love, someone real close to you.' He paused until Josh was able to look into his face again; then he said, 'I rode the Wall of Death, and it took strength and guts and it took knowledge. But it takes *more* than all that to love someone, to really love them. And if you do, you can't throw it away without losing part of yourself.'

304

Josh listened to him, feeling the words printing themselves into his mind.

'I been involved with a lot of women in my time and I've never been married. I'm sorry to say I treated most of them pretty shabby. Maybe when you're older, you'll know some woman and your feelings for her will help you guess what happened to your mom and dad.' Now his voice took on a special tenderness. 'I know what an oldest son means to his dad – a *first* son – because I was my father's first, and we were close until the old man died. Your dad's got cancer and you say he's getting worse.'

He paused and seemed to be figuring out how to say something. Finally he frowned, and his eyes communicated to Josh the sense of being at the brink of a tragedy. 'Josh,' he said, 'I know *I* couldn't bottom out like a virtuoso when the time came if I'd lost *you*, and you were my oldest son.'

Victor's words now evoked in Josh a chain of memories he had buried in the cold vault of his rage. His father carrying him out on the porch in his arms and pointing up to the night sky. 'Stars!' his father had said. He must have been very young. He remembered that night as his first sight of the mysterious heavens. He remembered his father's arms around him, his firm step as he walked the floor, singing some nursery song in a voice that croaked like a bullfrog's. His father had bought him his first guitar. When he was older his father had begun to teach him about motors and how they ran and why they broke down. One weekend he had taken him with him to the shop and they had disassembled a motor and put it back together. He would be able to take good care of his motorcycle because of what his father had taught him.

His sense of vulnerability began to dissipate. Victor's words were settling within him. Something was being rearranged. He heard him speaking again.

'Don't ever let bitterness get a foothold in your guts,' Victor said. 'Keeping bitterness is like swallowing poison. I know, because it poisoned me.' He didn't look at Josh now. He seemed to be staring into his own past, beyond the grass, the flowers, the grapes, and the maple tree.

Josh stood up and walked over to Victor. He had to bring the old man back. He bent down and sat on his haunches beside the chair. He put his hand on Victor's thin arm and pressed it firmly. Victor turned from his dark vision and looked at Josh. The boy's face was bright, and he spoke intensely.

'You're not bitter now, Mr Vendetti – *Victor*. You're the least bitter person I ever met. And I know you'll do all your bottoming out exactly right.'

'Thanks, Josh. I hope you're right.' Victor grinned and made a move to get up from his chair. 'I've had a long enough time to study it out.' He laughed. 'Give me a hand here, will you? I get stiff when I sit still a long time.'

Josh held out his arm, and Victor raised himself from the chair. A woman's voice was calling from the window.

'Victor! It's time for your medicine. I have to leave for the factory in a half-hour!'

Josh walked Victor to the back door, letting him lean on his arm.

'I've got to go too. I'm a busboy at Harry's Restaurant from five to ten,' Josh told him.

Victor held out his hand. 'Get in touch with me, Josh. Let me know if you work things out with your dad.'

Josh closed his hand over Vic's in a firm grip.

'I will, Vic. You gave me a lot to chew on. I have to figure out what's best to do, what I should say.'

'Don't worry. Words aren't always the key. Sometimes they gum things up.'

'I'll bring my new motorcycle by – as soon as I get it.'

'Good.' Vic grinned. The stunt-driver look gleamed in his eyes again. 'Remember. Punks bottom out on telephone poles!'

They both laughed. Josh saw a nice-looking lady waving to them from the back door. He waved back and walked away, rounding the house to the front sidewalk and his car. He stopped at the kerb and stood there for a few moments. The chimes at St Thomas' were pealing out a melodious song. The music sounded familiar. Now he knew what it was. It was an old hymn his father used to sing off key in the shower every morning. Something about a balm in Gilead. He wondered why the chimes were playing at this off hour. He decided it must be a feast day.

Chapter Twenty-Three

Several days after Joan Bentley's crisis, Christie arranged to meet with Dr Mulder in the Seven Main conference room. She arrived first. The window was open, and a slight breeze fluttered some papers tacked to the bulletin board. She stood at the window looking at the buildings that spilled along the hillside and the freeway with its snaking interchanges. The city traffic moved sluggishly, bathed in the torpor of summer heat.

She heard the door open, and Richard Mulder's solid frame moved into the room. He walked over and stood beside her. Both of them were silent looking down at the city. Finally Mulder spoke.

'Do you think Joan's levelling out?'

'Yes. I think she is. She *had* to blow. She took the sentence too calmly. Something had to give.'

Mulder watched her profile. She was staring down at the church – or the freeway. He cleared his throat.

'The priest – Franciscus – is a Godsend.'

There was a hopeful tone in his voice. Christie turned and faced him.

'It's obvious,' she said, 'that Prince doesn't want to hang around on this case. The other Godsend is that *you* take time with her.'

Mulder reached over and patted her on the shoulder. 'I think she's over the hump.' He walked over and sat down on a small stool near the wall sink. He leaned an elbow on the sink and rested his chin in his hand.

'There's a frivolous detail I want to mention to you, Christie. First of all, I want to say your massage rescued Joan from her crisis; but ...'

'But what?' Christie left the window and leaned against the table watching his expression carefully. He was looking at her with amusement and affection, but a hard seriousness lay behind his eyes. He leaned forward now, clasping his hands on his knees.

'But this: the story of the laying on of hands is all over the hospital. I've overheard some conversations. You're damn lucky you massaged Joan and not Kiley, or any other man, no matter how debilitated. As it is, the worst inference I've overheard is "lesbian".'

Christie looked down at her hands. She turned a small turquoise ring around on her finger. Finally she looked up at him. Her face was flushed, and her eyes were steely.

'I knew ... I always knew, I couldn't be on solid ground here. But is there any? Is there any, *anywhere*?'

Richard Mulder stood up and walked over to her. He put his hands on her shoulders and looked into her eyes.

'Christie, this is my last week here. My next duty is the Trauma Unit. I'm going to keep seeing Joan as much as I can. When I check out of Seven Main, I'd like to think the ice was a little thicker where you're skating. No more massages for a while, okay?'

Christie was touched by his expression, by his levelling with her, by his concern. It was going to be rougher with him gone.

'Okay.'

He walked back to the sink and turned to face her.

'Now, one more item.'

'Yes?'

'Prince is sending Martin Kiley to surgery early tomorrow morning.'

Christie's eyes widened. She stared at him. 'Surgery! Now! At *this* point?'

Mulder nodded an affirmative.

'*Why*? What do you think will . . . Can Martin live through . . .?' She was trying to speak all her fears at once. Mulder answered directly and firmly.

'I think he won't live through it. He's too weak. The anaesthetic alone . . .' Mulder was certain only a miracle could bring Martin out of surgery alive.

'What is Prince's logic?' Christie demanded.

'From what I gather, Prince reasons that if surgery is successful it might decrease his nausea and stop the vomiting,' Mulder said.

'Why don't they just stop the chemo infusions?'

'They finally did – today. Prince said that since Martin was going to die soon anyway, they might as well try one more last-ditch approach.'

Christie's face had registered shock. Now it changed to anguish.

'But if he dies before . . . He isn't ready yet, Richard! He has one more important thing to resolve. It involves his son. He is waiting for a way to reconcile with Josh!'

There was no doubt about it, Mulder thought, Christie was playing in a whole other ball game. A game with different rules. She could do it only as long as her game didn't interfere with the official game. He wondered how she'd made it this long.

'Josh?' Mulder responded. 'Martin's on the outs with his son?'

'Yes, the oldest one,' Christie said. 'A friend of mine has talked with Josh, and we think he is going to find a way to let his father know he really loves him. If they can bridge the distance between them, Martin's life will come full circle.' Christie's eyes appealed to Mulder again. 'I have to find out if Josh has seen Martin!'

He recalled a fragment from his busy schedule.

'Christie, when I saw Martin this afternoon, he mentioned that Josh was coming up tomorrow because he had something special to give him.'

'Tomorrow?' Christie's voice had a hollow ring. She stared

at Mulder with a look that sent shivers along his spine.

'Tomorrow will be too late,' she said. She whirled around and walked out of the room. He heard her call 'Thanks' as she went down the hallway towards the nurses' station.

'Jeez,' Mulder muttered to himself. He hoped she wasn't going after Prince. He had seen Prince in arrogant and tenuous moods lately. But today especially, he had given short shrift to anybody who came near him. Something told him he'd better follow her.

Mulder rounded the corner and saw the nurses' station. Mildred Schultz was on a stool chatting with the charge nurse. Two internists were going over their patients' charts. Roberta Smith was loading the medications cart to start on her rounds, and Mary was on the phone. Virgil Prince sat at a low desk on a swivel Chair. Christie moved like a guided missile.

Mulder halted at the drinking fountain. Prince had just slammed a chart on the counter – Kiley's, no doubt – as Christie whipped around the corner.

'Dr Prince,' she began, 'I have to talk with you.'

'Make it fast.' Prince didn't look at her. 'I have two meetings in the next hour.' He was writing in the chart he had slammed on the counter.

'They will keep,' he heard Christie say. 'What I must talk with you about now is more important.'

Prince dropped his pen and slid back in his rolling chair, giving Christie a drop-dead stare. Everything in the station had suddenly frozen: pens, medication-cart loading, mouths.

Christie glanced around and saw the fascinated audience. She dropped her voice to a whisper. Mulder began to move in closer. No one had noticed him approaching. Christie said, 'Can we talk in private?'

Prince leaned back with a languid and feigned patience, aware of his tingling audience.

'I have two minutes. What's the problem?'

Christie sat down, took a deep breath, and leaned forward.

'Please. You can't send Martin to Surgery tomorrow. He

310

is in the middle of resolving a critical problem.'

There was a ringing pause. It seemed endless. Prince appeared to hang between boredom and tedium.

'Oh,' he said.

Christie was pleading with her eyes.

'He could die in Surgery,' she said. She reached out and put her hand on Prince's right sleeve. 'He mustn't die until he and Josh are okay with each other.'

Prince pulled his cigarette case out of his jacket pocket, selected a cigarette, and lit it.

'He mustn't die "until"?' he repeated. He chuckled gently.

Mulder had kept moving, slowly, towards the station. He felt blessedly invisible. Christie searched Prince's face with her eyes.

'Christie.' Prince's tone had softened now. He spoke with the patience of a father who had finally decided it was time to dislodge his child's mind from the myth of Santa Claus.

'Christie,' he repeated, ' "mustn't die" is a fantasy statement. You have been on this Unit long enough to know we can't will people not to die.' Prince pushed back his chair and looked at his watch. Christie shifted her touch from his arm. She grasped his right hand.

'I know Martin is going to die soon, but he has to come full circle first ... or he will not be free.'

Prince looked at her for a full second and then released his hand by standing up. He looked at her again, with a lazy glance of assessment.

'No one dies with everything settled,' he said. 'You're living in unreality, sentiment. Martin's only chance for remission, now, is surgery. He is going to Surgery at 7 a.m. tomorrow.' He stubbed out his cigarette in a glass ashtray on the counter and straightened his tie. 'You should have had some classes in medical pathology before you came onto this Unit. It won't make any difference whether Martin Kiley has come full circle after he is dead.'

Christie froze and stared at Prince. She stood up. They were almost the same height.

'You are wrong,' she said evenly, her voice deeper and

stronger. 'You are wrong, and you are *evil*.'

The silence in the station was deeper than the silence of the grave.

Mildred Schultz moved a few inches in Prince's direction. She caught his glance. He addressed his next remark to her.

'If anyone pages me, I'm out of the building.' He had turned and walked about two feet when Christie grabbed his shoulders.

'Please,' she said. Her voice was beginning to break now. 'Please. One more day. If he has to die, I want him to be free.'

Prince turned back, and Christie's hands dropped from his shoulders. He looked her full in the face. For the first time she saw his full face turn towards her. She bit her lower lip. Tears were running down her cheeks. Mulder was studying Prince. He was struck by the absence of his usual cool. A bitter heat suffused Prince's voice. It was his last statement to Christie.

'Mrs Wilson,' he said, biting off the words, 'stop worrying. When you are dead you are free.' He slammed Kiley's chart back into its slot and left the station for the elevator.

Everyone became busy. Roberta Smith wheeled out of the station on her medications route. Mary disappeared. The two internists, after brief, curious glances at Christie, jiggled their charts around and left the station. A phone rang. The charge nurse picked it up. Christie stood motionless in the vacated station, remote as if she were back in the dunes.

Mulder advanced towards her cautiously.

'Christie?' he swivelled around the corner of the counter. He stood in front of Christie. She was staring past him.

'*Christie*,' he repeated. He took her arm and led her out of the station, towards the elevator. He pressed the button. When the doors opened they walked in. The soft whirr of the fan began. He put his arm around her. She had begun to shiver. She was shaking as if she stood in a cold wind, as if she were lost in a blizzard.

'Good try, Christie,' he said; 'good show.' She began to sob. He took her in his arms and held her until they reached the bottom floor. Then he walked with her to her office.

He put her in the chair and went to get a glass of water. Kate collided with him in the hallway.

She grabbed his hand. 'I heard, Dr Mulder,' she said. 'I already heard.'

Christie sat at her desk feeling empty and numb, accepting a paper cup of water and Dr Mulder's comforting presence. Kate came in behind him and sat on the edge of the desk.

'Christie, it's almost quitting time. I'll call Dick and tell him I'm going to be home late. How about you and me going to the Cave and cooling down?'

Christie seemed not to hear. She was staring down at her appointment blotter.

Kate patted Christie on the shoulder. 'I never would have thought you'd do it, babe. I have to hand it to you. You've got guts.'

'I didn't do anything. Nothing is changed. Martin's going to Surgery tomorrow – early.' Christie's voice was toneless.

'You tried,' Mulder pointed out. 'Nobody ever crossed Prince before.'

'Except Nippert and Bjord,' Kate said. 'You're up in the big league, Christie.'

Mulder looked at Kate.

'Nippert and Bjord crossed Prince?' he asked. 'How?'

'They refused to irradiate an old man who was dying when Prince asked them to,' Kate told him. She was snapping an emery board against the palm of her hand. 'They *won*. Prince can't operate the linear accelerator.'

'Well, you win some and you lose some,' Mulder cracked. He leaned back against the wall and thoughtfully studied the ceiling.

Christie picked up the small glass paperweight containing a toy mouse that a patient had given her. She was looking at the words: 'FRIENDS ARE TO REMEMBER.'

'I don't think I'll be welcome on Seven Main anymore.'

Mulder and Kate exchanged glances. She continued.

'I know you'll stick with Joan – and with Martin. Mary will too, and Randy.' Her eyes filled with tears again. She wiped them away with the back of her hand and looked at Kate. 'Thank God Kate's here.'

'Christie . . .' Mulder began.

Some clunky footsteps approached, and Margot and her platform Earth Shoes appeared in the doorway.

'If you're through with your conference, Christine, I want you in my office right away.' Her face had a look of excitement, shock, and resolute purpose. Kate stood up and followed her out of the room and into her office. The air conditioner droned away in the window. Kate faced her with a level glance.

'Knock it off, for today – okay, Margot?'

'My God!' Margot said, in a holy whisper. 'Did you hear what she *did*?'

'Yeah. I heard. Why don't you let it wait till tomorrow? She doesn't need any more confrontations today. She's fresh out of steam.'

Margot's eyes were large, round, and staring through the magnification of her steel-rimmed lenses.

'She's officially finished here as of tomorrow,' she intoned. 'Mildred will get the incident report down here by 8 a.m.'

'She's not coming in tomorrow. Why don't you send her discharge to her by mail? She knows the score. You can wait to gloat till the next meeting of the coven.'

'Watch your mouth, Katherine,' Margot snapped. 'I can write out two termination slips as easy as one.'

'Go ahead, Margot, terminate me. Just one thing you should remember: DeHogue knows you'd have to bust your joint asses to replace me. Nobody knows the jungle of nursing homes and home-care resources like I do. A week after you can me, this hospital will be in a traffic jam that will make 5 p.m. on the Eisenhower Expressway look like a cow pasture.'

Margot sank petulantly into the depths of her swivel chair and began to shuffle papers. Kate tossed the emery board she had been gesturing with into the wastebasket, turned on her heel, and marched out of the office.

She went back to Christie's cubicle and found it vacant.

There was a note on the desk held down by a stapler. It said:

I went on home. Can you call me? Thanks for being there when I needed you.

Christie.

Kate noticed that Christie's personal things were still there – some wicker file baskets, a picture of Carl Jung on the wall over her desk, and beside it, a wooden plaque. She hadn't moved out yet. Kate stood for a few minutes looking at the plaque. It said 'WORK IS LOVE MADE VISIBLE.'

PART III

Chapter One

Christie woke up to the sound of rain on the roof. It was a strange feeling. She had been accustomed to waking to the radio-alarm every day before she went to work. The bedroom was dim. She had left a glass slider partly open, and the smell of wet foliage drifted in. The dial on her clock said 7.30.

Martin Kiley already had his hypo now. He was on his way to Surgery. She closed her eyes and pictured his angel hovering over him. She imagined him held in an aura of protection.

She lay listening to the rain. The soft sound of its dripping on the leaves was somehow comforting. As her mind began to focus, she remembered two phone calls from the night before. Lance had called to tell her he had broken loose from his schedule and would fly to Brandenburg around dinnertime today. He said he would stay overnight and go back the next day. He couldn't have timed his visit more appropriately. The thought of being with him again dissipated her sense of limbo. The second phone call was from Mary. She told Christie that Joan was asking for her. She said that if Christie could run up to the hospital today, she would see to it that the 'coast was clear.' Christie had promised to come in the afternoon. She would be able to get back in plenty of time to greet Lance.

She sat up on the side of the bed and reached for her robe. The bedroom was cool, and she shivered in the damp air from the door. After she had closed it, she went to the bathroom to shower. It was lucky she had awakened early. She had a lot of things to do.

After she had dressed, she went to the glass doors in the

living room and raised a bamboo shade. The rain drizzled down on her small concrete patio and bowed the petals on the geraniums that bordered it. The trees and bushes were glistening. This was a day when rain came as a comforter. To see it and hear it was a kind of benediction, like a tender touch. She stood looking at the muted green of the leaves and the silver rivulets running down the trunks of the trees, making the bark alive and luminous.

She brewed some coffee and sat drinking it, imagining how Lance would see her room. It was small and unimpressive, but it was warm.

There were a lot of bright-coloured pillows strewn around. One wall was covered with her books. There was a large sawhorse table she used as a desk. The books, her hanging plants, and some coloured candles made the room cosy and inviting. Her collection of stones and driftwood still lay on the wide shelf.

The morning after her night on the beach with Lance, she had gone to visit the Moon Castle for the last time and had found a piece of driftwood shaped like a fish with feathery fins. It lay with the others now. She decided to walk down to the shopping centre and get some flowers for the table to celebrate Lance's arrival. She would get a bottle of Scotch, too, and something for a snack.

She put on her rainy-day gear – boots, jeans, and a vinyl slicker – and walked through the rain to the store. Joan had wanted to get home to her flower garden. She would get flowers to take to her, too.

She had just arrived home and was putting the things away when the phone rang. She set the flowers in a can of water and ran to answer it.

'Christie?' It was Stefan Franciscus.

'Yes.'

'I tried to reach you at work and finally talked to Kate. She gave me your home number.'

'Oh, good. I'm glad you called. . . . I . . . Did Kate say why I didn't come in?' Christie wondered if he knew what had happened.

'Kate told me about yesterday, and so did Dr Mulder. I've just come from talking with him. He was there when they came to take Martin to Surgery.'

Martin. Father Franciscus had just come from the Unit!

'You were with Martin? Father Franciscus . . . how is he?' Christie looked at the kitchen clock. It was ten-thirty.

'That's what I called about. Christie . . . I'd rather talk about this in person. Are you busy now? Could I come over there, or could you meet me somewhere?'

'Please come here. It isn't far.'

She barely had time to heat some nut bread in the oven before she heard Franciscus knock on the door. Beads of raindrops were glistening in his grey hair. His black raincoat was very wet.

'Come in!' Christie took his hand and smiled, but her eyes were anxious and questioning. 'I'll hang up your coat to dry.'

Franciscus looked around the room with interest. It was cosy and had an intensely personal feeling.

'I'm heating some coffee,' Christie called to him from the kitchen. 'Please make yourself at home.'

He walked over to the wall of bookshelves and looked at the titles.

'*Modern Man in Search of a Soul,*' he read aloud. 'You must be a student of Carl Jung. I noticed his picture on your office wall.' He turned as Christie walked into the room. 'You seem to have most of his books.'

'Most of the books came from my great-aunt when she died. They were her legacy to me.'

They both sat down on the sofa. Christie turned to Franciscus.

'Tell me about Martin,' she said.

Franciscus watched her with a grave and quiet expression. His intense eyes were, for the first time in her experience with him, blurred with tears.

'He died?' Christie whispered.

Franciscus nodded. He reached into his pocket and pulled out a handkerchief. She waited while he brushed it across his face. Then he leaned towards her.

'He died, Christie, but in a most unexpected way.'

She poured coffee into their cups.

'I went up to the hospital last night to tell him I would be there this morning before he went to Surgery. This morning I arrived about twenty minutes before they came with the cart to take him. He had been given his hypo and was drowsy, but he took my hand and said, "It doesn't matter, Father. It doesn't make any difference. Everything is all right." He sort of drifted off to sleep then.' He stopped for a moment, then continued.

'I sat beside him and held his hand, grateful for his state of peace, repeating the prayer I say at the anointing. I had done the sacrament before for Martin, you know.' He paused again, as if entering into these last moments of Martin's life.

'Well, they arrived with the cart – two Operating Room escorts and a nurse. Dr Mulder followed in behind them. The nurse walked over to Martin and touched his forehead. She said, "We're ready to take you to Surgery now, Martin. You're nice and sleepy already." Then the attendants pulled down the covers and started to lift him onto the cart. As they put their arms under him to lift him, he suddenly sat straight up in the bed and opened his eyes. His whole face seemed to have awakened. It was illuminated.' Franciscus' voice was a trifle strained in the attempt to describe precisely the sudden change in Martin.

'He looked ... he looked ... like a person who had been lost in a great desert and had suddenly found himself before the door of a palace that was marked with his own name. There was this total, intense awakeness, *aliveness*, in his face. His eyes – and he had been heavily sedated – were clear and shining. He had sat bolt upright, and he was looking straight at ... something!

'Everyone drew back, Christie. The attendants let go of him and waited. All of us froze. Then he closed his eyes and lay back on the pillow. He sighed a very long sigh. Then he was still. We all stood there for what seemed an eternity. Dr Mulder was the first to move. He walked over to the bed and put his stethoscope on Martin's chest. Then he put his little flashlight into his eyes, lifting his eyelids to do it. After a few moments he stepped back and said, "No heartbeat. The patient has just expired."'

Christie and Franciscus sat silently, alone with their own thoughts. Then Christie said, 'Where was Gretchen?'

'She must have been delayed in the trip through morning traffic. She walked in just after Dr Mulder pronounced Martin dead. I spent a little time with her before I called you. I think she was reconciled to it. Especially since she was in conflict about the surgery herself. Mulder is an interesting character. After he said, "The patient has expired," he began to walk out of the room. Then he turned, looked around at each of us, and said, "Well, it looks like Martin has finally managed to escape from the health-care delivery system."'

Christie had been close to tears as she listened, but now she bowed her head and both wept and laughed into her paper napkin. Franciscus put his hand on her knee.

'He died his own way, Christie – at least in part,' he said.

'If only Josh had been able to ...' she began, speaking through the crumpled napkin. Franciscus interrupted her.

'That's next,' he said. 'But before I go into the rest of my story, let me say I'm sorry about the ramifications of your encounter with Dr Prince. Christie, it was bound to happen. I've felt you were working against too much hostility for a long time. I see and hear things. ...'

'Have you heard anything about my job being terminated?'

Franciscus looked steadily at Christie. She was twisting her hands together in her lap. He said, gently, 'I heard. ... Dr Mulder said the word was out that the nursing office has asked Administration to terminate you. Their reason was "bad example to nursing staff"!'

Christie's eyes became steely.

'I told Prince I wanted Martin to be free. He said something I'll never forget. He said, "*When you're dead, you're free.*" Any kind of dead is free?' She looked at Franciscus, her eyes a perfect mirror of dread and anger. Then her face softened.

'You've been seeing Victor Vendetti as much as I have.

You know what he's accomplished – with your prayers and his own commitment. He has come full circle. He understands his past and is at peace with it. He loves Stella and has been able to give her a real sense of her own self – of her worth. It is all a miracle – and he has given me ...' Her voice wavered again. Franciscus saw that it was something too deep for speech.

'Father,' she began again, 'I took Martin's son Josh over to meet Vic because he is crazy about motorcycles.' She was tumbling the words out now, in a despairing voice. 'Vic really connected with him. And Josh told Vic he was going up to talk with Martin this afternoon. Then Prince arranged the early surgery –'

Franciscus reached out and grasped her hands. 'Christie! Listen to me! Josh did see his father before he died. He got up to the hospital late last night!'

Her eyes widened. 'He saw him last night!'

'Something must have given Josh a sense of urgency. He got up to see Martin rather late last night – after Gretchen had left. I had saved my call on Martin until the last. I knew he was dreading the surgery today, and wanted to see him before he went to sleep. I hadn't been able to get there all day.'

'Did you talk to Josh?'

'Let me tell you what I saw,' Franciscus said. 'I think that will answer all your questions.' He leaned back on the sofa and went on with his story.

'Martin's room was at the end of the West Wing, you know. As I came down the hall, I heard the faint sound of music. I was amazed to think Martin might be listening to his radio or TV. He's been beyond that for quite a while. The door was open a crack, but as I started to knock, I saw someone with him. I pushed the door open a little bit and saw that it was Josh. He was sitting on the big footstool by his father's bedside, playing a guitar very softly, and singing. Martin had the look on his face of a man who had "come full circle".'

Christie covered her face with her hands and wept again

324

with relief. Franciscus could barely hear what she next said.

'Victor ... Victor worked it out. He and the angel.'

Franciscus reached out for her hand, and they sat quietly. Finally Christie asked, 'Did you go back to see Martin before you left the hospital?'

Franciscus seemed lost in his thoughts for a moment. Then he let go of her hand and cleared his throat.

'No, I left word with the nurses to tell Martin I would be up to see him before his surgery this morning. I thought a visit from me would be anticlimactic, after Josh.'

Christie nodded her head. She wiped her eyes with a tissue and blew her nose. One of the things she loved most in Stefan Franciscus was his fine sense of timing.

'He's okay now,' she said. 'I know Martin is really okay now. I wish I could have left the hospital knowing Joan's life would end as well.'

Franciscus was silent for a moment. He had been so eager to tell her the outcome of Martin's situation that he had not mentioned the news of Joan.

'Christie,' he said quietly, 'before I left the Unit this morning I stopped by to look in on her. She has slipped into a coma.'

Christie got up and walked over to the sliding doors. One was open halfway. She stood with her back to him, looking out at the rain.

'Mary was going to smuggle me in to see her today. She said she had asked for me. She liked blue flowers. I bought some to give her.'

They both were silent for a time. Then Christie spoke again. 'Do you think she ever got over her fear of God?'

Franciscus walked over to the open door and stood beside her. They watched the rain falling in small crystal streams from the leaves of an oak tree.

'I don't know,' Franciscus said heavily. His sense of impotence made the words come slowly. 'The first time I saw her she told me not to discuss God. I respected her needs.

'But she brought it up twice. One day she told me that all she would ask of heaven was a human hand to hold when she

325

was frightened, so I often held her hand.

'The last thing she said to me – just yesterday – was about heaven again. This time she said she hoped it was only eternal silence. "Not pain," she said, "or anxiety, or fear. Most of all, *not love or hope*, because they bring such suffering."' Franciscus' voice broke as he said the last sentence.

Christie turned to Franciscus. 'No one knows what people feel or experience in a coma. I'll go up to see her and bring her the flowers anyway. I'll hold her hand for a while.'

Franciscus smiled. The rain seemed to be letting up. He turned to Christie and put his hand on her shoulder. 'Will you let me know what happens – keep in touch and tell me what you are doing? If nothing special comes up in work, I may have some ideas for you.' His eyes showed a shade of the confidence that had always communicated hope to her.

'I think that first I'll take some time off. Maybe I'll go to the dunes again – to Mary's place. The lake and the dunes have always been a refuelling station for me; a healing place,' she said.

Franciscus stood watching Christie's face as she spoke. He detected a mixture of wistfulness – not quite joy, and some kind of uneasiness. Her eyes, which were always a blueprint of her state of mind, had become guarded.

'Christie, I haven't wanted to probe,' he began, then hesitated, choosing his words carefully. 'You don't have to answer me, but after our meeting in the chapel when you told me about ... when you wouldn't pray ... there was a man, you said, whom you were seeing. ...' He waited now. Christie had dropped her gaze from his face. She walked away from him. Then she sat down on the sofa. He seated himself in a chair by the patio door. His voice was very gentle. Christie knew his concern for her was genuine.

'You seemed to be quite upset that day. I sensed that whoever the man was, he had affected you deeply – I should say, *profoundly*. Christie, how is it now? Are you still seeing him? Are you happy?'

Christie was silent for a while. She stared out at the rainy patio and chewed the corner of her lip. Then she too began to select her words carefully.

'I ... well, I have been terribly happy. He's very different from anyone I've known. He's ... he's *funny*. I mean he makes me laugh a lot. And he's serious, too; I think, quite intelligent.' Franciscus leaned forward and watched the moods and feelings flashing in her eyes, in her face.

'He is kind of crazy,' she said. 'Wild, and full of energy and strength, and ... persuasive when he wants something. He's very different from me.'

'Are you happy?' Franciscus asked again. Christie sat very still and looked into the priest's eyes with a steady, thoughtful gaze.

'When I'm with him I am. Excited and completely absorbed. But ...' She paused and thought for a moment. 'I haven't seen him for several weeks. He's been travelling. We usually see each other every other week. He called last night and he's coming here today, to Brandenburg, to see me.'

'He sounds almost bigger than life,' Franciscus commented. He smiled and continued to watch her face.

'Yes, he's a little scary.'

Franciscus had the feeling it had been an act of courage for her to say it.

'Why?' he asked.

She looked at him now with an expression he had seen often at the hospital. It was Christie when she was most herself, half raw courage and half ghost-ridden dread.

'Because he occupies so much of you,' she answered, 'like an invading army. You wonder what would become of you if you were really committed to him, really his, and then he left. I have seen pictures of gutted cities. They have no centre anymore.'

The strange sense of something he had never known hovered over Franciscus as she spoke. He had loved. Had his centre ever been completely occupied? He had known desolation. What kind of possession, what kind of love, could leave one like a gutted city?

He shuddered slightly. Christie stood up and walked to

the kitchen. She brought a hot carafe of coffee and filled both their cups, then put the nut bread on the table.

'It's damp,' she said. 'It's a damp day.'

They sipped the hot liquid slowly. Christie watched him now. He stared into his cup.

'Have you ever loved anyone?' she asked.

'Yes.'

'Did you ... did they ... did you lose them?'

'Yes.'

'Have you ever been – destroyed?'

'Yes ... but not by the absence.'

Neither of them spoke for a while. Christie's eyes were full of unasked questions.

'When you feel such a danger, it is all the more important to pray.'

Franciscus was aware that she was deep in thought and decided it was time to change the subject. He strolled over to the table where the driftwood was and picked up the gull.

'This is interesting,' he said. He held it in his left hand and touched the grooves on the sculptured wings with his right. 'It looks like a bird in flight.'

'It is a gull,' said Christie. 'It was formed by the movement of the water. I think that sometimes gulls are avatars.'

'Avatars?' Franciscus smiled at this paganism. There was something in Christie that was not entirely Catholic – or Christian.

Christie smiled. 'They bear messages, and they announce gifts – for people who do not have an angel of annunciation.'

He remembered Victor's saying Christie's angels were birds and bugs. He studied the gull, stroking its grooved and satiny surface. He put it back on the table and picked up the fish. Its grooving was finer than the gull's and covered more of its surface, giving a true feeling of the lacy quality of fins.

'This one is lovely too. And the other one?'

'The other is a porpoise. They are very playful and intelligent.'

'And the fish is the Christ symbol,' Franciscus mused aloud.

'Yes,' Christie said.

'Someday we will have to manage a little time for you to explain your theology to me, Christie. It sounds fascinating – a freestyle variety.'

'I would like that. But my theology is always still in formation.' She walked over to the table. She picked up the driftwood fish and put it in his hand.

'If you would like this . . . I want you to have it for a symbol of all we . . . saw together. No one made it but the wind and the water and the sun.'

Franciscus was surprised and deeply touched.

'Are you sure you want to let it go, Christie? You must have found it yourself, and it is unique.'

'I want to give it to you,' Christie answered, 'so I won't really be losing anything.' She took a deep breath and smiled at him. Suddenly she remembered something. She looked at her watch.

'I almost forgot! It's one o'clock, and Mary is going to smuggle me in to see Joan before she goes off her shift.'

Franciscus looked around the room. 'My coat must be dry by now.'

She got the coat and helped him into it.

'Thank you for breakfast, Christie. I will always treasure the fish.'

They shook hands.

'Thank you, Father,' Christie said, 'for everything.'

Franciscus walked out the door and down the sidewalk without looking back. She watched him until his car disappeared around a corner. She turned again to the apartment and her project of separating and arranging the flowers. She had a sudden hollow feeling in the pit of her stomach; a feeling of loss – not for the structure of the hospital and her job, but for the pain, the anguish, and the enormous hope she had shared with Stefan Franciscus.

329

Chapter Two

Christie returned from her trip to see Joan feeling exhausted, but also with a sense of completion. She had put the blue flowers on the pillow next to Joan's face in case she might still be able to detect their scent, and had sat silently holding Joan's hand for at least an hour.

She decided to rest before Lance arrived. The apartment was ready for his visit. The tables gleamed, the cushions were fluffed up, and the flowers sat at one end of her sawhorse table, lending the room a festive look. She took off her clothes and wrapped herself in a robe. Then she stretched out on the sofa and closed her eyes, drifting between sleep and wakefulness. The rain stopped, and a freshened breeze came through the open slider. She had planned to rest for a half-hour, then shower and be dressed for dinner before Lance arrived; but she fell into a deep sleep.

A loud knock awakened her. She pulled the robe around her and went to the door. Through the viewing slit above the knocker she saw Lance's eyes burning, as wild and blue as she had remembered them. She wondered how long she had slept. Either the sky was dimmer from the overcast weather, or it was dusk. She ran her fingers through her hair and opened the door.

Lance Bohrman stood motionless for a few seconds, searching her eyes, then assessed her figure in the long thin robe. He pushed through the doorway, filling it with his shoulders, which seemed massive now under the jacket of a tailored suit. He enveloped her immediately with powerful arms. He lifted her and carried her to the sofa, sitting down and holding her on his lap. He took her face between his hands and kissed her eyes, her hair, and her neck.

She pushed him away from her. 'Stand up,' she said. 'I have to really look at you.' She studied him with narrowed eyes. 'You're handsome. The suit civilizes you a bit.'

His suit was made of a smooth fabric of pale summer beige. He wore a white silk shirt and a broad tie with an abstract design in warm shades of orange, pink, and lavender. His thick grey-blond hair contrasted dramatically with the deep tan of his face. His eyes revealed a mix of emotions which she could not read. She laughed and put her arms around him.

'You wear my colours,' she whispered.

Lance dropped to his knees and wrapped his arm around her thighs. He parted the robe and kissed her belly, then slowly moved his lips down to her legs and her knees. He caught her arm in his hand and began to kiss her fingers, then her wrist. He held her thighs tightly with his other arm. Suddenly, she felt him freeze. He knelt there still holding her wrist in his fingers. Then he stood up. His face had changed. He stared into her eyes.

'There's a red streak on your arm. Did you cut yourself on something?'

'No. ...' Christie pulled her arm out of his grasp and looked at it. There was a smear of bright red as if some liquid, as thick as blood, had been pressed into her arm and dried. She hadn't noticed it when she put on her robe. She must have been too preoccupied.

'I didn't cut myself,' she told him. 'Something must have rubbed off – or dripped. ...'

'I tasted it on my tongue before I saw it.' Lance reached over and pulled the robe from her shoulders. She stood in her bra and panties. He turned her around slowly and examined her.

'You couldn't get that much blood on you without knowing you cut yourself. Are you bleeding? Is it your period?'

Christie shook her head, puzzled. Then she thought of

331

Joan. She remembered seeing a stained bandage on her arm.

'I remember,' she said. 'I just got back from seeing Joan. It must have rubbed off one of her bandages.'

'Is she dying?' Lance spoke with his lip curled against his teeth. In his eyes was a blend of fear and rage.

Christie nodded her head.

Lance stood and picked up the robe, which had spilled around her feet.

'Where's the bathroom?' he asked. Now he spoke quietly, more quietly than she had ever heard him speak. Christie pointed.

Lance tossed the robe on the sofa and took her by the hand. He followed the hallway to the bathroom and turned on the water full force. He held her arm over the basin and poured water over her wrist. He picked up a nail brush and ran it up and down her arm to the elbow, scrubbing the bloodstain until the water in the basin ran clear. Then he rubbed soap on the brush and turned the water to hot, scrubbing her arm again. He dried her arm with a towel. Christie leaned against the sink, breathing hard. He dried the sleeve of his coat where water had sprayed it.

'Goddamn it, Christie! Leave that job!'

'Why?' she whispered. She could not tell him yet that the hospital was behind her.

'Blood is precious. Get away from death.' He spat out the words like a drill sergeant. 'You've got dying people touching your body. You're touching people with cancer every day.'

She watched him closely. 'Cancer is not communicable,' she said quietly.

'The energy of death is communicable.' Lance's eyes penetrated her with the power not of fear and anger, but of a deadly loathing. There was another silence. She knew, now, how it would feel to be rejected by him. He was rejecting death. He was rejecting the death in her. A chill travelled over her body.

Lance took her in his arms and kissed her roughly, filling her mouth with his tongue, thrusting his tongue into her throat.

He released her with one hand and undid her bra. He tore off her panties and pushed her against the wall with his legs, cupping her breasts in his hands. He moved his mouth over the warm swell of her flesh, more devouring than caressing her. A sob shook his shoulders. Christie stroked his hair with her fingers.

He raised his head and looked at her. She saw again the fervent expression she remembered, the look reminiscent of sacrifices and offertories.

'Follow me,' he said, turning away from her. She followed him into the living room. Along the way he began discarding clothing. His coat hit a chair. He dropped his trousers, kicking them into a corner of the room, and pulled off his tie and shirt, tossing them in the direction of the coat. He kicked off his shoes and removed his socks and shorts. He picked up Christie's robe from the sofa and spread it on the carpet.

He lifted her in his arms, cradling her against him, and began to lower their bodies to the floor. He entered her suddenly and violently. His power enveloped her and filled her, not in the fullness of care, as it had at the beach, but with savage thrusts. His tongue pushed roughly into her mouth, pressing against hers. He held her so tightly she could not respond with her own body. He impaled her rigidly against him, burning and helpless in the fever of his heat. The act was all his, and it was an onslaught. He controlled her with a brutal grip, his arms shifting only slightly and at intervals, then renewing their bruising hold. She lost all sense of time, held in his hardness and his power.

Fierce thrusts, deep into her body, sent waves of sensation into her legs and arms, into her mouth. She struggled to move away, and he briefly allowed her body to twist beneath him. Engulfed in sensations she had never felt, she began to cry out. He covered her mouth with his hand, then lifted her tightly against him again, one arm beneath her hips, repeating his long and violent penetrations. Then he raised himself above her and looked at her, pinning her to the floor only with the contact of his penetration and his hands on her arms. The force of her orgasms finally relaxed his hold. He held her less tightly, allowing her to move. She twisted from side to side, biting her lips to keep from crying out.

Finally, he released her completely and lay beside her. He watched her body shuddering, the large spasms receding slowly until she lay completely still.

He reached out and touched her hair gently. It was damp around the temples and hairline. Her hair spilled on the carpet, an unruly and dusky web. Her body swelled and curved, at once luminous and shadowed in the twilight. She moved her legs slowly in her sleep, stretching, arching her back, and curling her toes. She sighed and turned, the round curves of her hips moving slightly, unconsciously repeating the undulations of love.

He touched her belly with his fingers, stroking her lightly.

She sighed and reached out her arms.

'Christie . . .' he whispered.

She touched him, her hips and belly moving slowly, lifting towards him. He leaned over her and kissed her mouth. She uttered a small cry and he covered her immediately, filling and possessing her again. They now wrestled as equals. The room moved from dusk into darkness.

Finally, they slept.

Chapter Three

For some time now Victor had been growing weaker and needing more pain medication, but there were times when he felt well enough to take short walks or putter around the house. Even though his body had lost its energy, his mind and spirit often grew restless.

A great affirmation had come to him through Josh. The boy had come back to see Victor as soon as he learned of his father's death and had talked with him for a long time. He told Vic how grateful he was, for he knew he would never have seen his father again had it not been for their conversation. Victor took great comfort from this knowledge. He had gained a new friend – a young one, who, in many ways, was much like himself in his late teens.

Stella encouraged Victor to move about as much as he could. She did not speak about her fears, but she knew if he retreated to the daybed completely, he would lose what strength he had.

As she went about her household chores, she hummed to herself. In spite of her concern about Vic's weakness, she existed in a new strength and happiness. Today she had put out a big wash to dry on the line. The wind had risen in the afternoon, and now the sheets were whipping as briskly as loose sails. Late summer sometimes brought cool evenings to Brandenburg.

Stella pulled on a sweater and went out into the yard with her clothes basket. She folded the sheets and towels as she took them off the line, holding them to her face to enjoy their sweet, fresh scent of sun and wind. Their house was a short block from the river. That spring she had watched its slow thawing, the ice floes forming, colliding, and breaking up as sun and wind made inroads into its frozen surface. The process had reminded her of her own life. The hardness in Vic had frozen her for a long time. Now all that was changed.

Before she left for work she would always settle him down with his glass of whiskey and water. It relieved his cough and helped him sleep. He always thanked her and kissed her goodnight. On weekends they would sit close together, watching television, and Vic would put his arm around her. It was the closest thing to romance she had known since she was a very young girl.

The wash was folded. She picked up her plastic basket and deposited it in the small, enclosed back porch where the old washing machine was. It was a combination utility and storage room, always cooler than the rest of the small house.

The soup kettle had been on all afternoon, and the aroma of stew beef and vegetables floated through the rooms. Victor was lying on the daybed in the last of the day's sunlight, his afghan spread over him. When she got home at night he was sometimes shivering. She would curl her body around him and hold him till the chill subsided. He smiled and threw her a little salute as she came through the door.

'Getting cool out there?'

'Yes. Looks like it might get real cool tonight. It's clouding up in the west, too.' She hung her coat on a hook in the kitchen and tied on her apron. 'Soup'll taste real good now. You inhale the steam when you eat it. It will help your cough.'

Victor heard the dishes rattling in the kitchen. She was humming from time to time. He turned his head to the window and watched the light grow softer. It became a pinkish gold before it went to lavender. It was that soft, last light he loved best, just before the blue shadows extended into night.

Stella bustled in and made a little fire in the coal stove. It was an old Franklin model. They hadn't had a fire since the cool nights of spring. Then they had sat together and watched the flames.

Victor watched Stella move about the room and thought about his luck. Well, it wasn't just luck. He'd had months of good time since his return from the hospital. He had been right about Franciscus. The priest was a good prayer. When Victor knew he was growing weaker, he had written a kind of testament to leave Stella when he was gone. The praying Father Franciscus had done had given him his reprieve, but the problem of dying was his own. A man's death had to be his own. No one could share it with him.

The Wall of Death had become a gauge and symbol. If he had possessed any genius at all, it had resided in his knowledge of balance and timing. A man had to know how long to remain on the rim.

He sat at the table with Stella, inhaling the steam from the soup. Stella was a good cook, but all the medications had blunted his taste. They chatted easily as they ate. Stella told him some funny stories about the women at work.

While she cleaned up the dishes, he lay back on the daybed

336

and watched the flames in the stove. When she brought him his glass of whiskey before she left for the factory, he would usually nurse it for at least an hour and finally fall asleep.

Tonight he watched Stella brushing her hair and getting ready to leave. She had cut her hair short, and Arline had given her a permanent. She applied some kind of makeup base and lipstick, then pulled on her blue coverall. She looked real smart. Her manner was no longer apologetic. She came over and kissed him good-bye. She set the glass of whiskey down on the table beside him.

'Ray and Arline might look in on you around eight,' she told him. 'There's beer in the fridge if they do.' She stood looking at him fondly for a moment or two; then she kissed him and walked out to the porch to wait for her ride.

Victor reached over and picked up the whiskey. He ran through his 'testament' in his mind. When he died, Stella would have the house. He had written a note for Franciscus too, and one for Christie.

Christie had come to visit him a few days ago. She had come to say good-bye before leaving for the dunes on a vacation with Lance. She had a lot of news for him: the story of her run-in with Prince, her termination at Broadcliff, and the circumstances of Martin's death. It had filled him with satisfaction. Josh had called him a few days after their meeting to say that he was learning how to play his father's favourite hymn on his guitar. Martin Kiley's angel had been as good as his word. Martin had bottomed out like a virtuoso.

He held his glass up to the fire and watched the amber lights, the deep red reflections from the flames dancing in them. They reminded him of the stage lights when the red velvet curtain lifted slowly at the opera house in Frisco, and they reminded him of the carnival.

He sipped the whiskey, turning the glass to get a prism effect. The colours merged and blended, bled apart and changed. The whiskey began to infuse him with its blessed warmth, bringing to his mind the reprise he had always courted. He remembered something Churchill had said: 'I have always got more out of liquor than liquor ever got out of me.' Well, Churchill had died in bed, an old man. The thought brought him back suddenly from his reverie. He had been very careful to project in his mind exactly what would be essential. He needed to achieve the precise moment between a warm rush in his blood, which gave him strength, and the vulnerability of drunkenness. He was just about there.

He raised himself from the daybed and stood up, looking into the fire once more. He lifted the whiskey and murmured a toast, taking one more slow drag from the glass. He walked to the back door and removed his coat from the hook, glancing around at the homely warmth of the kitchen. He inhaled the scent of the cooling soup pot. Stella would be all right now. He had given her something of value. Christie called it the gift of being seen.

Oh, yes – the notes. Now he remembered the notes. There were three of them. He had put them in an inside jacket pocket, next to Renée's knife. He dug into his coat and removed the three envelopes. They were labelled *'Stella'*, *'Fr Franciscus'*, and *'Christie'*. He laid them in a row on the table.

He left the house and closed the door behind him. He stopped only once as he headed towards the River Bridge. He looked back at the house and stood watching the smoke curl from the chimney. It was an old structure, but it had served its purpose. He lifted his empty hand and gave it a symbolic toast. Then he thrust the hand into his pocket and closed it firmly around the handle of Renée's knife. He was almost to the river.

Chapter Four

The first week after Brenda's departure for Chicago was a wilderness for Virgil Prince, punctuated only by deep inner conflict. He was forced to face the fact of his dependence on her presence, and his sexual need for her. He felt exposed without her buffer of protection between himself and the patients who were dying. He could not force himself to go into Joan Bentley's room. Now he simply initialled the residents' entries in the Progress and Consultation section of the charts. He saved his energy for the new patients and those still in remission.

Brenda's flight to Chicago had hardly taken off from the Brandenburg airport when Prince made his basic decision. He would have to drop the bomb on Dottie and ask for a divorce. There was no way he could continue with his work in the emotional desert of Brenda's absence. His despair and restlessness since her departure had resulted in severe insomnia. He tossed and turned in bed at night, finally falling into a fitful sleep, then waking in a sweat from nightmares in which he saw Brenda snuggling unknown studs in the velvet booths of her favourite Chicago bistros. One night he had awakened to find himself crying out. That night he had begun his use of Seconal.

The second night of Brenda's absence, he had moved into a motel near Broadcliff and phoned Dottie that problems on the Unit had forced him to initiate a series of conferences which would keep him in town late, and he would be too tired to commute to the lake.

The morning after his seventh night at the motel, he woke up groggily and knew it was another hot day. He listened to

the drone of the air-conditioning system and began mulling
over his strategy with Dottie. Everything depended on the
initial approach. He had learned that with his patients. No
tinge of doubt or hesitation must mar his presentation, and
he must not allow her to accuse him or put him into a
defensive position.

He had rehearsed his approach for a couple of days. It had
to do with sketching out for Dottie the vast change in his
own personality and life pattern since the time of their
marriage. He would point out to her that she was the same
person she had been when they met in college, with the
exception of her role as mother. He would emphasize to her
his appreciation of her expertise in that. But he would go on
to explain that the weight of his commitment to his
profession and the consuming needs of his patients had
drained him of time and of the psychic and emotional energy
for a private life. Virgil Prince the doctor-initiate was not the
same man as Virgil Prince the oncologist and medical
administrator. He must paint a convincing image of the
monastic isolation of a man with his decisions and
responsibilities.

Prince crawled out of bed and made his way to the shower,
first scrubbing in hot, soapy water, then letting the needles of
cold spray run over his head and tingle on his body and legs.
He wrapped a towel around his waist and began to shave. He
was beginning to feel half human again. He had convinced
himself that no one had dared to repeat to Dottie gossip
about his relationship with Brenda. No one who knew her
would want to hurt her. Also, Dottie was a veritable Melanie
Wilkes, who could not conceive of deception in anyone close
to her, since the capacity for it did not reside in herself. He
winced as the picture of himself, as conceived by his wife,
drifted into his mind. He knew she saw him as a man of high
integrity, faultlessly truthful, brilliant, and the victim of a
lonely and selfless commitment. All her confusion, he knew,
lay in his gradual abdication from any sexual and emotional
exchange with her. His hope for success lay in building on
her constant inner picture of him.

However, he was painfully aware that regardless of the success of his approach, her agreeing to a divorce would be costly to her. This he could cushion with a generous settlement and allowance. When he thought of the expression that would surely be on her face when they talked, he experienced the same dread that made him avoid the countenances of his patients who were facing death. Powerlessness filled him with aversion and guilt.

He had developed a routine for himself after Brenda left. He went to the hospital first and initialled the residents' entries in his patients' charts, then left for the office. After his appointments there he would head for the motel. He would sit in the dimly lit lounge and have a nightcap, listening to the insinuating beat of a jazz combo, then retreat to his room. He would try to render his mind blank, but was unsuccessful. His thoughts wound tortuously through the complexities of his problems with Dottie, how he would deal with the children, and how soon he could get Brenda back. The Seconal was a blessed relief. He began to see at first hand how continued pain and anxiety could invite the release of drugs and the slavery of addiction.

The discovery that he, with all his medical knowledge and personal power, could welcome the induced oblivion of even one Seconal filled him with fury. One afternoon, after a particularly bad night, he had visited the Unit and run into Christie Wilson while he was in the nurses' station initialling charts. There had been an unfortunate scene. It was over that damned Martin Kiley case. She had had the gall to ask him to call off surgery and then to argue with him about his decision. Jesus! Dying in surgery would have been a blessing for Kiley. If he survived it, it would have been an act of God. Well, he had received word the next day that Kiley had died before they got him to Surgery: maybe *that* was an act of God. Prince was aware that more and more, he was using religious slogans in his mind. He was also swearing more.

Always before, Prince had felt that Christie was gentle, and even somewhat reverent towards his own authority. That day she had spat at him like a cat in heat, and told him he was 'evil', with the entire Unit staff watching.

He splashed after-shave lotion on his face and began to
dress. The combination of Seconal and tobacco made his
mouth feel foul. He went back to the bathroom and gargled
some mouthwash. The night before, when he had lain
sleepless in bed, he had decided to drive to the lake and have
it out with Dottie today. He would get Bracebridge to see his
office patients – most of them just got chemo from the nurse.
Then he would call Dottie and drive to the lake. When it was
all over, he would call Brenda with the divorce news. When
she returned, he would be free.

A painful incident at Broadcliff the day before had
accelerated the urgency of Prince's decision to confront his
wife. He had run into Stanford Bracebridge as he was
leaving the hospital, and after some conversation about a
patient, was about to suggest he meet him for a drink and
dinner that evening. As they stood there chatting, Frank
Stone had come down the corridor and joined their
conversation. Stan Bracebridge had exhibited enough
delicacy to look embarrassed, but Stone had remained, with
an inane smile on his face, and had even begun a
conversation about Brenda.

'Well, I'm baching it for two weeks, Stan.' He had
addressed his remarks to Bracebridge, with only a slight nod
in Prince's direction. 'Brenda's gone off to Chicago for a
little sabbatical.' He had laughed in what was supposed to be
a demonstration of husbandly indulgence, and had then
gone on to slide his knife into Prince's solar plexus. 'She
called me last night. Said she's having a ball shopping
Bonwit's bare and doing the town at night with all her old
boyfriends.' His voice had an unfortunate tendency to
crescendo into a strained squeak when he was playing 'the
good fellow'. Prince mused over the fact that everyone said
he was a great politician and horseman. Well, he was a lousy
husband. At least, he had been a spectacle of ineptitude with
Brenda. Bracebridge had slapped him on the back and
drawled, 'You're a sly fox, buddy. After a splurge like that
she'll come back here purring like a pussycat.' Bracebridge

ad turned and winked at Virgil.

A wave of fire had surged through Prince's stomach. His throat and his gut contracted with pain and rage – although he guessed that Brenda had *not* phoned her husband.

He had gone back to the motel restaurant and put away three drinks. Then he had eaten – he forgot what – and gone to his room hoping to fall unconscious, but again his mind clicked endlessly through kaleidoscope scenes of Brenda, and rehearsals of his confrontation with Dottie. He had finally swallowed the Seconal. It had been his worst night.

He pulled a clean shirt out of his suitcase and began to dress. He didn't need a tie. At this point there was no need for worrying about the credibility of his outfit. He would tell Dottie at the outset that he had taken the day off in order to settle their problems. He threw his shaving kit, dirty shirt, and shorts into the suitcase and closed it. He looked up and caught the reflection of himself in the mirror. The face staring back at him was agitated and unguarded. He paused for a moment and studied it. He had often wondered what his life would have been like if his face had been formed in a unity – either a monsterish full mask, or clean and clear: at any rate, whole. If it had been the latter, he probably would have been a successful obstetrician or surgeon; if the former, some sort of medical research expert hiding in a laboratory.

As it was, the unmarked half of his face was handsome enough to make the whole intriguing. The other half was horrible, but it endowed him with mystery. He had seen its effect on others for many years now. As afflictions went, he vastly preferred it to having been born crippled, for instance. He had a well-muscled, well-proportioned body, and he was hung like a savage. His choice of being a cancer specialist had derived from his own conviction that a marked man must be something beyond the ordinary. He knew that his face, which had the brief initial effect of inspiring pity, had been his credential of entry into the confidence of anyone with cancer. Cancer patients were almost universally afflicted with a secret shame. They felt set apart from the rest of the world. When they first met him, they sensed a kindred

343

soul, someone they could trust. For his part, he was convinced that his disfigurement was his permanent inoculation against the disease he treated and his pre payment against other acts of God.

He picked up his jacket and threw his key to the room on the dresser. After he had checked out at the desk, he slung his suitcase into the back of the Mark VI, locked the car door, and went to the coffee shop. He bought a newspaper and glanced at it while he waited for breakfast. He sipped the coffee and began to feel better. No matter what kind of scene Dottie made, nothing could be worse than what he had been enduring. The heat of the weather matched the pressure inside his head.

He ate his breakfast slowly, experiencing the slowdown of a Seconal hangover.

He had a second cup of coffee while he finished his breakfast. The effect of the Seconal was beginning to wear off some. Then he went to the public phone and called Dottie at their cottage. The phone rang four times; then his youngest son answered.

'Hi,' Prince said. 'This is Dad.'

There was silence and the sound of the receiver scraping around.

'Can you get your mother to the phone?' Prince asked.

'We're feeding the ducks. She's on the deck,' Donnie told him.

'Go get her. Tell her I'm waiting.'

Prince heard the receiver clack, then Donnie's voice yelling as he headed for the deck.

After what seemed like a long time, he heard Dottie's voice.

'Hello ... Virg?'

'Yeah. I'm just checking to make sure you didn't drive into town. After I stop off at the hospital I'm coming out to the cottage. I'm beat from the heat and the conferences. I'm taking the day off. There are some important things I have to discuss with you.'

'Oh ... okay. Fine.' There was a small pause, and then he

heard her voice get softer.

'I'm glad ... you're coming. It must be hot in town. I'll ... Jill Smith is taking the children to a fair in Lakeshore Village. So you can just relax when you get here. The two of us can talk. They'll be back at dinnertime.' Her voice now contained a note of hope and anticipation. She waited for a moment, and then went on.

'I got fresh strawberries ... and I made a cake ... I thought you might get free today.'

Prince felt the familiar hot, twisting pain in the pit of his stomach.

'Yeah. Okay ... fine. I'll be leaving in a few minutes. It's hot in this phone booth.'

'Of course. Be careful. I'll see you soon.'

She hung up.

Prince swung his jacket over his shoulder, walked up to the counter, and paid his bill. He headed for the car. The asphalt lot was throwing up heat already. He got into the seat and pressed the automatic window opener. He wanted to breathe the outside air.

He moved the Mark VI expertly through a four-lane downtown street and drove towards Broadcliff. Traffic was light. It was midmorning. The speed and power of his car was one of his releases from tension.

The conversation with Dottie had undermined his resolution. The tone of shy anticipation in her voice had got to him. It had affected him in a way that her whining and interrogations never could. He made a determined effort to blot it out by summoning the expression on her face that annoyed him most: a look of reproach, sad and defeated, like a whipped dog. Her voice just now had reminded him of Dottie as she was when they had begun dating. She had been in two of his classes and had been terribly impressed by his intelligence. He had helped her with lab assignments. Her feminine appeal had rested in her dependence on him. Her admiration had given him his first sense of male power.

It would be so easy for him if he could be happy with her. But he could not. He had gone around some bend, passed

345

some invisible border, into a territory where return was impossible. Brenda's strange manipulative appeal had roused emotions and needs in him that only she knew how to satisfy. To go back to Dottie now would be like leaving graduate school to return to the eighth grade. It would violate his own evolution.

Chapter Five

Prince eased the Mark VI into his space in the doctors' parking ramp and headed for a rear elevator. He hoped he could make a swift trip up to the Unit, check the charts, initial them, and make his exit without any detours. The elevator was empty. It was fairly early in the morning and he had that in his favour. No families would be lying in wait for him, and most of the residents would be busy with their rounds. Thank God Mulder's tour on the Unit was over, he thought. Mulder had always managed to corner him about some problem Brenda could have handled.

The elevator stopped at Seven Main. As he walked out into the corridor, the stairwell door slammed open and Dr Lindsay bumped into him.

'Dr Prince!' Lindsay said, looking pleased and surprised to see him. 'What a coincidence!'

Prince was irritated. He hadn't had occasion to talk to Lindsay since he had left the Unit. Lindsay smiled rather crookedly.

'Funny I bumped into you, Doctor. I just came from the Emergency Room. Your "bad penny" has returned! They just admitted Victor Vendetti a half-hour ago. His cancer must have progressed. He evidently passed out when he was walking on the River Bridge. A police ambulance brought him in. They sent him up here to the five-bed ward. I was just going in to take a look at him.'

'Vendetti?' Prince felt a mild consternation. He had written in the chart: *'Advise no further admissions to Broadcliff. Vendetti refuses treatment.'*

Lindsay turned abruptly and started down the hallway towards the ward. Prince followed him.

'I made a note in his chart against further admission,' he told Lindsay. '*You* saw it.'

'Yeah. *I* saw it. He must have slipped through the red tape. He has a long record. The clerks probably haven't made their way through the notes yet.'

The two doctors passed the nurses' station and turned into the hallway of the East Wing. A small crowd was clustered at the door of the five-bed ward – several patients in gowns and robes and a few nurses.

'God,' Prince snapped at Lindsay, 'Vendetti must be in another standoff!'

Lindsay stretched out his long arms and parted the crowd like a pair of lumpy draperies. Prince followed in his wake. All the beds in the room were empty. Hugh was kneeling on the floor, cradling Victor Vendetti in his arms. Around them was a spreading pool of blood. Hugh was whispering something. It took several moments for the words to register on Virgil Prince.

'It's all right, Vic,' he kept saying. 'It's all right. . . . It's *all* right.' He was weeping silently. No sobs. No wails. Just the quiet falling of tears, like small rivers, down his face.

For a moment Prince and Lindsay appeared to have turned to stone. The room was totally still except for the sound of Hugh's whispering. Prince was the first to move. Something had caught his eye in the spreading blood near Vendetti's hand. It released him from his paralysis. He stepped across the room and crouched down to retrieve it. He pulled out his linen handkerchief and wiped the blood from his hand and from the silver knife. It was a graceful object, much larger than a pocketknife, more like a switchblade. Its handle was mother-of-pearl. A message was

347

etched in a delicate, frondlike design. It said:

> To Victor
> *For conquering the wall of death*
> *Always – Renée*

Prince knelt there reading the inscription several times. Then he felt someone touching him on the shoulder. He looked up and saw Lindsay's open hand. He dropped the knife into it gently, and looked at him. Behind the steel-rimmed glasses, Lindsay's eyes were bright with a totally inappropriate gleam of triumph.

'It looks like a *suicide*, Doctor. Something that never happens. Vendetti is dead. He must have known where to hit the carotid.'

Prince heard other voices behind him now. The head nurse was speaking nervously.

'He was dead when Hugh got here. It was too late. Someone put on a light. It was too late. We got all the patients out of the ward. . . . It was too late.'

Lindsay bent down and helped Prince to his feet; then he walked over to Hugh and whispered something to him. He knelt down beside him and put his hand on his shoulder. Hugh hadn't taken his eyes from Victor, and he hadn't moved. Prince forced his own glance to Vendetti's face. It looked incongruously, phenomenally, young. His shock of grey hair had been stroked away from his forehead. His thick eyebrows were raised, as if he had recognized some pleasure. His lips were curved in a slight smile.

Prince was aware that he was beginning to get shaky. He knew he must get hold of himself. He'd seen massive haemorrhages before. He turned to walk from the room. He was a little dizzy and his knees felt like putty. He made his way through the group remaining in the doorway. Someone was coming with towels and mops. He heard the wheels of an approaching stretcher. The patients from the ward had been deployed to a conference room. Prince saw a young nurse pass by him, entering the ward. Her face was wet with tears.

348

It was Mary. He turned and saw her hold out her arms to Hugh.

Prince sped along the freeway towards the lake. He had opened the windows wide, and the warm wind tossed his hair like invisible fingers. After he had made his way out of the hospital to the car, he had dropped off at the Cave and downed a double shot of bourbon. He had stayed there in a dark corner booth until his shakiness and the weakness in his knees diminished. The sight of Vendetti's face, the sound of Hugh's voice, and the horror of all the blood had blurred.

Vendetti was dead, he told himself. He had waved a knife before, at a room full of people. Damned lucky he had killed *himself*. It could have been an innocent bystander. He must pack the incident away with the thousand other deaths that had occurred at Broadcliff since he had come there.

He focused his attention outside the car. The industrial sections of the outskirts of Brandenburg began to melt into green areas, woods, and marshes. From time to time a few ducks rose out of the swampy reeds and took off across the highway into the small lakes that abounded between Brandenburg and the big lake. Prince began to feel a little of the sense of freedom that comes to all travellers on the open road, suspended between what they are leaving and what they hasten towards. The wind, the swift motion of the car, and the last vestiges of the Seconal, reinforced by the bourbon, gave him a sense of floating – of euphoria.

He decided to take the next turnoff, which he knew connected with the old highway between Brandenburg and the lake. It passed through a few villages, curving through the hills and crossing streams. It would be more private and allow him to pass closer to the woods. The freeway always intruded itself between man and nature.

After the turnoff, he skimmed along the old two-lane highway, passing an occasional farmhouse. But there were mostly meadows and forests. The car rode smoothly and silently, undulating over the rises and curves like a dancer. It was that rare time in summer when the wild asters bloomed.

At the summit of each hill, Prince looked out over miles of green-and-lavender meadows. A choir of insect voices rose from the lush ground cover. The earth seemed alive with a soft, sensual fatigue, like lovers after a day of passion, and the aura of Brenda enveloped him. A surge of longing swept over his body.

The old highway was now joining the Shore Drive, and he could feel the air becoming cooler even before he saw the lake through the trees.

This stretch of road, as always, affected him deeply. He slowed down and paused along the edge of a broad, sandy beach, the beach he had sometimes stopped to walk along at sunset. Now the sun was high and the blue waves glinted with sparkling crests. A few gulls walked along the sand. He saw a group of sailboats far out, their coloured spinnakers billowing forward as bravely as banners. The morning beach and all its colours was a scene of innocence and joy. It brought him back to his own youth and the long days of summer that had then been unshadowed by the weight of tedious decisions.

The road abruptly turned and he was plunged into olive darkness and the arches of tall cathedral trees. He drove along slowly, enveloped and penetrated by the brooding mystery of the forest, which was pierced by sharp, intermittent shafts of light. No church had ever communicated to him the sense of awe and worship he felt in the depths of these trees.

He shivered slightly as the car emerged into the next stretch of open shoreline. He was relieved to feel the full sun again; to be released from the grip of mystery. He knew he was on the last stretch of road between the turnoff and his cottage; a few miles and he would be facing his meeting with Dottie.

He must not think about it. He pressed his foot on the accelerator as if a burst of speed could banish his dread of the confrontation and could bring him closer to freedom. He was rounding a long curve in the road, heading into the woods again, when something suddenly appeared, a hundred feet ahead, and stood motionless in his path. It sat up on its haunches, alerted by something ahead in the woods. It froze on the spot, oblivious to the car bearing down on it.

Prince's action was instinctive. Some reflex too deep for thought, some dark grace bestowed by the forest road blurred his mind and alerted the muscle in his leg. He jammed his foot on the brake. There was a sudden lurching movement; the sensation of being at the centre of a whirling vortex; a singing, keening, drowning sound in his head; and then a green silence.

Chapter Six

The denseness of the silence into which Virgil Prince had plunged held him in a merciful pause. It faded slowly. The first sounds that entered his consciousness were a soft rustling of leaves, the chattering of squirrels overhead, and the mingled calls of birds. A jay shrieked and others answered. The gentle voices of doves sounded a minor key in the distance. At first he thought it was morning and that he was being awakened by the chorus of voices he heard often at his cottage. But he became aware of an aching in his neck and sharp pain somewhere in his upper torso. He wondered what he had done to induce muscular pain. He could not remember any unusual exercise.

He tried to roll over and found that he could not move. He opened his eyes and saw the frame of a windshield and the right fender of his car smashed against a tree trunk. Now he remembered. He had been on the back road to the cottage. A man's voice broke into the convocation of birds. There was a sound like sirens in the distance.

'Don't try to move, buddy. The ambulance is on its way.'

The accent sounded as if it belonged to one of the rural residents of Lakeshore. He saw the man's face now, tanned and leathery, bending towards him outside the door. Bloodshot eyes reflected pity and terror. He had cracked up in the boondocks.

My God. I'm probably pinned in – or worse, injured badly.

Now he was fully alert.

Injured! Jesus. It could be anything. I have to force myself to stay conscious. The waking terror of every doctor was a car crash in the countryside where he might be rushed to a one-horse hospital and screwed up by an incompetent staff with no sophisticated equipment. He heard his own voice now, strangely thin and cracked.

'Get me ... tell them to take me to ... Broadcliff ... Brandenburg ... the Trauma Centre.... Don't let them ...' The siren drowned out his voice. The man's face faded. Everything vanished again in the green silence. He drifted between dreams and consciousness, unsure which was which. He heard the voices of medics.

'It's okay. We got you out. It's okay. Try to relax.'

Did the man get the message? God! Let them get me to Broadcliff.

'Unit one two zero. On scene with forty-two-year old white male, doctor's insignia. In motor-vehicle accident. Multiple injuries. Vital signs stable. Pulse one ten. Resp. twenty-four. Blood pressure one hundred over sixty.'

Prince strained to hear the rest.

Thank God. Don't fade out. Stay awake. Listen!

'Patient gaining consciousness. Decreased breath sounds on right. Belly soft. Unable to move legs. Request protocol.'

The certainty of protocol! Legs. Legs. How much injury? If it's a neck injury ...? My God. What can I move?

Prince's mind raced like a rat in a maze. He must be calm. He must listen carefully. *Protocol. They would call back the protocol.*

'Broadcliff Base to Unit one two zero. Protocol three. Start I.V. with LR titrate to pressure. Transport on back board. Philadelphia cervical collar. Advise of change in condition. Request ETA.'

'Less than an hour. Estimate arrival one p.m.'

Prince watched them put in the I.V. Well, he had lucked out on the paramedics. They weren't clumsy. They moved expertly, following directions. He forced his mind to stay alert, clocking their motions. They lifted him into the ambulance and pulled out into the Shore Drive, opening the siren immediately.

He knew he was locked into the Trauma system and that the Emergency Room would be ready. The swaying of the big van and the screaming of the siren enclosed him, and he rested for a time between reality and revelation. After some minutes he moved his fingers under the blanket, confirming that much mobility; opening and closing his hands, bending and unbending his elbows. Then, for a while, he shut his eyes, insulated within the motion and the noise, separated from the past, not yet entering the future.

Suddenly the image of Brenda bled into the void behind his eyelids. He began to remember. He had been driving to the lake on a serious mission involving his freedom; his freedom to have Brenda. Now, in the space of an hour, all the logistics of freedom had been altered. A new panic overtook his mind. He must smother the panic. He must be calm and aware. He glanced out the window at the swiftly moving landscape. They were winding down the freeway below the bluff that stood above the river. He saw vaguely through the pines the high walls and red roofs of the buildings on Seminary Hill. They were approaching the city.

The ambulance screamed up to the Emergency Room entrance. Two nurses rushed to the rear door. The medics eased him out on the stretcher.

The faces of the nurses hovering along beside the stretcher were arranged in the acceptable expression of professional cool, but their eyes were eloquent with excitement and dread. They managed to keep their hands on the blanket as the medics rushed through the double doors with him. One was shoved between the wall and the stretcher, scraping her

353

arm. The other yelled, 'Which Trauma room?' Now there were more people. An intern barked, 'One-five-eight!' The medics bore the stretcher down a short hallway.

From the hard surface of the examining table he squinted his eyes against the cruelty of overhead spotlights and watched a swarm of white-clothed figures encircling him. The two nurses were poking into his arms to start more I.V.'s. Suddenly his eyes focused on a familiar face. So Mulder was the Trauma resident now. Well, if vigilance meant anything, he was in luck. Mulder laid a hand on his arm.

'Everything's okay, Doctor. Just try to relax.'

You ass. Everything's shot to hell. I can't feel my legs! God. Don't let those nurses put in the Foley.

Now the Emergency Room resident was shouting orders.

'Three I.V.'s with lactated Ringers. CBC. Lytes. Type and cross for six! Where the hell is X-Ray?'

I must be bleeding. Inside? Where? I can't feel my legs.

Mulder was feeling his belly, looking at his pupils with the light. He was speaking to the ER resident.

'Get me Surg, Ortho, and Neuro residents, stat.'

All three walked in the door as Mulder was giving the order. Prince knew the news had spread through the whole hospital. Mulder was busy now examining his neck and airway. The Neuro and Ortho residents were mauling him somewhere. Where? They kept moving around the table.

'Do you hurt anywhere?'

'Can you move your toes?'

'Can you feel me touching you? Is it sharp or dull?'

The last was the Neuro man.

Was he touching me? God. Was he touching me? Where? Prince shook his head.

'Feel like you're gonna throw up?' That was the ER resident. He shook his head again. He was beginning to feel a little dizzy.

It's the damn lights. The eyes.

There were millions of eyes. They spun around the room now like tiny jewels, glinting and glaring. Alien. Demonic. He heard the Surgery resident clipping off words.

'No breath sounds on right. Trachea has shifted! Get portable X-ray!'

The room was swirling. The eyes were a blur.

'I think he's got a pneumo!' the Neuro resident hissed.

'No DTR's! Toes down. No bulbocavernosis reflex!' The words bounced off the walls of the room.

Take me into the Green Silence.

'He's losing pressure!' The voice was a nurse.

'It's a tension pneumo. Give me a chest tray.' Mulder's tone plunged them into a wordless tension. Their movements were swift and certain.

'He's arresting.' The ER resident's statement was a low hiss.

'Shit!' The Orthopaedic resident spat out the word and glared around at them. Mulder had received the chest tray from a nurse. He incised the skin and stabbed the chest tube in with one powerful thrust. The group were poised on a periphery of the silence Virgil Prince had entered. They were barely breathing. They stood listening to the bubbling sounds as pressure was released from Prince's chest. Moments passed. Finally, one of the nurses spoke.

'Pressure and pulse returning.' Her voice was laced with caution. They stood motionless, watching the dials, the vials, the tubes now inserted squarely into Prince's veins.

Mulder was the only one watching Prince's face. He was the first to move, the first to speak. He turned to the ER resident.

'We can get the X-rays now.'

'He should be stable enough to move into the ICU after that.'

Mulder nodded. The X-ray machine was being rolled over to the table. Prince was again aware of pain in his chest. He heard the X-ray plates being slammed into the machine and taken out. Then he saw the Neuro resident moving around the table again.

'Can you feel me touching you?' The questions were repeated.

He shook his head and closed his eyes. He had watched

long enough, been conscious long enough, to know the
score. He would shut out the added torture of the glare. He
knew they would read the X-rays before they moved him. He
felt intensely weary now, as if he had suffered a beating. His
upper body was a confused field of pain. Below it there was
nothing. The pain and the activity around him somehow
became merged. They flowed together and formed a sea in
which he sometimes floated, sometimes pitched and tossed.
Mulder's voice came to him from time to time like a sheet
anchor, guiding him through the chaos; familiar; a sanity out
of the past which he seized and held. He heard the sounds of
X-rays shuffling in the view box, voices commenting.

'Cervical spine looks okay.'

'Thoracic spine okay.'

'Here's one hell of an LS fracture.' The Ortho resident's
voice had dropped an octave.

'Looks like a displaced fracture L-four on five,' Mulder's
voice concurred. The shuffling sound continued as more X-
rays slid into the view box.

'The pneumo reexpanded. Lung's open.'

'Couple of broken ribs. No flail segment.'

Mulder was dialling the phone. He turned to the other
residents.

'I'll get attending staff.' There was a pause. Then Prince
heard his voice again – the reality link: 'Look, Dr Ransahoff,
we have Dr Prince here with multiple trauma. Looks like
minor closed-head injury. Had tension pneumothorax. Resp
arrest. We put tubes in. He's okay now. But we got a big
problem. He has an LS fracture. Significant neuro deficit.
The fracture isn't stable. We need surgery.'

A long pause again; then Mulder said, 'Want me to talk to
the family, or stall? Okay. They're here ... Okay.' Mulder
hung up. 'Transfer him to ICU. The Neuro Department
Chairman is on vacation. Ransahoff will do the fusion. He
says don't let the interns near Prince.' Mulder's eyes locked
with Dr Graham's. Graham was the Neuro resident. They
walked over to a corner of the room. Mulder's voice was
barely audible.

'You want to give me some statements I can pass on to Mrs Prince? Bracebridge is down in the conference room with her.'

Graham averted his eyes and nodded. One of the nurses was inserting a Foley catheter into the patient's penis. The room entered a diminuendo.

Dr Mulder stared down at the face of Virgil Prince, whom he had recently thought of as the devil. Now he lay motionless and apparently unconscious. In his face Mulder read the intense vulnerability of all human life plunged into the truth of its own frailty. He sighed and turned away to the basin to wash. He decided to take Graham with him to give Prince's wife whatever information they could now be certain of.

Chapter Seven

The news that Virgil Prince was in the Emergency Room, a trauma case, spread through the hospital like grass fire. Francine Lindemueller was standing by the desk monitor when she heard the Unit clerk whispering excitedly to the head nurse. An intern stood near them, a look of shock spreading over his face. Several of the Unit staff gathered in a small knot, talking fast.

'God! It's Dr Death! On his way to the Unit!' The intern whistled through his teeth. Francine heard more fragments: '... bent out of shape ...' '... one-car accident ...' One of the nurses suddenly glanced at her over her shoulder, and the group dispersed towards their duties on the run. Francine followed the head nurse.

'Who is it?'

'Virgil Prince.'

Francine stood rooted to the spot, her mind reeling.The

head nurse turned into one of the private rooms, the resident just ahead of her. Francine recovered her mobility and joined them. An intern and two nurses were milling around, checking equipment, adjusting the bed. The head nurse spoke fast to Francine over her shoulder.

'LS fracture. A bad one. Neuro damage. He arrested. Three I.V.'s and a chest tube. Foley. Nasogastric tube. He goes to Surgery early in the a.m.'

Jeez! Francine's mind clicked into position. Brenda. She was in Chicago! They had met for lunch just before Francine had driven her to the airport eight days ago. The whole conversation at the restaurant had centred on Brenda's explaining her new strategy with Virgil Prince: a two-week vacation, which she would spend with old friends in Chicago. She was going to stay at some posh hotel. Her absence would force Prince to cool his heels, worry, and above all, miss her. She'd given him an ultimatum: divorce his wife, or forget their love affair. Francine had been amazed and impressed, as always, by Brenda's cool, analytical mind. It was Brenda's style to have a big fish like Prince on the hook and then loosen the line while he was hot for the bait. She was always ready to take big chances. Francine thought of the day Brenda had announced to her the opening of her campaign to get Virgil Prince.

'God, Brenda,' she had responded in an awestruck voice, 'he doesn't even look at legs and asses. He's remote. He's Mr Dignity. He's got a wife and kids. They're big church people.' She leaned into Brenda's face and measured out the words impressively: 'My brother and his wife sit in the same pew with the Princes at Blessed Redeemer!'

They were conversing in a booth at the Cave. Brenda had looked across at her over the rim of her Margarita glass, her green eyes at the same time alert and slumbrous. Francine thought of a leopard in ambush, observing its kill. Brenda put down her glass and ran her tongue daintily along her lips, retrieving salt; then she leaned back in the booth and smiled contentedly, like a prim little girl who had memorized her lesson.

Francine felt someone shaking her elbow. It was the head nurse. 'Check Adgate's monitor! The desk is flashing!'

Francine snapped into the frame of the present.

'Look out!' warned the intern. 'They're bringing Prince through the door now!'

Francine flattened her plump body against the wall and took a swift look at Prince as the stretcher passed her and was rolled up even with the bed. His eyes were closed, but they opened as the stretcher wheels stopped moving. He looked around the room, and his eyes met hers for a second. She felt he was aware of her friendship with Brenda. He always spoke cordially when they passed each other in the hall. Now he turned his head away. She shivered involuntarily and hurried from the room. Thank God she had been assigned to old Mrs Adgate today – a heart bypass post-op. She would have been utterly rattled if Virgil Prince had been in her care. They would probably assign Esther to him. She was Mrs Impervious, and she wasn't interested in status.

Francine went into Mrs Adgate's room and saw that she was fibrillating. She waved through the glass window to an intern who was still at the main desk. Her mind had become clearer. As soon as she went out on her break, she'd put a call in to Brenda at the hotel in Chicago. She had written down the name of it. In fact, she had asked Brenda for it at the last minute. She was Miss Careful. Too careful for her own good. Well – she smiled to herself – she might just be Miss Intuitive also. Something had told her to get the name of the place where Brenda was staying. Now she could be the one to break the terrible news. Brenda wouldn't have to hear it from her husband, who would rub it in, or any of the staff, who were not really her friends. From her position on the ICU, she could provide her with inside information she couldn't glean from the chart. Francine would be a key player in whatever new drama was about to unfold in Brenda's life.

Chapter Eight

Richard Mulder stood alone in an anteroom of the Trauma centre. An important part of his commitment as a physician was to the human needs of the patients he saw. He had learned about the emotional turmoil of the sick and injured and their families by experiencing it on all the units of the hospital. He had also shared in the need of physicians to insulate themselves from it. He felt that he owed a peculiar moral debt to Virgil Prince. Prince, more than any other doctor he had encountered, had demonstrated in graphic dimensions the cruel distancing which his own vulnerability might one day construct as its defence.

His monthlong duty on the Cancer Unit had made obvious to him the pressures and contradictions in Prince's private life. The hospital underground had for some time been observing and discussing Prince's obsession with Brenda Stone. Mulder knew Brenda was no powder puff, but his psychological knowledge of women was too meagre to grant him clues with which to project her reaction to Prince's predicament. His first task was to go with Dr Graham to give Mrs Prince the first medical information about her husband. He knew much less about Dottie Prince than he did about Brenda Stone. He knew Dottie had children and that they were young. He knew that she had been waiting, with Bracebridge at her side, for at least an hour, twenty-five feet down the hall.

Dr Graham walked into the room, interrupting his reflections.

'He's safely plugged into the ICU. Ransahoff will do the surgery at 7 a.m. tomorrow. He should be levelled out by then.'

Mulder was thoughtful. 'What can he have for pain? He would be damned uncomfortable even if all he had was the pneumo aftermath – the chest tube.'

'I ordered codeine. It's all we can give with a closed-head injury,' Graham told him, then added, 'Tomorrow there'll be the residue from general anaesthesia.'

Mulder stroked his red beard and studied the floor for a few seconds. Then he drew a deep breath and turned towards the door.

'Let's go,' he said. He and Graham walked the short distance to the conference room in silence. Mulder tapped on the half-open door and walked in.

Today Bracebridge looked even more dishevelled than usual. His face resembled the pained and puzzled countenance of a sad clown. There were food stains on his jacket lapels, and his eyes looked tired. He stood up, at the same time reaching to touch Dottie Prince on the shoulder. Dottie looked directly into Mulder's eyes, then into Graham's. Her face was swollen from weeping. Some used tissues tumbled from her lap as she stood up. She clasped her hands together. The fingers of her right hand curled around her wedding ring and trembled as they rubbed it. She was a plain-featured lady with a trim figure. She had evidently rushed to the hospital in her gardening clothes; her khaki pants and white sneakers were caked with dried mud. Her nose was red. She picked a tissue out of a box beside her and blew her nose. Bracebridge wrapped an arm around her shoulders.

'What's up?' His drawl had not been altered by crisis.

Mulder cleared his throat.

'We've got him through the preliminaries. He's just been taken down to the ICU.' He kept eye contact as he spoke with both Bracebridge and Dottie Prince. He waved his arm in the direction of the sofa.

'Sit down, Mrs Prince,' he said. He turned to Graham. 'This is Doug Graham, our Neurosurgery resident. He went

361

over your husband thoroughly. We'll both tell you what we know.'

Mulder and Graham pulled up chairs close to Dottie and Bracebridge. Dottie's eyes were huge now, frightened and anxious.

'He's alive? He *is* alive? He's going to be . . .? He isn't . . .?'

'Your husband is alive. He's a very strong man. He has come through a very bad accident resulting in serious trauma. We've managed the first challenges very well. He's resting now, in the ICU so we can keep a close watch on him.'

Mulder was keeping his voice low, gentle, and reassuring. Bracebridge looked from him to Graham.

'What injuries are confirmed?'

Graham glanced at Mulder. His eyebrows lifted slightly. Mulder spoke carefully, clocking off the facts confirmed by the X-rays.

'He has a couple of broken ribs. His cervical spine looks okay. So does the thoracic spine. The main problem is a displaced lumbar fracture, L-four on five.' Mulder paused. His eyes locked with Bracebridge's for a moment. Then Bracebridge turned to Graham with a carefully blank gaze.

'Responses?' he inquired, levelly.

'A significant neuro deficit.' Graham kept his eyes on Bracebridge as he responded.

'Dr Ransahoff is doing the fusion surgery tomorrow, early,' Mulder stated. 'Decompression laminectomy and Harrington Rod placement.'

'Where's the Chairman of Neuro?' Bracebridge's tone was sharp and a bit testy. 'Where's VanderGeist?'

'Dr VanderGeist is in Colorado. He's on a rock-hunting expedition in the mountains and unavailable.'

Dottie looked around at the three men. She was anxious and confused.

'Is Dr Ransahoff . . . is he . . .?'

'Don't worry, Dottie.' Bracebridge patted her hand with his big paw. 'He's no butterfingers. It's just that Virg equals a department chairman. It's protocol.'

Mulder leaned forward and spoke directly to Dottie.

'Your husband is getting the best care this Trauma Centre can offer, Mrs Prince. We've already pulled him through the trickiest stage. I know all these medical terms are confusing. What it amounts to is that his main injury is a lower-back fracture with displaced vertebrae. The surgery is being done to stabilize that break and to stop the damage it is doing to his spinal cord, hopefully, reverse part of it.'

'When can I see him?'

'You can see him very soon. They are getting him settled into the monitors now. We want him levelled out and ready for surgery tomorrow. That's the next important part.'

Dottie watched Mulder closely as he talked, fear and hope mingled in her face. Tears welled up from time to time.

'Thank you, Dr Mulder. You're a very kind man. Thank you, both of you, for getting my husband this far. I hope – will *you* be with him in surgery?'

'Yes,' Mulder told her, smiling, 'and so will Dr Graham. I'll go up to check on him before you see him. He'll be glad to know you're here. Then you should go home and get some rest before the surgery tomorrow. You'll have an important part in his recovery.'

Dottie absorbed Mulder's words as if they were vital plasma being dripped into her own veins, registering and processing each sentence. Then her eyes filled with tears again. She bent over the tissues, and her shoulders shook.

'Virg . . . took hopeless patients . . . no one else would take.' Her voice was muffled; she was speaking between sobs. 'He wanted to heal people . . . everyone else had given up on!'

The three doctors exchanged glances. Mulder moved over to the sofa and sat beside her. He put his hand on hers and kept it there until her sobs subsided. He longed to make her some promise, offer a certainty that would make the next hours and days more bearable, but he could find no single promise within the scope of the vast battery of technology now amassed in the cause of healing Virgil Prince.

Bracebridge had risen to his feet again while Dottie was crying. He took Graham by the elbow and led him to a corner by the open window. They stood shoulder to shoulder

363

staring out at the freeway interchange and the hills.

'How bad is it going to be?' Bracebridge muttered under his breath.

Graham reached for a handkerchief and wiped perspiration from his forehead and upper lip before he continued. The conference room was not air-conditioned.

'He arrested. A tension pneumo. Mulder had the chest tube ready and took care of that problem. We got back the pressure. Lung's draining now.' He took a deep breath and went on, 'Examination showed no bulbocavernosis.' He looked at Bracebridge, whose face wore an empty expression. His lips barely formed a response.

'God. No more screwing. Life in a wheelchair.'

Graham glanced over his shoulder quickly. It was okay. Mrs Prince had her face in her hands and was weeping into the tissue too noisily to hear. He looked back at Bracebridge, who now seemed to be communing privately with the stream of freeway traffic or his own soul. He seemed to be whispering.

'"He whom God loveth" . . . ' There was a short, dry laugh. 'I thought he had enough stigmata already.'

Bracebridge turned to Graham. His eyes were alive with the gleam of irony.

'He'll live,' Bracebridge intoned audibly, and with a comforting assurance. 'We'll pull him through at any cost.'

Dottie's sobs had subsided. Mulder still sat silently beside her. Graham and Bracebridge had walked to the door. Mulder waved at them to leave. When they had closed the door behind them, he took his courage in his hands and made a very unphysicianlike statement.

'Mrs Prince . . .' He waited for her to blow her nose again. He wanted her complete attention.

'I haven't been a doctor for as long as your husband has. I'm only in my last year of residency. I can't honestly make any medical promises, although I want to very badly. But I can promise you this: if you love your husband as much as I think you do, and if you're the gutsy woman I think you are, your husband has the best chance in the world of making it.

364

Love and courage can accomplish things that medicine can't.'

He waited, feeling somewhat embarrassed. He wondered if his instincts were out of joint. Dottie sat there quietly. She didn't move or speak for a while. Then she gathered up the wet tissues and dropped them into a wastebasket. She walked over to the window. Her back was turned to him. He stood up, preparing to leave. Then she turned around and smiled at him.

'I'm glad you're my husband's doctor, because you're right, Dr Mulder. Love is a shaky promise, a shaky guarantee.' Her voice shook as she said 'guarantee.' She lifted her chin a little and went on. 'However, it's the only real weapon, the only real power I've got.'

She ran her fingers through her brown hair, arranging and smoothing it a bit. Then she walked over to him and took his hand.

'I'm ready to see my husband now,' she said.

Chapter Nine

Virgil Prince lay and watched the ICU staff move efficiently around his bed, checking the three I.V.'s and the drainage from the chest tube and a nasogastric tube which had been inserted to remove pressure from his stomach and to insure against the aspiration of vomit, should he become nauseated. He had already been subjected to the insertion of a Foley catheter by the ER nurse. He saw that he was hooked up to all the electronic monitors. He closed his eyes again. Summoning darkness had become his only shield against the assault of each new reality. In the oblivion behind his closed eyelids he could temporarily erase the tentacles of tubing which imprisoned him. But darkness stimulated the sensory nerves which held him to his pain. The side of his chest where the tube had been inserted still throbbed, differentiated only by the degree of its intensity from the aching in his arms and torso.

He opened his eyes to the room again. Nothing was dripping from the I.V.'s but plasma and the normal glucose-saline fluids. A nurse was standing by the bed. She slipped a thermometer into his mouth. The codeine they had given him before he left Emergency was beginning to dull the edges of sensation. He was terribly tired.

'Try to sleep, Doctor. We'll take care of the rest. I'll be with you until your surgery tomorrow. But before you sleep, Dr Ransahoff and Dr Mulder want to speak with you, and your wife is waiting outside. She can only stay ten minutes.'

Dottie. Well, he had been spared one confrontation and handed another. Dottie held all the cards in this one. What had he done? He had always been an expert driver. The Mark VI was as obedient as his own body. His own body! God. Even his chance thoughts presented him with galling ironies. What careless move had he made? He couldn't remember seeing a car coming at him. Oh, yes. Now he remembered. The rabbit! He had seen a rabbit standing in his path as he rounded a curve. It was small, stupid and vulnerable. The accident was a gauge of the intelligence behind the cosmos: a rabbit's life for his.

He heard heavy footsteps beside his bed and looked up to see Ransahoff and Mulder standing beside him. Mulder placed a hand on his arm. He was aware it was the first human touch he had felt since the accident, other than in the course of medical procedures. He experienced a wave of some unidentifiable emotion and the reflex of tears. Mulder spoke to him in an easy voice.

'Dr Ransahoff came over to have a look at you, Doctor. He's already checked the X-rays.'

Ransahoff was tall, lean, and muscular, with a perpetually unreadable expression. His upper lip somehow remained motionless when he spoke. He greeted Prince with a quick twitch of his lower lip, indicating a smile, and nodded his head. Prince had never been a social acquaintance of Ransahoff's. The surgeon had always avoided social contact with his colleagues. He was an enigma, but respected in his field.

'I think you understand that there has been a serious fracture of your lumbar spine,' he began. His voice was as dry and crisp as a fallen leaf, 'L-four on five displaced. I will do a decompression laminectomy with Harrington Rod placement. I am doing the surgery since Dr VanderGeist is unreachable in Colorado.'

Prince watched and listened carefully. Then he looked at Mulder.

'I can't feel my legs,' he said in a thin voice. Ransahoff cleared his throat.

'Yes. The Neuro resident has told me about the deficit. We want to do the surgery early tomorrow. We hope to reverse some, or all, of whatever damage has resulted from the displacement.'

Prince closed his eyes. Now he recalled the Neuro resident's voice. It had reported 'no bulbocavernosis' while he was in Emergency. The nasogastric tube was irritating the back of his throat. He swallowed hard before he spoke again.

'How bad can it be?' He looked at Ransahoff as he asked the question, but his eyes moved to Mulder's and held him in its meaning. He read Mulder's face as he listened to Ransahoff's reply.

'I can't make any statements on prognosis until after the surgery.' Ransahoff's mouth twitched again at the edge of his lower lip. His eyes were as blank as before. 'Well' – he tapped the manila folder he was holding on the blanket beside Prince's legs – 'I'll see you early in the morning.'

Mulder watched him leave the room, but remained at the bedside.

'Your wife is waiting outside. She is very anxious to see you,' he said.

'How bad can it be?' Prince's voice sounded stronger as he repeated the question. Mulder's face was serious. He looked directly into Prince's eyes.

'You know it can be very bad if you don't regain the neuro loss. But even if that happens, there's plenty to work with. You're strong and you're alive.'

Prince turned his face to the wall. His voice was muffled. 'A half-life,' he murmured. 'Not even that. An existence like senility.'

'Let's wait and see.' Mulder had begun to sense that a part of himself he had not yet discovered had become host to an eccentric hope. He would manage to table it until the surgery was accomplished.

'Doctor, your wife has been waiting almost two hours to see you. She got here just behind the ambulance. One of your neighbours recognized you and notified her. Do you feel up to seeing her?'

'Yes.' He closed his eyes again. Was there a possibility that surgery could reverse the nerve damage? Not without the aid of angels. He thought of Martin Kiley. Kiley's angel must have lifted him out of his bed to spare him the surgery. A hope began to kindle around the edges of his mind. There was a possibility he could die in Surgery. Ransahoff was going to perform a tricky operation. He felt weak from the short exchange with the surgeons, and dread at facing Dottie. The speeches he had rehearsed, the strategy he had evolved, the negotiations he had been travelling towards had all been cancelled. There was nothing left to negotiate. Nothing to be given and nothing to take away.

He heard a sound beside the bed and felt a hand brush across his hair.

'Virg – oh, Virg!' It was Dottie. She kissed him on the forehead, on his closed eyelids. He did not move or speak.

'Shh. Don't say anything. You don't need to talk. I'll just sit here and hold your hand.' She sat on a chair beside the bed and slipped her hand into his. Everything was quiet. There was only the sound of the pumps and monitors. After a little bit he felt her cheek laid against his hand. A strand of her hair caught in his fingers. He moved his hands slightly, comforted by the silky texture sliding along his skin, eased by the discovery of a touch that did not carry pain. He heard

368

Dottie's voice whispering near his ear.

'I know you're going to be all right, Virg. I know you are. If God hadn't needed you for something important, He wouldn't have sent Larry Goldsmith along the back beach road in time to get help for you. God couldn't *spare you*, Virg. You're going to be all right.'

Her voice faded as the effect of the codeine and his own exhaustion took him into sleep. He dreamed of being led by long strands of silken thread through the canyons of an alien country he had been ordered to explore.

Chapter Ten

Neither Stella nor Father Franciscus had expected Victor to take his own life. At first, Franciscus speculated that when he had regained consciousness and found himself in the ward, he had chosen death rather than the entrapment he hated. But the notes he had left on the kitchen table disproved that theory. Their contents made it perfectly obvious that Victor had decided not to wait until he was too debilitated to act. The note he addressed to Franciscus explained that he feared, ultimately, the cancer would affect his ability to reason as well as act; that he would end his days as a grotesque burden on Stella, short-circuiting all she had accomplished in her work.

Both the presence of Franciscus and the existence of the notes, particularly the one he had addressed to her, had eased Stella through the shock of Victor's loss. The funeral had been a small one, but Franciscus thought of his memorial talk about Victor as one of his best. For one thing, Victor had died leaving no loose ends. Like Martin, he had come full circle. He had left his own living memorials. The priest had used that theme as he talked to the group which had gathered in the smallest parlour of the Taggenhorst Funeral Home.

Present to pay tribute to Victor were Stella's friends Arline and Stan. They sat on either side of her in the first row. Behind them were Mary, Hugh, and a couple of nurses who had taken care of Vic during his first incarceration on the Cancer Unit. After the service, they tearfully told Franciscus of Victor's great spirit. They said he had flung water pitchers and urinals at them and that they would always remember him. The absence of Christie, as a noticeable void, expressed almost as much as her presence might have. No one knew where to reach her. Everyone knew she would return. In the row behind Hugh and the nurses sat Josh with his mother, Martin's first wife. Just as the ceremony started, a tall figure entered the room and slid into a seat in the back row. Franciscus was startled to recognize Dr Lindsay, the resident he had seen with Virgil Prince at the start of Victor's odyssey. Lindsay blew his nose frequently during the service and disappeared as soon as it ended, without speaking to anyone.

After the services, Franciscus went back to the house to chat with Stella. She made iced tea and they took their drinks out into the yard.

'He loved this yard,' Stella said, 'especially the flowers.'

'And he planted them for *you*,' Franciscus reminded her. Stella responded with a remark she had made several times before the funeral.

'I don't think what Victor did was an angry act,' she said. There were still threads of concern in her tone. Franciscus nodded in agreement, listening attentively as she continued. 'I've heard that people always commit suicide to punish someone, but I don't think Vic was trying to punish anybody. He didn't have any more hate left in him. Not for a long time.' She sat looking up into the maple leaves. 'You know, in the time when Vic was silent and brooded around, well, sometimes he was mean and he threw things – before he got taken to Broadcliff. I think it was *himself* he hated,

Father. Something made him stop hating himself.' She sighed, relaxed back in her chair and wiped some tears from her eyes.

Franciscus smiled. 'You're right, Stella,' he answered.

Now Stella looked a little anxious. She watched the priest's face as she spoke.

'Vic never made a formal confession of faith,' she said. 'That worries me.'

Franciscus returned her gaze. His eyes were serious. He sat for a while with his hand under his chin, apparently trying to phrase his thoughts into an adequate answer. When he spoke, the certainty in his voice reassured her.

'I think Victor made a confession of faith when he asked me to pray for him, when he hoped for time to rebuild his life with you.' Franciscus paused, watching relief soften Stella's face. 'And he made a deep confession of faith when he helped Josh understand that he and his father needed each other.'

Stella dabbed at her eyes again. 'Josh Kiley even called me – after you let him know about Vic.'

Franciscus continued: 'The two Beatitudes that will always bring Vic to my mind are "Blessed are the merciful for they shall obtain mercy" and "Blessed are the peacemakers for they shall be called sons of God." I'm sure, Stella, Vic would qualify for a place in His house.'

Stella didn't speak for a while. Her glance moved around the yard and rested on the grape arbour.

'We'll have a lot of jelly this year. I'm going to take some to my friends at the plant. Stan says he might make some wine from the grapes, too.' Her voice wavered slightly, but she controlled it and went on. 'Last year the grapes rotted on the ground, but Victor mended *everything*. He mended the arbour too.'

Franciscus looked at the arbour, sharing her pleasure.

'I'm not afraid to be alone,' Stella went on. 'It's like part of Vic is still here, and I've got Stan and Arline next door. And I'm doing good at my job.' She smiled proudly. 'I've been promoted.'

'A lot of things have changed,' Franciscus answered

warmly. He saw she had more to say. She was making a count of all her blessings.

'I memorized part of the note Vic left me. Some women whose men even *married* them and gave them kids never got a farewell note like Vic left me.' Stella narrowed her eyes and looked at a place beyond the top of the priest's head and recited: ' "You gave me so much, Stella, so much patience and devotion. You were more loyal than a lot of wives. I consider you *were* my wife. You gave me your pride in me and your love. . . ." ' Her voice began to break now and she finished in a whisper. ' " . . . So I don't want you having to watch me wind down like a broken clock, to have to leave your job to nurse me. We had good days." '

As she finished the quote, Stella's voice grew stronger. 'I got a lot to be proud of, Father.'

Franciscus reached for her hand and pressed it; then he rose from his chair. Stella had one more thing to communicate. She looked up into his eyes.

'Father, I'm worried about how we can let Christie know about Vic. He worried about her, and he left her a note too. Do you expect to be seeing her?'

Franciscus didn't answer for a moment.

'I hope when she gets back we'll . . . hear from her. Mary might see her. It seems Mary and her husband have a cottage up somewhere near where Christie . . . was going.'

Stella sensed that the priest was uncertain about more than Christie's geographical whereabouts. She reached into her pocket and handed him a white envelope.

'Would you give this to Mary next time you see her at the hospital?' She frowned. 'Christie was like a favourite niece to us. I know she really loved Vic. I hope she's all right.'

Franciscus slipped the envelope into his breast pocket. 'I hope she's all right too,' he replied.

They pressed each other's hands, and she stood watching him walk out to the alley and get into his car. He waved to her as the car started.

She heard Arline's voice calling to her from the next yard. Arline and Stan had asked her over for supper. She looked around her at the late-summer lushness of her small garden. The roses were heavy with blooms and with new buds. They were a warm pink, and she had always kept a bouquet of them on the kitchen table for Victor to smell and look at. The roses had graced all their meals since June. She walked to the shed and retrieved her clippers. The roses would brighten Arline's table tonight. She would find out how to root new shoots. An exciting idea struck her. Maybe she could root enough shoots to give small bushes to all the people Victor had loved. She smiled to herself as she gathered her roses, and she hummed an old song.

Chapter Eleven

August was a hell of a month for a trip to Chicago, Brenda had told herself more than once. But the timing of her trip had been built around an issue far more critical than avoiding a heat wave. What she hoped to accomplish was well worth the discomfort of big-city humidity. Besides, all the places where she spent time were air-conditioned. Her room at the Drake was elegant, understated, and cool. The service was superb. They knew her there. Chicago had been her home town for a few years after she married Frank Stone. Now whenever she went back to visit as Mrs Stone, whether with her husband or not, she made the Drake her headquarters.

She had worked out a schedule of diversions to take her easily through the two weeks of self-imposed exile. She liked to breakfast alone, either in her room or at Les Oeufs, which was nearby. She spent her mornings walking on the Boulevard, shopping, or having her hair done, and she lunched with friends.

One of her favourite friends, Dana, had a penthouse above

the North Shore Drive. Brenda had spent the best two days of the week with her. She preferred the atmosphere of the city, even in summer, to the poshest suburban setup. Suburban wives always managed to be dreary.

Dana was the perfect female friend, Brenda had concluded. She was sophisticated and had a quick intelligence. She moved in eclectic circles. All her friends were wealthy, or interestingly eccentric, or both.

The eighth night of her stay in Chicago, Dana dropped Brenda off at the front entrance of the Drake following an evening of dining, jazz, and exchanged confidences. She leaned over in the cab and kissed Brenda's cheek.

'Bring him over soon, darling; he sounds delicious!'

'Don't forget to mention him to your Department Chairman friend,' Brenda reminded her. She had just hatched the idea of prying Virgil loose from the limitations of Brandenburg and ensconcing him in the more interesting freedoms of Chicago.

Brenda swung away from the cab, shook her long hair from her face, and headed through the revolving doors. She mounted the red-carpeted staircase with easy strides, pleasantly aware of heads turning in her direction. She felt the crossfire of male glances as her heels clicked along the terrazzo floor of the lobby. She paused a moment at the elevators and then decided to drop by the small bar off the lobby for a nightcap.

She sat listening to the music from the piano bar. The pianist was singing an old popular song and doing some kind of medley with the piano based on the melody. It was 'My Reverie.' The waiter came with her drink. He was friendly, but unobtrusive. She could come into this bar at any hour and never worry about the intrusion of attempted pickups. The bartenders knew her as a rich attorney's wife, and so did the waiters. No one would dare to approach her.

She allowed herself to daydream a bit. This was the eighth day of her separation from Virg. She knew he was as frustrated as she was. Undoubtedly, much more so. He had been forced to remain in the surroundings where they had been together. She had the advantage of change. Even more crucial, he was tasting the deprivation of continuing his work without her presence and support.

She let herself imagine their reunion. The music lent itself to the evocation of sexual images. Her greatest delight was the strength of his responses after a day of subtle manipulation during which he could not touch her. He was as strong as a bull and as responsive to nuances as an artist. God – she wondered if he had confronted Dottie about the divorce yet. What if he could not bring himself to? ... No. That was unthinkable. She would not even let the shadow of the idea take hold in her mind. He had responded perfectly to all her moves concerning him.

She remembered suddenly that her visit with her friend Dana had taken her away from the hotel all day. It was possible that he had already talked to Dottie and had tried to reach her. If he had, the message light on her phone would be flashing. She signalled the waiter and signed her bill.

When she opened the door to the coolness and order of her room, the small red light on the base of the telephone indicated a message. Brenda smiled to herself. It was Virg. He had been on her mind all day.

She walked over to the window and opened it to feel the night air and the distant noises of the traffic. Her room was near the top floor, and the buildings of the city glittered around her like a display of precious jewels on black velvet. Along the length of the Boulevard and the Drive, headlights moved like tiny chains of diamonds. She took a deep breath and stretched, undoing the small buttons on her silk dress and letting it slip to the floor. She threw it over a chair and kicked off her high-heeled sandals. The maid always turned down the bed and left ice in the thermal bucket. She stretched out on the sheets in her lace bra and panties and dialled the operator. A breeze from the lake caressed her warm body.

'Yes. This is Mrs Stone. I believe I have a message.' She waited, smiling to herself while the operator checked the records. Finally her voice came back on the phone.

'Yes, Mrs Stone. You have a message to call a Miss Francine Lindemueller at Broadcliff Hospital.'

Brenda felt a sharp twinge of annoyance as the operator read off the number of Broadcliff and Francine's home number.

'She said it was very important you call as soon as possible. She has left three messages today.'

'Thank you.' Brenda mumbled an obscenity under her breath. It was just like Francine to bother her in Chicago with some idiotic item of news or gossip she fancied as important. She had a mini-FBI chain of information. In some ways it made her indispensable. In other ways it made her an impossible nag. Francine was seldom able to discern what was vital information and what was peripheral gossip.

'Were there any other messages?' Brenda found it hard to accept that Virgil had not tried to reach her.

'No,' said the operator, 'that's all.'

Brenda hung up the phone and lay looking at it with frustrated annoyance. Now her mood made her too restless to sleep. She might as well call Francine at home. She'd probably wake her up, but she deserved it.

She dialled the long-distance operator and placed the call. She reached for her cigarettes on the nightstand and lit one, taking deep drags and exhaling slowly, listening as the phone buzzed. On the fourth ring she heard a click and Francine's voice saying 'Hello.' Its high-pitched, nasal quality was missing, and it sounded rather faint. At first she thought she had got a wrong number.

'Francine? Is that you? This is Brenda.'

'Brenda?' Now the familiar squeak – or was it a whine? – had crept back into her voice. 'Brenda?' she repeated. The voice was an octave higher.

'Yes. What in the world is it? It's nearly 2 a.m.'

'Oh, Brenda.' The voice dropped again to a strange new key. 'Brenda ... are ... you alone? I mean, are you in bed? Or sitting down ... ? Brenda, I have terrible news. I don't know how to tell you ... I called three times.'

'Spit it out, Francine.' Brenda's annoyance was turning

into anger, but she tried to control her voice. 'If you've called three times, you must know what you have to say.'

'Brenda, it's Virgil – I mean Dr Prince.' Brenda heard Francine's voice begin to waver now. She wondered why Virg would give Francine a message to pass on. Francine was gaining control of her voice again. She was nothing if not dramatic, Brenda reminded herself.

'Dr Prince ... Brenda, he's had an accident – a *terrible* accident. He's ... he's in the ICU now.' She was speaking more quickly and had stopped stuttering. 'He's scheduled for *surgery*. It's early tomorrow morning. I knew ... '

Brenda's mind had cut off at the term 'ICU.' She felt as if she had turned on her car radio and got an announcement, an ultimatum, broadcast from one of the planets. She looked at the cigarette in her hand and could not feel her fingers holding it. Someone else's hand seemed to hold the phone. She heard her voice speaking. It seemed to be a long way off.

'Accident?'

'A car accident, Brenda. A bad one. They won't know a lot till after surgery. I've been asking around. I talked to the head nurse and overheard the Surgery resident, and I read the chart. I'll pick you up at the airport.' There was a pause. The sound of Francine's voice rattling on began to give Brenda a sense of her self again, and the time and the place. Now there was a silence at the other end of the line. The silence alerted Brenda.

'Francine ... ' She thought of a question. 'Have you seen him?'

'Yes, in the ICU when they brought him in.'

'Was he ... conscious?' Brenda lifted the hand that held the cigarette. It was hurting. The fire had burned it. She stubbed the cigarette out.

'Yes.'

'I'll ... I'm going to be leaving, Francine ... ' Brenda paused. Her eyes roamed around the bed, fastening on objects to connect her to herself. She saw the suitcase, then the bottle of Cabochard on the dressing table. Next to it was a leather toilette case Virg had given her for her birthday.

'When?' Francine asked. 'I'll meet the plane.' She paused a moment. 'Are you going . . . *home*?'

There was a silence. Home. Brenda's mind had made the round trip back from bedlam.

'Of course,' she told Francine. 'You don't need to meet me at the airport. I'll take a cab. Just hang in there. Find out everything you can. I'll be in tomorrow morning, whatever time I can get a flight.'

'Okay, Brenda. I'll keep my eyes open. Take care!'

Brenda put the phone back on its cradle and lit another cigarette. She took deep drags and watched the panorama of the night city until she could feel herself getting back together. She must keep cool. She still had to get all the facts. Francine said he was conscious. A good sign. She needed to call for a reservation, and she needed a decent rest before she appeared at the hospital. She would need all her wits about her there. Bracebridge would tell her everything. A sudden thought dealt her a below-the-belt blow. Dottie Prince, who had always been in the dim background of hospital affairs, would now be in prime evidence. Well, she would handle that as it presented itself. The plane reservation was number one on her agenda.

She phoned the airline. The only available space on a flight to Brandenburg was at 1.30 p.m. Then she walked over to the dressing table. She opened the toilette case and took out a small bottle of sleeping pills. Brenda knew herself well enough to realize that she must turn off her mind for a while, or her imagination would trip her up. She needed facts to work with.

She swallowed the capsule and washed it down with water. She carefully removed her makeup. There was plenty of time to pack in the morning. She left a message with the operator to wake her at eight. Then she stretched out between the sheets to wait for sleep.

Chapter Twelve

Lance and Christie were at the dunes. The morning after their arrival, she awoke to the sound of waves breaking against the rocks and the voices of gulls. She turned her head on the pillow and saw Lance looking at her. He watched her silently for a few moments, then quickly arched his body above her. His mouth moved over her face. She had begun to relate her first awareness of morning with the hard strength of Lance's body and the searching of his lips.

Up until last week, his impact on her had been incomplete. But now the vestiges of her old life had been consumed in a totally new environment. All her duties were gone. She moved within the freedom – and the limits – of an entirely sensual world of sun and wind, rain and night, water and sky. Nothing had come with her from the old life but the meanings embodied in her pieces of driftwood: the porpoise, the gull, and the fish which she had given to Franciscus.

Christie buried the knowledge of Lance's wife and his other life – which he still inhabited – together with her sense of sin, among the realites of her past. But even when she was in Lance's arms, shaken with the sensations his strength and subtlety evoked, an inner knowledge told her she existed in some strange corridor, some anteroom of life. The intensity of her experience contained a warning. A small pocket of fear waited in a corner of her mind.

Meanwhile, she observed and wondered at the new facets of Lance's personality revealed by their extended time together. His abrupt changes of mood were sometimes delightful, sometimes puzzling or shocking, but the chemistry of their mutual attraction continued to delight her. As the days passed, he became slightly less meditative and concentrated in his manner towards her. Occasionally he would spring out of bed while she was still foggy and limp from their lovemaking and sit naked at a table by the window, suddenly gripped by an idea for solving some problem at the foundry. She would lie in bed and watch him drawing diagrams, staring out at the lake with narrowed eyes and printing words on the page in his childish, uneven lettering. He made love, almost always, in the same way he worked, with a devoted intensity, almost as if he were engaged in a holy task. Yet occasionally he could be crude and almost savage.

This morning he had been tender, watching her with his eyes, taking time as they made love. Afterwards he had jumped out of bed and gone to his papers on the table again. Christie lay and watched him as he worked. The sun shone through the leaves of an oak outside the window and made shadow patterns across his face. His hair had fallen over his forehead. From time to time he glanced out the window, then returned to his paper pad and drew furiously. After about fifteen minutes, he stood up and threw down the pen. He approached the bed, feigning a frown.

'Why aren't you in the shower? Don't you see the sun? You're going to turn into an indolent kept woman if I don't become a drill sergeant!' He jumped on the bed and imitated a bear, crawling around her, pawing, biting, and nuzzling until she was weak with laughter and screamed for him to stop. He scooped her up in his arms and carried her out to the deck.

'Put me down! I'm naked! Someone could be on the beach!' Christie protested. He stood at the edge of the stairs, holding her so that she faced the shoreline.

'Look at all of them down there! The swans are white with shock! Look at those gulls circling to stare at you! They're screaming, "Horrors! Christie is naked as a jaybird, and so is Lance!" They may evict us from the beach club!' He kissed her gently and put her down. He smacked her on the behind.

'Hurry and get into the shower. We'll have breakfast on the deck and hike to the rockfall.'

All week Lance had been telling Christie about some rock caves down the shoreline near a spill of large boulders. He remembered it from past summers when he had gone exploring. This area of the lake was more remote and rugged than the beach where Mary lived, near Pacifica. Their first days had been spent walking along the shore looking for rocks and driftwood and climbing into the dunes near the cottage. They always carried a pack with them containing a blanket and food. Some evenings they had stayed at the cottage, watching the sunset or the formation of a storm, making love beside a bonfire.

Lance was a great storyteller. He told outrageous tales, half mythology and half slapstick comedy. Christie laughed at Lance's stories, curled between his legs, wrapped in a blanket and watching flames leaping into the cool night air. A few nights Lance had taken her into some of the nearby resort towns where there were good restaurants and entertainment. They would sit at small corner tables, holding hands, touching bodies. She would watch Lance's face, a mask of devotion, his eyes closed, his head swaying to the beat of some jazz combo. She was amused at the way he drank. He cupped his drink in both hands and sipped with a kind of reverent contemplation. His face looked like the face of a priest drinking from a sacred cup. Lance the profane. His God, she decided, was Dionysus.

She ran into the bathroom and showered quickly. She put on lipstick, brushed her hair, and tied it back with a band. She pulled on her bikini and stood looking at herself in the mirror, intensely aware of her body. She could feel the tautness of every muscle, yet she was relaxed. She was getting very tanned. Her flesh was all close to the bone.

She heard Lance talking on the phone again. She could tell by his tone that it must be a client. The aroma of fresh coffee drifted through the house, and the smell of bacon frying. Lance was a great cook.

Christie walked into the living room and heard the end of the phone conversation.

'Great!' Lance was saying. 'The weather's super here. We'll have a ball! Tell the girls we even have nightlife.' There was a pause. 'See you Friday!' He put down the phone and grinned at Christie.

'Who's coming?' she asked.

'This guy is a buddy of mine from Chicago. I try to combine business with pleasure when I can. I've been trying to figure out a design for a casting he wants. I worked it out this morning.' He stood up and walked over to Christie, put his hands on her shoulders, and looked into her eyes.

'See, you're good for me, Christie. I never work better than after we make love!' He snapped the elastic of her bikini pants and walked towards the kitchen. 'I'm starved': he announced it in a mild yell. 'Let's get the food on the table.'

They carried the food onto the deck and sat sipping coffee and eating, watching the activities of the water birds. Lance always ate with his face close to his plate, and with gusto. He devoured a forkful of eggs.

'These people aren't your type. They're not intellectuals, but they're . . . sophisticated, and rich. It's time you had some exposure to the real world. Life is to live. You need more experience.' He munched on a strip of bacon and regarded Christie objectively and critically. 'Look at you. You're beginning to look like a red-blooded woman. Before we leave here you're going to look like an Indian.' He got up and kissed her on the cheekbones, then sat down and wiped his toast around in the egg yolk.

'Eat your eggs,' he told her. 'You need stamina. The rockfall is over two hundred feet high.'

Christie cut up her egg and bit into a piece of bacon. He was right. Her life had been isolated, stiflingly narrow. It was such a relief to simply laugh, and to feel pleasure; to live in the sunlight and play like a child, or an animal. She thought of Victor and Renée. The time of their good days in the West must have been like this.

Lance got up and went into the kitchen for more coffee.

382

She sat quietly for a few minutes. The gulls were close now. They shadowed the deck with their wings. God, but they were beautiful! Two passed slowly and low over the deck. She looked up at them, and suddenly, with complete irrationality, tears threatened. Why? Why, in this strange new happiness, could two gulls bring her to tears? She heard Lance moving around the house. A cold draught, emanating from nowhere, made her shudder. Something within her still existed alone in patient exile outside this experience with Lance.

Sometimes during these long, golden days at the lake she had tried to bring that part of her self out of its banishment and let it share her life. When she tried, she sensed that familiar withdrawal in Lance. She knew now that all that was inward, that hinted of darkness, was off limits in her life with Lance.

One evening as they lay beside a bonfire, listening to the sound of waves, she had tried to tell him about her driftwood and Father Franciscus. She had described the fish and why she had given it to the priest. He had changed the subject, and finally slept.

Lance's voice brought her back from her musing. He was watching her closely.

'Finish your breakfast, Christie. What's the matter? You look like you're in a trance.'

'Nothing. I was just thinking.' She broke a piece of toast into bite-sized pieces. Lance watched her for a few moments, then fell back in his chair and laughed. Now he leaned forward, touching her hand.

'I was just thinking too. You eat like a cat. You walk like a cat. You sleep like a cat. Did anyone ever say that before?'

Christie looked at him curiously.

'A cat?'

He nodded. She went back to toying with her toast and bacon. They were both silent. His eyes watched her. She took a sip of coffee and cleared her throat.

'Do you think a sin . . . doing something evil . . . could ever be – well, necessary? A necessary process in finding God?'

383

She looked at him. Her eyes gazed directly at him, waiting for some indication he had understood the question.

Lance moved his shoulders as if he were shrugging off a shirt that constricted him. He smiled slightly.

'God again? Look, Christie, there are only two sins in my book: not taking advantage of everything in life while you're alive, and taking someone's life when it isn't in self-defence.'

Christie dropped her eyes and looked away, down at the circling birds. Lance continued.

'I think if something makes you feel good it's not bad. If God exists, He – It – is a force. Maybe it brought me out for a climb in the same dune you were sleeping on.'

'Do you know what an avatar is?' Christie asked. 'It's a messenger of God. Blue dragonflies are avatars.' She leaned forward and touched Lance. 'Sometimes I think spiders and grasshoppers are, and that you are.'

Lance threw back his head and laughed.

'Jesus! Now I know why I'm in love with you. No one ever compared me to a dragonfly or a grasshopper. Maybe a roach – the spoilsports.' He stood up and stretched his arms above his head, flexing his shoulder muscles and cracking his knuckles. He was at the edge of the deck looking out on the water. 'You're nuts. You know that, Christie?'

Christie nodded absently. She watched a gull that had floated down again, low, over the deck.

'Let's get going,' he told her briskly. 'We should climb to the top of the rockfall by noon. We'll have lunch down by the grotto.'

Christie began to clear the table. He followed her into the kitchen, grabbed her by the shoulders, and forced her to look at him.

'Look, Christie,' he began, 'talking about God depresses me. Get *off* it, okay?'

Christie nodded her head and looked away. She felt an intense and sudden loneliness. Lance kissed her hard on the mouth.

'You got a cute ass,' he said. He slammed through the doorway and went to the closet to get his knapsack. The blanket was already stuffed inside. He put the wine beside it. As he got the gear together, he whistled a theme from Mendez: 'Slow, Hot Wind.'

Chapter Thirteen

Virgil Prince's first awareness as he emerged from anaesthesia was the presence of a nurse who was doing something in the area of his groin. Of course, he thought: the Foley. Its plastic bag had to be emptied. The Foley had come to symbolize his helplessness. He detested the idea of strange women dealing familiarly with parts of his body he associated with power and sexual intimacy. The irony of this reaction assaulted his mind like a shock wave. He could not feel her moving the catheter. He still could not feel anything below his waist.

The nurse smiled at him and spoke brightly.

'You're awake, Doctor! Well, the surgery's over. You came through it just fine!' She lifted his penis and adjusted the Foley. He still felt nothing. The damned bladder catheter was a trifle, an insult almost microscopic in comparison with the vast wasteland of shame and impotence that lay ahead. He looked around his bed. He was hooked up to all the monitors. The I.V.'s were dripping their fluids into him: life-giving fluids. He could feel the pain of the chest tube. It was still draining reddish-yellow liquid into the bottle.

A wave of drowsiness swept over him, and he drifted into sleep again. He awoke on and off during the day – or was it night? – and saw the faces of Mulder and Dottie. He heard the name 'Dr Graham' and 'Neuro resident.' He heard voices talking. Once he woke with his head fairly clear. No one was in the room. He heard only the sucking, humming, and pulsing noises of the monitors and pumps. The I.V.'s still contained only blood and a glucose-saline solution. If only he had needed a potentially lethal drug. He might have managed the reach to the valve and released a fatal rush before they could check on him.

It was a futile thought. They would even dole out the codeine, knowing they could not dare to risk more medication with the neuro situation unstable. He thought of pulling out his tubes, but knew it would be an idle gesture, no more than a nuisance.

In an intensive-care unit where the care came through plastic tubing and electronic transistors, he lay with the companionship of monitors. He felt a terrible sense that he had become unreal; that life lay within the equipment that surrounded him, and that he himself was only some kind of function – a valve that fitted into the mechanism and kept it working. He shuddered before the suspicion that now his whole identity would be passive; a conduit within the system of his own intensive care.

Vendetti's face, in death, appeared behind his closed eyes, so absolutely washed of tension it was young again. The smile mocked him. Even Vendetti, the epitome of power-lessness, his body eaten away from within, had pulled off a suicide that would do credit to a healthy surgeon. Now he, who could summon every force the hospital boasted, could not effect his own demise.

When the face of Victor Vendetti faded, other images invaded the room. Sometimes he saw forgotten patients who had torn tubes from their veins. The memory of Julius Hoffman and the long, stoic silence through which he had ushered himself into his own death came and brooded over Prince's bed like a sorrowful presence. If it was truly a spectre, it did not accuse him. It offered him companionship. It shared his suffering. Prince saw with painful clarity that only the spirits of men who had known imprisonment like his own could comfort him. Those who had been bonded to him by his power over their helplessness would become part of himself, an immutable structure within his own spirit.

Suddenly the hot necessity to rebel tensed the muscles of

his arms and pounded through his head, but he instantly fell limp against the pillows. He could not resort to violence. They would carefully reinsert any tubes he pulled out. They would pity his loss of control, and it would anger and annoy them. He saw the nurses, or his own physician, making entries in his chart. *'Paranoia,'* they would write, or *'Schizophrenic incident.'*

Richard Mulder had sent Dottie Prince home to rest after the long vigil of the surgery. During the preceding night he had awakened a couple of times and been struck with the irony of his own personal schedule. He had finished his month on the Cancer Unit and been transferred to the Emergency Room just a few days before Prince's accident. He had been glad to be done with the suffering and futility proliferating there. It was frustrating in direct ratio to his inability to affect or change the system. He could only rejoice that Martin Kiley had escaped before the ordeal of a useless surgery, an escape that would have done credit to Houdini himself.

Mulder still slipped up to the Unit once a day to see Joan Bentley, the last of the living with whom he had dealt closely. Though she had been in a coma for days, Mulder always touched her and spoke to her softly in case she could feel or hear. Mulder often found Franciscus sitting quietly beside the bed, Joan's hand in his. He guessed the family had been unable to cope with the long last stages of her illness.

His last days of duty on the Unit had been a struggle with mounting anger. There were the families some of the attending physicians took great pains to avoid. And there were several patients who had been admitted by Virgil Prince for diagnostic tests and who had lain there for days with no orders being given for them and no sign of Prince. When he did appear on the Unit, he seemed totally distracted, wrote a few orders in some charts and disregarded the others. It had been a relief to end his tour of duty there and feel he was moving on to more solvable problems.

Now fate had dealt him the problem of Prince himself. It was one of the worst cases he had ever faced. If there was a single man in his experience who was least constituted to cope with life as a paraplegic, it was Virgil Prince. Everything, including postsurgical examinations, pointed to the fact that he would have permanent nerve damage. Barring unforeseen changes, not only would Prince never walk again, but he would never function sexually. From all he had seen of Prince's wife, he would lay heavy bets on her hanging in there and contributing all she could to help him master his plight. But there was the other factor in the equation. The word around Broadcliff was that Brenda was off on a vacation. No one knew when she would be back. In the brief moments when Mulder had time to think about the situation, he anticipated her return with dread and an undeniable curiosity. Brenda was unaccustomed to being thwarted, least of all by blind acts of destiny.

It was almost five o'clock on the afternoon following Virgil Prince's surgery. Mulder was grabbing a sandwich in the doctors' dining room. He had been in to check on Prince twice since he had returned from Surgery. Prince had appeared groggy each time. This was fortunate. The more Prince could drowse through the aftereffects of surgery, the less pain he would have to suffer. They had to continue to be circumspect with any medications that could alter neuro response.

Mulder finished his coffee and walked down the ground-floor corridor to the elevators, preoccupied with his knowledge of Prince's prognosis. It would be only a couple of hours before Prince himself was sufficiently oriented to begin asking questions. He was approaching the bank of elevators when a vaguely familiar scent, alien to the hospital potpourri of floor wax, faeces, and disinfectant, alerted his attention. He glanced behind him and saw a white figure moving swiftly in the direction of the executive lounge. The stride and the twitch of the buttocks confirmed Brenda as the scent bearer.

Christ. She must have just arrived. He wondered if she'd

been to the Unit yet. Well, he wouldn't be the one to face her. Her *modus operandi* was to go to the top first. She'd be seeing Ransahoff, or Bracebridge, or both. Now he heard a muffled squeal behind him.

'Brenda!' a voice called. He turned and looked again. Francine Lindemueller was trotting heavily along the composition floor, her crepe soles squeaking like hysterical mice. Brenda wheeled around and waited for her to catch up.

Well, maybe she was going to the bottom first this time, he thought. Francine was an ICU nurse and had ears all over the hospital. She could give Brenda Prince's chart information and whatever private comment had come straight from the mouths of every surgeon and resident who had examined him.

Brenda turned and continued to the executive lounge with Francine just behind her. She opened the carved door and swished into the air-conditioned comfort of Broadcliff's VIP room.

'Shut the door,' she told Francine. She sat down on the larger of the two leather sofas and tossed her shoulder bag on the floor beside her. She waved to one of the upholstered swivel chairs that were grouped around a nearby table.

'Sit down,' she said. Francine pulled up the chair and dropped into it with a groan.

'I came down as soon as I could. I've only got ten minutes,' she said. Her round face was quivering. Her brown eyes were anxious and excited.

'That's okay,' Brenda answered. She pulled a pack of cigarettes from her uniform pocket and lit one. 'Stan Bracebridge is meeting me here in a few minutes. I want to see him alone. Start talking and tell me what you know.'

'Well' – Francine leaned back in the chair, and the smooth contours of her face drew into a frown – 'he's out of Surgery, and I haven't seen any Surgery reports yet, of course, but I did hear some conversation between Dr Graham and Dr Mulder, and – '

'Mulder?' Brenda spat out the name, interrupting Francine's recitation.

'Dr Mulder was on ER duty when they brought Dr Prince in. He was the Trauma resident.'

'Who did the surgery? Have you seen the chart?'

Francine held up her fingers and methodically counted off the facts she knew.

'Number one: I've seen the chart. Number two: Dr Ransahoff did the surgery on him. Number three: He had an LS fracture with four-five displaced vertebrae. The surgeon wrote on the chart, *"Decompression laminectomy and Harrington Rod placement".*'

'Ransahoff?' Brenda was frowning and appeared to be calculating something. 'Why Ransahoff? VanderGeist is the Department Chairman.'

'I heard someone say he was on vacation.'

A look of intense annoyance flickered over Brenda's face. Then she returned to business.

'What nurse has been with him? Have you talked with her?'

'Esther Burroughs. You know how closemouthed she is. She won't talk to anyone about patients unless it's necessary to treatment. But Brenda, I read some things in the chart that Dr Graham wrote.' Francine had been leaning towards Brenda, her face eager and animated; now a slightly pained expression returned to her features.

'Yes?' Brenda said impatiently. 'Hurry on with it. I want you to be gone when Stan gets here.'

'Well, Brenda, Dr Prince still has no feeling below his waist, and Dr Graham said "no bulbocavernosis." I heard him and Dr Ransahoff discussing that as if it were – well, important, and so I looked it up.' Francine paused. She sighed, and her nose sucked into a pinched expression. She folded her hands in her lap and looked down at them with her eyebrows arched, as if she were praying.

'For God's sake, Francine, get to the bottom line.' Brenda looked at her watch. This had already taken ten minutes. She wanted to be alone when Stan Bracebridge arrived in the

VIP lounge. He wouldn't be comfortable discussing Virg in front of Francine. Besides, there was psychological advantage finding her here alone, before she even saw Virgil.

'Well, Brenda, I looked it up in my medical dictionary, and it has to do with the sheath of the penis – the term, that is.'

'Term?' Brenda snapped.

'Bulbocavernosis – what he hasn't got. Well, I've been listening and keeping my eyes open, and just before I came down here I saw Dr Ransahoff go into the ICU conference room with Dr Bracebridge, and I stood around the corner listening. They didn't close the door.' Francine's voice was getting excited, and she spoke fast. 'Well, I heard Dr Ransahoff say, "Dr Prince still has neuro deficit below the waist, and there is no bulbocavernosis".' She took a deep breath and paused. Brenda closed her eyes and counted silently to ten. Francine leaned forward again. Now her face was smooth and pure, almost transfixed, with pity.

Brenda was confused. She had never before seen pity, bold and unconcealed, on the face of someone who looked at her.

'Brenda, I'll never forget the sound of Dr Bracebridge's voice. I couldn't see his face, being I was behind the wall. He said, "Poor Virg. Poor son-of-a-bitch. He'll never get it up again".'

Brenda sat absolutely motionless for so long that Francine began to wonder if someone could faint with their eyes open. Then she saw a tiny muscle at the corner of her lips begin to twitch. My God. Brenda had tears in her eyes! Brenda was going to cry. Brenda, who had always been Miss Invincible, even Miss Terrible. She was going to melt like a snowflake and begin to cry. Francine stood up and moved to take her in her arms. She could finally give Brenda something she didn't have. She could give her comfort.

A sharp, stinging blow caught her between the left eye and the chin. The room reeled. She heard Brenda's voice, low and venomous.

'Get out!'

Francine staggered backward and leaned against the wall.

391

'*Get out!*'

Brenda must be going mad with grief. Francine put her hand to her cheek to see if it was bleeding. It was only very hot.

She looked at Brenda closely and was truly frightened. The tears had disappeared. Her face was a murderous mask. There was no grief in Brenda to comfort. All Francine could see was rage and hate. The friend she had admired and tried to emulate, had spied for and even lied for, detested her.

Francine shrank back against the wall, her face the colour of paste. She felt behind her for the door. Suddenly she knew she was going to throw up. Her hand reached the knob, and as she turned it, the door jerked out of her hand and she walked into the pale beige bulk of Standford Bracebridge. She quickly clapped her hand over her mouth.

'Excuse me,' she muttered. She heard the door close behind her and fled down the hall to the women's toilet.

Stanford Bracebridge executed a half-spin on one foot and wound up standing with his back to the wall. The look on Brenda's face confirmed his awareness that he had interrupted a scene. She was leaning against a table near the sofa and breathing as heavily as if she had just run a mile. She must have heard rumours before he could reach her.

'Brenda ... ' He squared his shoulders, hiked up his trousers, and moved towards her very slowly, as if she were an animal in a trap. She studied his face as he approached.

'It's true, then, isn't it?' Her voice had always been low, with a slight growl. Now it seemed weighted with lead. His tactic had always been to approach Brenda obliquely in the clinches. He had learned the strategy through dealing with his more difficult patients.

'What was the matter with your friend?' he asked.

Brenda moved to one of the swivel chairs. She dropped into it with the weightless languor of a rag doll. She had not taken her eyes from his.

'I have my friends at court.' Her voice was simply toneless now. 'This was one of her juicier tasks.'

392

Bracebridge slung his attaché case over onto the sofa and fell into the other swivel chair.

'What did she say to you? Doesn't she work in the ICU?'

Brenda lit a cigarette. Her hands were shaking.

'She told me that Virg had a low spinal fracture and that the accident had made him permanently impotent.' She inhaled and slowly exhaled the smoke and read in Bracebridge's eyes a confirmation of Francine's statement. They were a mixture of sadness, embarrassment, and guilt. She had been puzzled before by the presence of guilt in the eyes of certain persons who dealt with the suffering of others. The strangeness of it and the sense of *déjà vu* momentarily distracted her.

Bracebridge cleared his throat and assumed a facsimile of his professional manner.

'Ransahoff hasn't committed himself to a prognosis yet. The surgery was only at six o'clock this morning.'

'They know what the injuries are. Don't temporize with me, Stan. Francine says he can't feel anything below his waist.'

'That's not unusual following the injuries he sustained. We can't be certain of anything for at least a week.'

Brenda narrowed her eyes and flared her nostrils. 'When I go into the ICU to see him, I want to know the score! He's impotent, isn't he?'

Bracebridge folded his hands and leaned towards her with his elbows on his knees. His face looked sorrowful.

'Brenda, it looks that way. It *looks* that way. But let's not finalize things in our minds until we get all the clinical data. Ransahoff will want to order further tests later to determine the extent of permanent neurologic deficit ... '

Brenda stood up and paced across the room and back, dragging on her cigarette. She blew out two jets of smoke through her nostrils and glared at him.

'Don't lay the old medical mumbo jumbo on me, Stan. I'm not one of your idiot patients. I've seen men with low spine fractures before. I believe the layman's phrase is "He'll never *get it up* again"!'

393

Bracebridge sat with his shoulders slumped over and examined his folded hands. He said nothing for a while. It was remotely possible that some of the deficit could be reversed. He sighed and murmured, a bit lamely, 'Don't forget, they're doing a lot with physical therapy ... '

Brenda had walked over to the small table. There was a medical dictionary lying there. She picked it up and hurled it across the room. It crashed against the wall and lay open on the floor. She covered her face with her hands. Her shoulders rose and fell with long sobs. Bracebridge put out his hand to touch her and then drew it back. Brenda was terrible in anger and forbidding, even in tears.

The room was quiet for a long while except for the sound of Brenda's sobs. When they had become quieter and finally stopped, Bracebridge spoke to her again.

'Everything possible is being done to reverse the damage, Brenda. Just tell me what you want from me.'

Brenda had settled again into the swivel chair opposite him. She played with her cigarettes, dropping them into a faille case and pulling them out again. She didn't look at him. Her mouth twisted down at the corners. When she spoke, her voice was low and bitter.

'You can go in with me to see him, if they'll let us in now. What else can you do? I have to figure out where I'm going from here. What I'll do with my life.'

Bracebridge had not been certain towards what goal Brenda and his colleague Prince were steering. He had been observing the situation with some anxiety, as Prince became more and more uptight and distracted from his work. He had received calls from Dottie that were unmistakable double checks on Prince's whereabouts. Virg took Brenda on all his bona fide medical trips and on some that were not so bona fide. He knew Dottie would now be in the hospital, at Virg's side, as much as possible. Of course, Brenda's job was to keep track of his patients for him, so she would have reason to see him too, but only after he was far enough out of the woods to go on with his work. Bracebridge projected that he should be out of the ICU and into a private room in a week, barring complications.

He leaned forward and assumed his fatherly posture.

'Well, you seemed to keep yourself busy up till now being Virg's head honcho and deputy. His injuries won't prevent him from going on with his work, even though he may have to do it in a wheelchair.' He watched Brenda closely as he spoke. She did not look at him and continued to play with the cigarettes. He pulled out an ace he had been keeping up his sleeve.

'Roosevelt ran the country and was commander-in-chief of the greatest war in history from a wheelchair,' he reminded her.

Brenda jerked the cigarette pack out of the case and threw them both down on the table. The case shot off onto the floor. She looked directly into his eyes now.

'Before I went to Chicago, I gave Virg an ultimatum: I wasn't returning until he asked his wife for a divorce. I knew we couldn't go on much longer living together apart. Dottie or Frank would have blown the lid off. I could see it coming. I wanted to jump the gun on that. I wanted a neat switch.'

So that was what was behind Virg's growing irrationality.

'Did he ask her for the divorce? How long were you gone?'

'Eight days.' Brenda leaned her head against the chairback and shut her eyes. 'Maybe I'll never know if he asked for a divorce. Is she here now?'

'I think Mulder sent her home to rest after Virg got out of surgery.'

Bracebridge's mind was busy with conjectures. Brenda's eyes remained closed. She spoke quietly.

'She'll stick with him day and night till he's passed all the danger points.'

' . . . And then' – Bracebridge leaned forward – 'he'll need you to help ease him back into things when he can go to work again.'

Brenda sat up and folded her arms in front of her. The old expression of smug amusement played over her face.

'*If* he makes it – and I don't mean just survival as a cripple. Can you imagine Virg getting pushed around by some

395

lackey, or pushing buttons to move his butt around in a motorized chair? Can you imagine Virg a neuter?' She shuddered. 'If it happens, if it *has* happened, I don't want to be there to remind him he is dead. He wouldn't be Virg anymore. The man I loved wouldn't exist – even if he could go on managing his war.' Brenda spoke with the old gutsy irony he had always admired, but some evil behind the words reached out like a cold hand to steal a vital core of meaning from him.

'Virg doesn't exist for you now that he's damaged?'

She smiled a bitter smile. It was not pretty, even with the small white teeth and the display of dimples.

'Virg and I are – were – powerful together. Part of my power was his sexual strength and how I moved it. The sex together and the work together were interwoven.'

Bracebridge felt with uncomfortable certainty that he was observing Brenda's memorial service for Virgil Prince. He averted his glance before the last hymn.

He rose to his feet and walked across the room. He stooped over and picked up the medical dictionary, returning it to the table. Then he retrieved Brenda's cigarette case from the floor. He risked a glance at her and saw that the ceremony had been concluded. She was doing something to her eyes with a tissue and a little brush. She applied some lipstick. Then she stood up and smiled at him – a thin smile, but one that told him she was ready for the next step.

She walked over to the sofa and picked up her shoulder bag.

'Can we go up and take a look at him?'

'Sure,' Bracebridge said. 'But I don't know if he'll be awake, or too aware if he is.'

'Who is taking over his patients?' she asked.

'Leonard, the other staff oncologist. I check on some of them myself.' They were walking through the door now. A profound sense of sadness made Bracebridge's head ache. He walked with a heavy step. 'The ranks have thinned out lately. A few went home, you know.' He paused. Brenda had walked on ahead of him, her hips undulating and her hair swinging around her shoulders. '... And a few died,' he added, speaking aloud, but to himself.

Chapter Fourteen

It was midmorning when Lance and Christie started out along the beach towards the rockfall. Christie could feel the energy of Lance striding beside her. Walking with him gave her joy in the strength of her own legs. He moved easily in the hot sun, brown as a savage, not seeming to notice the weight of the heavy knapsack he had slung over his shoulder. A cool breeze blew across the lake from the west, ruffling their hair and flapping their shirts. They had walked for about twenty minutes when they rounded the foot of a dune that had hidden the curved shoreline ahead. Christie was absorbed in the pattern of white sails and gulls' wings against the intense blue of sky and water. Lance grabbed her arm.

'Look, Christie! Up ahead!' He pointed down the beach, and Christie saw a long paleness, different from the colour of the dunes, ascending upward from the beach. It was a steep spill of white and grey rocks. At the top was a craggy bluff. At the edge of the beach, extending out into the water, was a rock formation in the shape of a large arch. Boulders surrounded it creating a cavelike structure. She stood still, fascinated by its shape. It had the aspect of a primitive castle built into the water. Its floor must be the moving tides above rock and sand.

'Let's run,' she whispered to Lance. 'I want to go inside it!'

They raced off together, Christie running on the packed sand next to the water. Lance outdistanced her immediately, then slowed his pace by cutting, sometimes into the water, sometimes into the deep sand, in a zigzag pattern ahead of her. They arrived at the grotto together and flung themselves down in its shadow to get their breath. Lance put down his knapsack and scooped up water, throwing it over himself and Christie. They lay back on the sand and looked up at the arch of the grotto.

After a while Lance stood up and shook himself like a dog. He fanned Christie with the tail of his soaked shirt. Then he removed the wine bottles and food from the knapsack.

'Follow me and I'll show you the grotto. I'm going to stash the wine between some rocks in the water.'

Christie followed him under the arch of rocks and inside the shelter of the boulders. While he looked for a good place to store the wine and food, she climbed around on the rocks exploring the grotto's dark niches and chambers.

'It's like a magic cave!' she exclaimed. The sun filtered through openings around the arches and cast paths of quivering light on the water. Its reflection on the stone around and above made her think of the undulations of some enormous silver-scaled reptile. She watched the changing patterns. The eerie mood of the grotto seemed to breed both promise and foreboding.

Lance crossed the rocks to where Christie was standing. He held her close for a moment, then took her by the hand.

'Let's go. We'll climb to the top of the bluff before it gets too hot. When we come back, we'll get in the water and cool off. Are you hungry yet?'

Christie shook her head.

'Good,' Lance said. 'I want to see what kind of climber you are.' They left the dimness of the grotto. He took the knapsack, containing only the blanket and the thermos, and strapped it around himself again.

'Is anyone likely to be prowling around here?' she wondered.

'No. I doubt it. I've been here before and I've never seen anyone around the bluff or the grotto. There are no cottages on this section of beach.' He walked to the edge of the water and called her over to him. 'I'm going to start climbing from there.' He indicated some flat rocks leading upward from the sand. 'Watch where I put my feet and step where I have been.

I'll be testing the rocks before I put my weight on them.'

'Okay,' Christie said. 'Let's go.'

She was looking up above her. Some gulls perched on the rocks. A few engaged in their ritual ballet, wheeling again and again above the water. Occasionally, one would dive down and come up with a small fish.

'Even if I can't swim, I've always been a good climber.' Christie's voice was confident.

They began the ascent, Lance picking his way, testing the stability of the rocks. He moved upward in a circuitous route, avoiding rocks that were too large and selecting those whose shapes made good footing. Christie moved behind him, keeping up with his pace, her feet securing a hold where he had been. They stopped from time to time to enjoy the perspective from where they stood, watching the waves and the shorebirds getting farther away.

As they moved away from it, the grotto seemed like a fortress rooted in water. They continued on to the summit, where some grass shaded by an old tree provided a good place to rest. Lance threw his knapsack on the ground and pulled the blanket from it, spreading it out beneath the tree. Christie arrived at the top just as he pulled the water from the knapsack. She threw herself down on the blanket.

'Thank goodness you brought the thermos! I'm dying for water!' Lance poured water into the thermos cup and they took turns drinking from it.

'I love to climb,' Christie said between sips. 'I haven't done it for years. I used to climb in the hills near our house when I was a little girl. My father took me on hikes.'

'You never mentioned your father before,' Lance remarked.

'They – my parents were killed when I was thirteen, in a plane crash. I went to live with an aunt,' Christie said. She looked out over the water. The sails of the boats were smaller than the wings of the gulls.

'What was your father like?' he asked.

She was silent for a while before she answered. 'I used to confuse him with God. He was strong. He was kind and wise.

399

He gave me the first sense of my identity.'

'And your aunt?' Lance lay back on the blanket and closed his eyes. Christie lay beside him and nibbled on a tall weed she had pulled from the turf.

'She was my mother's sister. She was very neat and tidy. Everything in her house was polished and protected. She was a great reader, a student of philosophy until she died. I went back to live with her after I left my husband.'

'Weren't you bored – living with an old lady?'

'It seemed like a haven of peace. I owe a lot to my aunt. I was her only niece. She died a year after I came back to live with her, and she left me enough money to finish college.'

'Good for the old girl.' Lance's voice was blurred. Christie heard the drowsiness in his voice and turned to look at him. His eyes were closed. His chest rose and fell with long, even breaths. It was still a source of fascination to her to see him unconscious. His body at rest compelled a kind of awe. She had the feeling of observing a dynamo that had come to a grinding halt. Tiny beads of sweat covered his forehead. The sweet curve of sleep was on his mouth.

The sudden arrest of all action somehow emphasized his energy. He had, from the first day she had seen him, symbolized life to Christie. It was life itself which had overtaken her, life which embraced her through his arms, life which filled her when they made love. When he left her, would life withdraw itself? She turned from Lance and looked above her. A wide circle of sky was circumscribed by the tall grass that surrounded them. Weed tendrils, heavy with tiny seeds, etched themselves against the blue background over her head. In the centre of the sky the twisted branches of the tree bent towards them, its leaves shining in the wind. It was an ancient oak which had withstood many storms. Cradled in the grace of the blowing grass, affirmed by the solitude of the tree, Christie dared to return again to the memory of the child she had aborted. In destroying the child, she felt she had condemned herself never to have another. The Scriptures described such women as barren. Barren was hard and dry, like the rocks they had just climbed. Barren was a woman who created nothing.

She looked at Lance's face, tanned and almost childlike in repose. How could she explain the darkness in her, and its counterpart of hope, to Lance? Part of her longed to stay with him forever in the sunshine and be happy there. But all that she had learned with pain told her that his time and his space were only temporary. Hers was a place of struggle and redemption, because acknowledged or not, evil, she knew, was real.

She watched him rest for a while, loving his sleep. Whenever she looked at Lance the possibilities of the lost child came alive again in her mind and she imagined that it ran into the meadow behind them. It would stay with her for a time, descending the rockfall and searching with her in the sand for wood and stones. She allowed tears to run down her cheeks and be absorbed into the grass. This child could never be wounded. No act of brutality could touch it. It would never fall victim to its father's pride or his foul temper.

She felt the light brushing of a blade of grass across her shoulders and breasts and opened her eyes to see Lance smiling at her.

'Did you fall asleep? I went out like a light. I'm ready to go back down and have some lunch. Are you hungry?' The dynamo was in action again. Lance stretched and stood up. He reached for her hand and pulled her to her feet. She watched him roll up the blanket and place it in the knapsack with the thermos.

'You'd better put that shirt back on,' he told her. 'The sun is at its zenith now. We don't want any moving parts to become dysfunctional.'

Christie untied her shirt and slipped it on, knotting the tails together at her waist.

'Okay,' he said when he'd strapped on the knapsack, 'do just as you did coming up. It's even easier to slip in the descent than in the climb.'

They made a smooth progress down to the bottom of the cliff. Christie took the last five rocks in small jumps and wrapped her arms around him.

'You are a fantastic guide,' she told him. 'I would let you take me over the tundra on foot!' She turned and walked to the grotto, then waded into the cool eddies around its rim. Lance dropped the knapsack beside a rock and pulled the wine bottles out of the water. Glasses had been stashed with the food. He pulled them from the sack, uncorked the wine, and filled them.

They took the food to a broad, flat rock outside and used it as a table, sipping wine and enjoying the breeze. Then Christie lay back and stretched out on the rock. She shielded her eyes and looked up at the sky. Lance had removed his shirt. He leaned over and kissed her.

'Are you hungry?' he whispered.

'I'm beginning to be.'

Lance had begun to untie her shirt. He slipped it off her shoulders and unzipped her cut-off jeans. Christie wriggled out of them and sat up to drink some wine. She leaned over to kiss Lance, then stretched out on the rock again.

'I love it here. I never want to go home. Can we feed the gulls some of our bread after we eat?'

Lance's finger followed the midline of her torso from her breastbone to her pelvis. She shivered, in spite of the sun.

'You are getting thin, Christie,' he said. 'I will have to stuff you with grilled steak and buttered potatoes tonight.' He bent over and kissed her ribs, one at a time, counting them off. Then he sat up and unpacked the food from the knapsack. Christie refilled their wineglasses, and they lunched on dark bread, sausage, and cheese. They ate mostly in silence, content to watch the action of the birds and the surf.

When they were finished, Christie said, 'I'm going to feed the gulls.'

'Go ahead,' said Lance, 'but over there, at the rocks. I don't want a thousand gulls hovering over my table.'

Christie walked across the beach and climbed to a position on a sharp, jutting rock about fifty feet above the shore. She tore the bread into pieces and threw it onto the stones a short distance from her. Within minutes, the air above her was filled with the beating of many wings. The cries of the gulls surrounded her as they circled her position. She knew that this moment would be with her forever. She stood on the high rock among them until the last crumbs of the bread were gone. Down below her, Lance stretched out on their table-rock. She stood watching him for a while, committing to memory the grace of his brown body against the grey stone and the white sand.

When she returned to the beach, Lance had picked up their blanket and was spreading it out in the shadows of the rocks close to the grotto. He stood up and took her in his arms. She felt the swell of her breasts, the curve of her belly, and the pressure of her thighs locked against him. They fell to the ground, joining in the midst of their embrace. They moved together slowly for a time; then both lay still, containing the heat of his penetration without urgency. They touched everywhere, their bodies locked together in a motionless union. A slow, fierce strength moved between them. His tongue explored her mouth. The palms of his hands pressed into hers. They lay joined together for a long time. Then they began to move with each other again, lithely as a single dancer in a dream. As their motion accelerated, they clung to each other, losing all sense of the boundaries of their flesh, their bodies tensing towards the final convulsion, a shuddering spasm of freedom.

They slept in each other's arms. The shadows of the pillar rocks shifted in the sun. The surf rose, and the waves crept further up the beach. Christie felt the coolness of the froth creeping from the grotto pool and licking around her hips.

'Lance,' she whispered. She raised herself on one arm and pushed back her hair with her fingers.

He opened his eyes and looked at her as if he saw her from a great distance. He threw one arm behind his shoulder and touched the water lapping onto the sand.

'Shall we start back?' she asked. She kissed him on his eyes and on his mouth. He sat bolt upright.

'How long have we been sleeping?' he said.

'I don't know. The shadows of the rocks have changed.'

The breeze had become a strong wind. Eddies of sand blew like a haze along the shore. He put his head into his hands and rubbed his eyes, then stood up and walked to the pool. He knelt there and splashed water over his head. When he came back, he studied Christie's face with a strange expression in his eyes, as if he searched for something. He put his arms around her, holding her in a close grip for a few moments; then he released her.

'Let's pack up our gear,' he said. They walked over to their table and gathered the remains of the food and the empty bottles. They picked up their scattered clothes and dressed quickly. He slung the pack over his shoulders again.

'The lake is getting rough. The horizon looks hazy. We should start back,' he said. He hesitated and looked over his shoulder. 'I want to show you something, Christie. It's just a short way beyond the grotto.'

His face was very intense. His eyes were bright and excited, but distant, engaged in some anticipation she could not share.

She glanced at the lake. It had a peculiar grey-green cast. The waves had grown higher, and there were whitecaps on them. The boundary between the lake and the sky had become confused. The horizon looked like a cloud of smoke.

He led the way behind the grotto, over the sand and boulders. The wind whipped Christie's hair around her face as they approached the long finger of rocky land extending upward and outward into the lake. They reached a stony path that wound upward unevenly to the land's end. Lance followed it with Christie close behind him. As they neared the tip of the bluff, their path was blocked by a weather-beaten wooden fence with a sign on it:

IT IS FORBIDDEN TO GO BEYOND THIS POINT

Lance turned to her and put down the knapsack.

'Wait here,' he said. He jumped the fence and ran to the end of the point. The extension of rocks stood in a circle, separate from the point, deep, well-spaced crevices between

404

them. A boiling foam of waves churned at their bases. Lance paused at the edge of the point. The wind blew his hair wildly around his head and whipped the tails of his blue shirt. He gave her a little salute and leaped from the bluff to the nearest rock. Christie leaned on the sign, her eyes riveted on him. He was balancing on the slippery rock like a tightrope walker. He stood there, poised, for a moment, then leaped again, landing safely on the second rock. It was narrower than the first. She felt her heart pounding heavily. He looked back at her and grinned, holding out his arms, pretending to roll and bank like a plane. She tried to look away, but couldn't drag her eyes from him. She saw him bend his knees slightly and leap again. He was now on the third rock, balancing on one foot, still holding out his arms like wings. Finally, he jumped to the fourth. He had designed a game, Christie thought: a duel with death. Perhaps it was his secret dance of life.

She bent over the sign and covered her eyes with her hands. She felt the wind whipping her hair and heard the waves pounding as they hit the rocks. Finally, she forced herself to look again. Lance stood with his back to her, still on the fourth rock, gazing at the darkening sky. The gulls circled above him, floating, resting on the wind, coasting downward in long, lazy curves. He watched them for a few moments. Then he turned and leaped to the last rock. It was not as close to the ledge as the first. One foot slipped slightly as he hit its rounded surface. He paused, using his arms to get his balance. Then he made the last jump, the longest. He flew through the air in a ballet leap and landed lightly on the edge of the bluff. Christie turned and leaned against the fence, letting the wind dry the anxious sweat under her arms. She heard Lance's feet scraping on the rocks as he walked back up the path. He reached the fence and climbed over it. He turned her around and kissed her. His face and hair were soaked with spray. He was smiling broadly. She shivered now from the wind. The sun had been swallowed in the cold smoke of the approaching storm.

Lance threw back his head and laughed. He was breathing

hard and perspiring. His face was alive, awake and eager. He was in full possession of himself.

'Let's go,' he said. He smacked Christie on the behind and took the lead again. They turned back along the path and headed for the cottage, racing home ahead of the storm.

Chapter Fifteen

Every time her mind returned to the past, Brenda was confirmed in her conviction that it would be depressing to remain in Brandenburg. Stan Bracebridge would be glad to keep her on in her old 'honcho' role, but her heart would no longer be in it. The motivation was gone. Hanging around Broadcliff would only deepen the contrast between the excitement of the past and a dim present until her loss became an obsession. She was uncertain whether Frank regarded her with fear or with pity. They had slept in separate rooms for months now. She had managed to avoid spending any time with him in the few days since her return. He left for the office early and she stayed out late, either by herself or with Stan.

She detested the curious stares of the hospital 'field hands'. Some of them veiled their glances, but she could hear whispering in her wake as she moved down the halls.

The problem was that she had to manage at least one meeting with Virg alone. She owed him that. She was going to have to think of some ploy to smooth Francine's feathers. She needed her help one more time. She had to find out which hours Dottie was camped out in Virg's room and when he was most likely to be alone. She had to see him before she could pack their relationship away. The only way she could summon Francine's loyalty once again was to plead crazy. Well, she probably *had* been wild with shock.

And Francine had dragged out the whole informing process in such a maddening way.

There was no one else she trusted enough to ask Dottie's schedule. It had to be someone in the ICU. She would manage to corner Francine tomorrow and say her little speech. Meanwhile, there were other things to do. She had stayed home today to putter around the house and think things out. Now she curled up on the chaise next to her bedroom phone and dialled her friend Dana in Chicago. She had no intention of leaping out of her situation with Frank until she had something organized in Chicago.

Virgil Prince lay in his bed half-listening to the nurse who was bustling around the room chattering to him. She had adjusted the blind, and now she was fluffing up a soft thermal blanket his wife had brought him. The hospital blankets were narrow and never warm.

The thin beginnings of a new attitude had begun to mingle with his rage and despair. It was a kind of exhausted surrender, a response which took him back to the helplessness of childhood and its benefits. Simply to give in to the inevitable was a relief of sorts; to allow oneself to be cared for like a child. He began to concentrate on the simplest things around him: the sun on the yellow blanket, the leaves of a plant, the hypnotic hum and movement of the freeway traffic. His anger and rebellion had not left him. They came back to him in waves. In their wake, they left weakness and emptiness.

Brenda resided permanently in his awareness, part of the underlay of all that had been irretrievably lost. Much of Virgil Prince's arrogance and self-confidence had derived from what he now knew was a superstitious notion: that the facial blight he had borne from birth was prepayment against further bodily afflictions. Because of this mystical conviction which he had harboured secretly, he had been singularly free of the uneasiness suffered by many of his colleagues who worked with cancer patients. He had moved without fear or guilt among the diseased bodies he treated. Now the awareness of something worse than impotence was added to his losses. He was no longer invulnerable. Loss could be heaped upon loss. He was no better than the stupidest, or the most miserable, of the patients he had treated.

Part of his mind hoped that Brenda would never come to see him. When he contemplated the moment when she might appear at his bedside, he felt as flimsy and insubstantial as a ghost confronting a living being. Yet some irrational need, not yet suffocated by the signals of reality, made him wish to see her.

Stanford Bracebridge had told him that Brenda had returned from Chicago on the day of his surgery. She had come to visit him in the ICU, but had left when she saw that Dottie was with him. She would be in soon, Bracebridge assured him. She would probably wait until his postsurgical grogginess had receded and they could have a good chat. Prince had not replied. He could think of nothing to say. Why should he share with Stan the now obsolete saga of his decision to confront Dottie with divorce?

He was aware of silence in the room now. The nurse must have left. He had fallen asleep during her morning prattle. The I.V.'s and the chest tube had been removed; so had the nasogastric tube. He felt less impaled now. The hum of the traffic below lulled him into a drowsy trance. He slept for a while and did not hear Brenda come into the room. He felt someone touch the blanket near his arm and opened his eyes to see her slender white figure standing beside him.

Brenda had been relieved to find him sleeping. She took pains to approach the bed quietly, giving herself time to observe him before there was any conversation. He looked the same, but paler and a bit drawn. His hair had been brushed away from his forehead and lay against the pillow. It had always been unruly; she had never seen him when it was not falling over one side of his forehead. It occurred to her that she had never really seen him inactive and unaware. They were always working together, driving together, matching wits with each other, or his body was assaulting hers in the heat of passion. Sleep made even a healthy person look vulnerable. The paleness of his face and what she knew about his body made him appear not only vulnerable, but vanquished. She swallowed against a tightness gathering in her throat. There could be no weeping. The last thing Virg would want was a maudlin abandonment to tears.

With a sense of shock she realized that she was *frightened*. Whenever she had faced a threat of any kind, she had coped with it through anger and action. Now she was face to face with a kind of dread she could not master with those weapons. She could not think exactly what it was she feared. She needed to pull herself together. She was, after all, a nurse. She had never panicked, even in the face of massive haemorrhages and *grand mal* incidents. She squared her shoulders and reached down to adjust the yellow blanket that covered him to his chest.

He opened his eyes and looked at her. After his look of recognition, she saw a flash of pain. It resembled the reflex of someone receiving an unexpected blow. She thought of Francine's eyes a moment after she had slapped her across the face. She reached out and took his hand.

'Hi, Virg.' She managed a smile. 'You're a hell of a person to get to see. You've either got visitors or a gaggle of nurses fussing over you.' She kept her tone jaunty and her face empty of any concern which might reinforce in him the horror of his condition.

He held on to her hand. She was surprised by the strength of his grip. His eyes searched her face. A spark of the old passion had kindled in them. He held her eyes with his and did not speak. The silence built until she felt that all the strength she had ever known in him had focused in his eyes. For a moment, that power and the heat in his hand sent an aching surge of desire through her body. Then the passion in his eyes turned to tenderness. She saw them begin to glitter and grow wet. He continued to press her hand in his. Finally his eyes closed and he bit his lip. Brenda's dread warred with the memory of love. She smiled at him and withdrew her hand. She pretended to straighten the blanket and patted him on the arm.

'You're looking *great*, Virg – really! I can tell you've made it through the first challenge with flying colours. Stan tells me the surgery went off without a hitch and that they're going to begin physical therapy soon.'

Prince turned his head away from her, towards the window. He waited to speak until he felt the thickness in his throat diminish. Brenda was sauntering around the room examining get-well cards along the shelf and some flowers on a stand near his bed.

'How was your trip?' he asked. 'Was it hot in Chicago?' He was proud of his voice. With admirable control he had kept it even, almost impersonal.

'Oh, great! Yes, it was hot, but everything's air-conditioned. I have a lot of neat friends who wined and dined me. It was a nice change from Brandenburg.' She spoke casually and eagerly. He could sense the relief in her tone. They were on a neutral ground where she could find her balance.

She came back and sat on the foot of the bed. Her bottom accidentally pressed his leg and pulled the blanket taut. She looked self-conscious for a second, then shifted her hips away from him, loosening the blanket. She began to talk again, her voice bright and businesslike.

'As you know, Stan is keeping up with your patients. I'll drop by to see them and let you know any important changes. Don't worry about work yet. Take your time. It'll pay off in the end. You should be patient with the physical therapy and keep at it. They're doing wonders with that, you know.' She paused, feeling a little awkward, remembering he knew all that she knew, and more. He was watching her with a kind of chilled fascination. Brenda the lover, Brenda the passionate woman, whose body his own flesh knew with such an intimacy it had become his second self, was prattling on to him like the day nurse, clocking off facts and priorities, extolling modes of therapy. He had lost half of himself and she had not asked him how it happened, how it felt. She picked up where she had left off.

'Are you feeling much pain, Virg? You know that if they're being chintzy with the medications, Stan will intervene.' She waited and looked at him, her professional nurse facade now securely in place. She looked self-confident and totally impassive; helpful, cheerful, and unreachable. He began to stammer as he responded.

'No ... I mean, I know ... he will. They're pretty good here. I've slept a lot. They give me codeine and Valium.'

'Well, if you should have any trouble, just page us. I'll be in mornings to check patients with Stan for a while, until ...' She broke off suddenly and took a deep breath. She had no intention of discussing her Chicago plans with Virg, or her own divorce. The most feasible course with him was a gradual phasing out. By the time a few weeks had passed he would see the logic of the move. He would be busy with all the problems of his own rehabilitation.

'Until ...?' He brought her back to her unfinished sentence.

'Well, until things are back to ... you're back in the swim again.'

'You know, Brenda,' he began with an effort; 'you know what my injuries are. Stan must have told you. I'll be ... I won't have the use of my legs.' His voice broke slightly. He watched her carefully. She responded with a toss of her head, flipping back her hair with a finger. It was one of the charming attitudes he always saw in his mind when he thought of her; that, and others more moving still, which he dared not think of.

'Of course!' she smiled. 'He told me the injuries. We all know no one can predict your rate of recovery. Each patient is different. A lot depends on attitude. Also, you're healthy and strong. You have a lot going for you.'

He listened to her voice. She could have been talking to any one of a hundred patients. The speech was pat. It was professional protocol. He had rattled it off himself. It seemed an eternity ago. He wondered if he should try to tell her about the accident, about his insomnia in the motel, the agonized debates, and his decision. He thought of the rabbit in the road and his reflex which caused the wreck. The last item would enrage Brenda: braking a car to avoid a rabbit!

411

He suddenly felt tired again. Exhausted. He sighed and closed his eyes. He heard her move towards the bed.

'You just rest now. I've disturbed you long enough.' She patted him on the shoulder. 'I have to meet Stan in a few minutes, anyway.' He felt her lips brush lightly across his forehead, a sterile benediction.

'Thanks for coming, Brenda.' He managed a polite smile. His voice sounded weak and hollow.

'See you tomorrow!' she called cheerily. She went out and closed the door.

Prince lay staring at the wall across from his bed. It was a muted pastel green. He was in the new hospital wing, where all the walls had been decorated in a colour code psychologically tested and proved to be calming and rest-inducing. He tried to relax and let go of the knot in his throat, the tight band of tension in his head and chest. Tears began to course down his cheeks. He let them fall. The vice in his chest broke, and he began to sob. The sobs became deeper. He heard them like great, ragged shouts in his ears, alien and terrifying; and he knew why men had for so long forbidden themselves to weep. Their weeping was not like the sobbing of women, not a wail or a moan. It was the sound of a great wrenching, as if giants uprooted ancient trees or tore granite from the centre of the earth.

Gradually the violence of his sobs subsided and he lay quietly in the silence. A kind of detached clarity began to replace his anguish, and a strange notion came to him. If Brenda had been able to share his grief, if she had entered his loss with him and wept, the terror and the sting of the injuries would have become bearable. He might have been blessed. He remembered how her eyes had filled with tears after she had kissed his face that night as they lay on the sand. It was the last night they had been together, the night of her ultimatum.

Now she was gone, and he knew, finally, that the spirit which gives birth to certain tears is a presence which power finds too costly to sustain.

Chapter Sixteen

The storm that hit the shore the day of Lance's jumping feat was the first of a series, marking the beginning of weather changes. Christie and Lance would linger on the beach and watch murky thunderheads gather over the horizon, turning the water from blue to leaden grey. They watched the storm's power sweeping up like an ominous curtain descending on the stage of summer.

During their evenings indoors Lance played his records on the stereo. They ran the gamut from meditative to thunderous, from classical to Greek cabaret. Christie had begun to feel that the vibrations of the music had penetrated her bones as deeply as the sun and the water.

Lance often worked on problems connected with the foundry, sketching out designs for castings. But he became restive in an atmosphere that was without challenge too long. While Christie was absorbed and happy watching the fire, reading, or listening to music, he paced the floor; he sometimes took her to taverns or bars in nearby towns to watch the action.

The night of the second storm, he brought out slickers and they walked down the beach in the wind-driven rain for half a mile, finding their way by lantern, bombarded by thunder and the crashing waves.

The next afternoon, Christie climbed one of the dunes and lay at the top near a stand of birches that edged the sand, interrupting the forest of venerable pines at the dunes' crest. This place was one of her favourite retreats because of the birches. Their branches lifted and swayed slowly, as if to

413

some silent music. Their leaves trembled and shimmered like thousands of green wings. The trees communicated joy to her sometimes; sometimes acceptance or sorrow. The sandweed spoke of tenderness and the subtleties of love. Now the dragonflies had gone and the weeds were alive with the energy of grasshoppers. One even occasionally alighted on her arm or leg.

This afternoon she had noticed some of the birches turning yellow. There had begun to be a diminishing of the sun's light. An autumnal cast pervaded the atmosphere, like the amber glow of wheat fields at sunset. When she had driven out for groceries with Lance that morning she had seen isolated branches turning orange and red. The prophecies of summer's death were all around them. Once that week they had noticed a small tree near the deck whose leaves had turned entirely brown and were beginning to fall. Lance had grasped the trunk in his hand and shaken it, as if to hurry it on its journey into winter. She wondered if he could seize winter by its throat and countermand the oblivion of snow.

She welcomed her moments alone at the dunes, away from the intoxicating whirlwind of music, power, and sensation.

In a few days September would begin, and their time here was almost over. Lance would return to Chicago next week, and she to Brandenburg. He was laying plans to bring her to Chicago for weekends or to meet her in the dunes, in addition to the trip to Mexico. Somehow she could not see the myth of their union existing anywhere but at the place of its inception.

Lance had driven to the airport to pick up two of his guests. The other two had business on the way and were driving down. She felt a nameless dread about the weekend. It was as if invaders were moving themselves into the magic circle where she and Lance existed. She had tried to be sensible, to laugh at her superstitions. She told herself they rose from the remark Lance had made to her about his friends being from a different world. From the beginning he had wanted to expand the limitations of her world.

She put the evening from her mind and fell into the relaxed and empty state her place beneath the trees always brought her. After a while she became aware of the chill in the air and saw that the sun had moved closer to the rim of the lake. She felt clear and refreshed and knew that she had slept. She picked up her blanket and wrapped it around her shoulders. Her mind turned to the cottage and Lance. He must be back by now. She would be a strange hostess, coming on the scene after the arrival of the guests.

The sinking sun bled pastel hues into the landscape. As she walked homeward, her footprints made lavender shadows in the pink sand.

Approaching the cottage, she saw five people on the deck. Lance was standing at the edge, waving something on the end of a long stick. She recognized one of her silk skirts as a flag in shocking pink. Lance put his fingers into his mouth and emitted a piercing whistle. The sight of Lance and his flag made her laugh. She broke into a fast trot and was out of breath by the time she had climbed the sandy bank up to the cottage.

'We were sending out signals for help. We thought you were kidnapped!' He reached out and pulled her up onto the deck. 'This is Christie, folks. Christie, this is Billie Gilmore ...' He patted a tall, slim, languorous-looking blonde on the shoulder, then turned to the other girl. '... And Tiger Eye, here is ...'

Everyone burst out laughing. A girl with taffy-coloured hair and strange amber eyes reached out her hand.

'I'm Gil Smith. Nice to meet you, Christie.' Her voice was husky, almost gravelly. She smiled faintly, penetrating Christie with an X-ray glance which noted every detail. Her yellowish eyes were shrewd and predatory. Christie instinctively felt her guard go up as she took her hand.

Christie heard Lance speaking again. 'This is Sloane Belding ...' The taller of the two men nodded and smiled at Christie. He had perfect white teeth, brown curly hair, dark eyes and a ruddy tan. His face was puffy with the look of a man who had drunk too much for a long time.

'... And Van Turner.' She turned to the voice behind her and saw a shorter man reaching to take her hand. He had greying sandy hair and an open, pleasant face. There was something very comfortable about his presence. He smiled easily, but his eyes held a kind of weariness.

Christie looked around at them.

'Sorry I'm late. I fell asleep up there.'

'Oh – the birches again.' Lance laughed. He had stuck his flag in a crack of the deck. 'We'll have to make that place off-limits.' He put his arm around her. 'What'll you have to drink, Christie?'

'I want to get rid of this sand. Let me shower and dress; then you can fix me a Scotch and water.'

She showered quickly, dried, and splashed herself with cologne. She was smoothing body lotion on her arms and legs when Lance came into the room. He walked over and sat next to her on the bed.

'Need help with that?' He grabbed the bottle, poured some on his hand, and began rubbing it on her legs. Christie had wrapped herself in a large bath towel.

'Don't get dressed up,' Lance said as he lifted her leg and smoothed the lotion on. He bent his head and ran his tongue along the inside of her knee. 'It smells great, but' – he wrinkled his nose – 'you taste better without it.' He gave the bottle back to her and rubbed his hands together to get rid of the lotion. 'They decided they'd rather cook steaks here. They get enough restaurant dining in Chicago.'

Lance went to the closet and pulled out a lavender tie blouse and a pair of white shorts.

'I like these on you. Will you wear them?'

'Okay.' Christie noticed a kind of suppressed excitement in him. He was obviously looking forward to the evening and wanted her to make a good impression.

'Are these old friends?' she asked as she brushed her hair.

'The guys are flying buddies. We belong to some of the same clubs. They're both divorced. Poor Sloane. His wife really cleaned him out – even got the plane. Billie's an old girlfriend of mine, but I didn't meet Gil till today. She's some

416

babe. Her grandmother left her several million. The family made a fortune in the soap business. Now Gil has nothing to do but spend it. Sloane met her at a skydiving meet. She's something else. You'll get a kick out of her. She dives and she's a hang-glider. How'd you like to hang-glide off that cliff we climbed?'

'Billie's an old girlfriend?' Christie had stopped brushing her hair and turned to look at Lance. 'How *old*?'

Lance's caught-in-the-cookie-jar smile spread over his face.

'Oh – a couple of years ago we ran around together. She's a great swimmer and dancer. She's a model around Chicago.' He saw the tentative look on Christie's face and walked to the dresser and put his arm around her. She had begun to brush her hair again. He turned her face with his fingers and made her look at him.

'We were buddies, Christie. It wasn't a romance. It wasn't like with you.'

'Isn't it a little incestuous getting your girlfriends together in a small group?'

'Listen, Christie. You don't have to worry. They all think you're terrific. You bowled Sloane and Van over. I could tell by their faces. They'd love to be in my shoes.' He pulled off the towel Christie had folded around her and held her against him. He turned his face so that he looked at their image in the mirror. 'Look, Christie – see how we fit? Look at us.'

Christie turned her face and looked at their bodies and faces touching. They were both brown. The unexposed part of her skin looked like a white bikini. Lance's face, arms, and legs were a gold-bronze against his blue shirt and shorts. The heavy hair on his arms and legs was bleached almost silver. She tried to imagine Billie's tall, boyish body against Lance's, the waist-length pale blonde hair brushing against him. She wondered how it felt to go to bed with a sporting buddy. She thought of his wife, and could not evoke the picture of Lance embracing either of them. There was a mental barrier which protected her.

'I'll go mix your drink.' He took his arms from around her. She felt suddenly frail and alone.

'Hurry and get dressed. We're all two drinks ahead of you. I'm going to start the charcoal.' He walked quickly from the room and shut the door. Christie picked up the lavender shirt and knotted it under her breasts. Lance had bought her a thin silver chain and given it to her when they arrived at the cottage. She put it around her neck and pulled on the white shorts. She applied make-up carefully, and let her shoulder-length hair hang loose and fluffy. She surveyed herself in the mirror. She looked pretty good. Not quite up to Lance's old girlfriend and 'Tiger Eye', but interesting. A drink would relax her. She would try to be open-minded and get to know them. She sprayed a mist of cologne over her hair and arms and left the bedroom to begin the evening.

Lance had put on some samba records, and music was filling the house. Everyone was out on the deck. Lance had set up a bar there. The outside edge of the deck was a low-backed seating arrangement scattered with brilliant blue cushions. The same cushions covered some lounge chairs arranged around a low table.

Everyone was sipping a drink. Lance had just said something outrageous and everyone was laughing. Gil was perched on the railing looking out at the lake with binoculars. She wore tight pale blue jeans and a white shirt. There was a certain toughness about her reminiscent of the swagger in young street bullies. It was an interesting adjunct to her sexy figure and insinuating manner with men. Billie lounged on one of the cushioned benches, her long tanned legs stretched in front of her, bare feet propped on a lounge chair. Sloane walked over to Christie with a Scotch and water.

'Here's your drink, Christie.' He flashed his white teeth in a smile and lifted his own drink, clinking their glasses together. 'A toast to changes,' he announced. He walked over to the bench and sat down, indicating to Christie the cushion beside him. She saw Van coming up the dune from the lake carrying a piece of driftwood. He walked to the table and put it down. Christie went over to look at it.

'An odd shape, isn't it?' he said. 'I just washed it in the lake. It's darker now from the water, but it's really a pale grey.'

Christie lifted the driftwood and ran her fingers over it. Its contours were not symmetrical. It was full of hollows and whorls, but it had been worn into the shape of a rough cross. Its beams were longer than her hand. She looked up at Van.

'I love the shape and the grooves. It almost looks as if an artist had carved it.'

Lance was checking the progress of the charcoal fire.

'You people are lucky I had steaks in the freezer. You might have had to settle for eggs when you decided not to go out.' He placed some foil-wrapped potatoes in the grill and put on the lid. He walked over to the table. 'Driftwood?'

'I found it half-buried in sand, down the beach a way,' Van told them.

'You'd better hide it if you want to keep it.' Lance laughed. 'Christie collects driftwood. She has a pile behind the cottage; enough tinder to burn the joint down.'

Sloane came over and took the cross out of Christie's hand. He turned it around, examining it.

'Goddamn. It's a crucifix.' He laughed, a bit self-consciously.

Van was looking at Christie with interest.

'You collect driftwood?'

'Yes,' Christie said. 'I have some pieces at home. I can't go back with all I collected this time. I'll have to sort out the most important ones.'

Sloane dropped the crucifix on the table and returned to his seat by the railing, and his drink. Christie picked up the driftwood, closed her eyes, and ran her hand over it.

'You can really feel its shape when you don't see it,' she told Van.

'You should have it for your collection,' he said quietly.

Christie opened her eyes. 'Don't you want to keep it? It's very unusual.'

He smiled at her again and pulled a pipe from his pocket. He struck a match, lit the pipe, and puffed on it awhile before he answered.

'Consider it a gift from me,' he said.

The two girls had stretched out on the cushions and were whispering and giggling. Gil put the binoculars down on a cushion. She looked at Lance for a moment and then whistled to get his attention. He had his back to her, stirring the charcoal.

'What do you do while she collects driftwood, big fella?'

Lance turned around. 'I snorkel sometimes. Christie doesn't like deep water.'

Billie spoke for the first time. 'What's to see here underwater? You don't have coral like we saw in the Virgins.' Her smile was a trifle mocking.

'Shipwrecks, baby, and a grotto where a sea serpent coils around. Buried treasure and all that.' He walked over and patted her on the thigh. 'The charcoal will take a while. Anyone for another drink?'

Sloane moved over and sat next to Billie. She ran her fingers through her long mane and shook it back so that it fell on his shoulder.

'You wanna snorkel?' he asked, looking at her mouth. She had very pale blue eyes rimmed with long, mascaraed lashes. She lifted her drink and sipped it, smiling at him.

Christie and Van still stood by the table.

'I mean it,' he said. 'It's yours.'

'Thank you,' she said. 'I'll put it on the dresser so it doesn't get lost or burned.' She put down her drink and went through the house and into the bedroom. When she returned, Gil was standing next to Lance at the edge of the deck.

'Are you kidding about a grotto? Where is it?' Christie heard her say. She was standing with her back arched. Her breast brushed against Lance's arm.

'I'm not kidding.' He laughed. 'There's a natural grotto down the shore. Maybe we can sail down there tomorrow, and swim in to see it. Tomorrow we'll explore.'

Christie felt a crushing sensation in the pit of her stomach. The grotto was hers. Hers and Lance's. Gil did not belong in the grotto. She took a deep breath and walked over to the far side of the deck, swallowing several sips of the Scotch.

'Lance,' she called to him, 'do you want me to tear up some lettuce?'

Lance turned around. 'Yeah, Christie. Tear up some lettuce. I'm roasting potatoes in foil. That's all we'll need.'

She took her drink out to the kitchen and opened the refrigerator. Billie came and stood in the doorway. Her eyes looked friendly.

'Can I help?'

Christie put the lettuce on the counter and found a large bowl.

'Sure. Do we need any more cheese or smoked oysters out there?'

'No,' Billie said. She began to tear the lettuce and throw it into the bowl.

Van came into the kitchen with the ice caddy.

'Lance says you've been having storms here,' he commented. He scooped ice into the caddy. 'The sky looks pretty good now. Just enough clouds to give us a good sunset.' He started to walk out. 'Come on, you two. Hurry up with the lettuce and come out on the deck.'

When they heard the sliding screen click, Billie turned to Christie.

'How long have you been seeing Lance?'

'Just since July. About a month and a half.'

'I went with him for a year,' Billie said. They tore the lettuce and threw it into the bowl. Christie was busy with her own thoughts.

'Of course you know he's married.' Billie shook back her mane of hair.

'Of course.'

'Are you seeing anyone else?'

'No.'

'That's bad.'

'How could you be involved with Lance and see anyone else?'

'I know what you mean. Force yourself. Try to do it anyway.'

There was a pause. Finally, Christie said, 'There wasn't anyone in my life when I met him.'

'Well, he'll never leave his wife. He just leaves ... whatever it is that distracts him, ultimately. And he leaves his mark on the people he leaves, rather indelibly.'

The lettuce was all torn now. Christie covered the bowl and put it into the refrigerator. She turned to Billie.

'You're trying to warn me. I appreciate that. It's too late to change anything. Whatever happens will happen.'

'Do you have a job?' Billie asked.

'I did have.'

'I quit my job, a long-term contract with a cosmetic firm, in order to follow Lance on a junket to Venezuela.' Billie wound a strand of hair around her finger and stared out the window.

'I didn't quit mine,' Christie stated. 'I was fired.'

'Where did you work?'

'In a hospital.'

'You're a nurse?'

'No. A counsellor – on a cancer unit.'

Billie turned and leaned against the sink. She looked at Christie as if she hadn't seen her before.

'You're tougher than you look. You might survive. Just remember: Lance is a form of cancer himself.'

Christie stared at her.

'He taught me a lot,' Billie said in an even, dispassionate voice. 'He taught me how to play.'

They walked out onto the deck. The group was getting a little mellower and a little louder. There was a lot of laughter. Lance disappeared into the living room and Christie heard vintage Sinatra coming from the stereo. He danced out onto the deck with the steaks and put them on the grill. He came over and put one arm around Christie and one around Billie.

'You girls getting to know each other? Good!' He grinned warmly at them both.

Christie went over to the cushioned bench and sat next to Van. He put his arm around her. He puffed on his pipe. They sat silently, listening to the laughter and chatter. The sun was becoming a red globe in the dusky mauve sky. Lance danced around the deck to the music with a drink in his hand. Sinatra was singing ':... change partners and dance with me.' Gil walked up to him and pressed her body against him. She slid her hand in to his. Christie heard Van's voice beside her.

'I envy him,' he said quietly. 'He believes life is more valuable than any of its parts. It prevents him from staring at things long enough to be destroyed by them.'

Christie looked at him quickly, startled by the statement and its implications. They sat and watched the scarlet, weakening sun. It moved very slowly, falling into the dark substance of water and the night.

'What do you do?' Christie asked. 'Your work, I mean.'

'I make valves. I own a manufacturing company.'

'And you fly. Lance told me.'

'I fly to escape my work – and myself.'

Lance and Gil were laughing. Lance had spun her out, and she fell back on the cushions, catching her breath. Lance walked back to the fire and checked it.

'Steaks go on pretty soon,' he announced. Sloane was pouring himself another drink. Gil got up and stood beside him.

'Take it easy on the booze,' she murmured under her breath. 'I've got some good stuff for you, baby.'

Billie walked over to them and pulled a small silk pouch from her pocket. 'Grass?' she asked in a lazy voice. 'I have a little here myself. Good Columbian stuff.'

Lance was busy turning the steaks. Christie crossed to the bar and dumped some Scotch and ice into her diluted drink. She walked to the edge of the deck where she could see Lance's face. He was sipping his drink, grinning and talking to Sloane. Someone touched her arm. Billie was holding a small white pipe to her mouth.

'Try a puff of this,' she said.

'I don't smoke,' Christie told her.

'Oh.' Billie looked at her sharply and smiled. The Scotch

423

was making Christie feel warm and remote. The sun had finally dropped beneath the horizon.

'Christie!' Lance called. He was checking the food on the grill. 'Everything's ready. Go get the salad and the plates. I'll clear the table.'

She left the deck and walked into the kitchen. She put dressing on the salad and stacked the plates and silverware on a tray. There were a lot of drawers in the rented kitchen. Most of them were unexplored. She finally found a tablecloth and napkins. She was about to begin carrying it all to the table when Van walked in again.

'What can I do?' he asked. Christie noticed that he seemed to anticipate need. She wondered about his divorce.

'I'm glad you're here,' she told him. 'You can carry out the salad and the dishes as soon as I put a cloth on the table.' They went back through the house together.

'Anyone hungry?' Lance took several gulps from his drink and looked around the deck. Sloane and the two girls were passing the white pipe around. 'Let's eat,' Lance suggested.

Everyone finally got seated. Lance produced some hurricane lamps and lit them. The last pale light of the sun hung silver edges on black thunderheads that had begun to gather on the rim of the lake. The water looked rough and forbidding.

Christie ate absentmindedly, her eyes on the drama building in the sky. She sipped the Scotch that remained in her glass.

'Looks like the sail you promised might have to be cancelled,' Van remarked, watching the storm clouds.

'No. It clears up every day. We've been having these storms at almost the same time each night,' Lance told them. He patted Christie on the shoulder. 'Eat your steak, sea urchin. There are no gulls to give it to now.' He laughed. 'She's nutty about the gulls,' he said to the group in general.

'We brought some wine,' Sloane announced. It was the first time he had spoken for a while. He had seemed to be watching the action around him, after his third drink, from a remote plateau.

'God! I forgot the wine!' Lance jumped up and went to the kitchen.

When he returned he poured some into his own glass, then filled Gil's, Billie's, and Christie's. He began to pour some into Van's. Van covered the glass with his hand.

'I'm fine. I just want to sit back and watch the fireworks.' As he said it, they were startled by a long streak of snake lightning which pierced the centre of the horizon. Van puffed on his pipe. The smoke curled around their heads, its aroma nostalgic to Christie. It recalled evenings in her childhood when her father had read to her. Security had always been linked to the aroma of pipe tobacco. The wind had risen, but was still warm. Gil looked behind her at the waves breaking noisily on the sand.

'Maybe we'd better get this stuff in the house,' she said. She was looking at Lance, who studied the sky.

'You're right. The lightning's getting closer.' He stood up. 'Anyone want more steak? Salad?'

They were pushing their chairs back with murmurs of 'No, thanks.' Christie went into the kitchen to store the food and stack the dishes in the sink. Lance changed the records again. Greek cabaret music filled the rooms with its feverish beat. A clap of thunder struck, rolling, reverberating, and diminishing like the growls of an angry giant.

They all gathered in the living room. Lance stood near the stereo, a glass of wine in his hand, swaying to the music with his eyes shut. Christie knew that the Greek music got into his blood as much as the wine. Sloane lay back on the sofa with Billie and Gil. They all puffed on the pipe from time to time. Sloane appeared stupid with lethargy and the girls languorous. Christie stood at the door to the deck, sipping wine and looking out at the lightning. Van moved over and stood beside her. They were silent for a while, absorbed in the heightening of the waves revealed by flashes of light.

They heard husky laughter and then a sudden shout. They turned to see Gil standing in the centre of the room unbuttoning her blouse. She tossed it into Sloane's face. Her yellow eyes were half-closed, excited and predatory. She smiled and slid her hand between her breasts, pulling out a silver chain with a tiny silver spoon hanging on it. She began to tease Billie, running the spoon along her lips. Then she walked to one of the tables and opened a small jewelled box. Billie followed her.

'Save some of your dust for me, honey,' she murmured. She pulled her T-shirt off over her head and threw it at Lance. He stopped swaying to the music and opened his eyes. Gil had completed her ritual at the table and was undoing her bra. She threw it in the direction of Billie's shirt, and it caught Lance across the mouth.

Sloane had roused himself to the action with effort. He emitted a long, low whistle and slapped Gil on the seat of her tight jeans as she danced past him. He looked over at Lance and shouted, 'Hey, Buddy! Didn't I tell you she was some kind of crash-and-burn babe?' He fell back on the sofa, laughing.

Van opened the door and led Christie out onto the deck. The wind whipped their hair into their faces.

'Looks like they're going to play rough.' He was raising his voice against the noise of the waves.

'What can we do?' Christie looked back over her shoulder and saw Lance sitting cross-legged on the floor. She felt very alone. The two women were kneeling in front of him, facing each other.

'It's too dangerous for a walk on the beach.' As Van spoke they felt the first drops of rain. A great streak of lightning turned the deck white, and a clap of thunder followed it instantly.

'I think I'd invite Lance to the bedroom and lock the door,' he told her. 'Voyeurism isn't my thing, so I'm heading for my room. If you need me, call.' He put his arm around her and led her to the door. 'Lance should have warned Sloane that he didn't have a playgirl up here,' he muttered, half to himself.

They went back into the house. Billie and Gil had now stripped naked and were dancing together very slowly around the room. Sloane lay on the sofa staring at them, his eyes as glassy as a ceramic pig's.

Christie went over to Lance and put her hand on his shoulder.

'I'm going to our room, Lance.'

It was a full minute before he turned and looked at her; then he pulled her down on his lap.

'Don't go, Christie! The party's just getting exciting!' He reached down and began to untie her blouse. He put his lips against her ear. 'Take off your clothes, Christie! That'll revive old Sloane.'

She turned her head and pressed her face against his arm.

'Please, Lance, come with me. I don't want to be here.'

He didn't move or speak, but she could feel him turning away from her.

'Then go to bed,' he said. His voice was empty and uninvolved. She lifted her face and looked at him. He was watching Billie and Gil. They had stopped dancing and lay on the floor together. His eyes glittered in a frightening way.

She shrank back from him and walked away into their bedroom. She heard Van's footsteps retreating up the wooden stairs to the loft and the guest rooms.

She closed the door behind her and lay face down on the bed. A crushing sensation knotted her stomach briefly; then a kind of paralysis crept through her. She felt nothing. She could think of nothing. She lay empty and motionless for a long time; then with an effort she rubbed her cheek against the woven bedspread. Its rough texture brought back some feeling.

Beyond the door, Lance's Greek music swirled through the house with its confused cacophony of sounds. It muffled the noise of the thunder. She was losing something. She could not calculate the loss. She turned over and fixed her eyes on an object above the bed. It was a bad painting of an autumn tree. With almost pointillistic precision the artist had delineated every leaf and branch and texture with his brush. Some need, or instinct, now compelled her to trace the detail with her eyes: the outlines of the leaves, the stems, the twigs, following them into the branches, and the branches' various connections to the trunk. She memorized the structure. Her eyes came to rest at the earth. She stared at the ground, itself a minute representation of a carpet of fallen leaves. Then her mind began to see the invisible web of filaments beneath the ground, more extensively fine, more intricate than the leaves and branches. She heard a noise beside the bed.

'Christie?' a voice whispered. She turned and saw a slender figure standing beside her, cupping small breasts in her hands. Billie knelt on the bed with one leg. She lifted strands of Christie's hair and brushed them against her thigh.

A huge surge of energy surprised Christie, absorbing her inertia like a sponge. She leaped free of the bed and stood against the wall, breathing hard.

'Get away,' she told Billie, startled by the tone of her own voice. 'Go back to your games. I'm odd man out. If Lance is the one who taught you how to play, he should go back and revise his rule book.'

Billie backed off the bed, slowly. She stood and pouted for a moment, stroking her own long hair. Then she uttered a dry, mirthless laugh and left the room, slamming the door behind her. Christie walked to the door and stood with her back against it for a minute, getting her breath, calming her mind.

She pressed the bolt in the latch and went into the closet. She pulled out her suitcases and emptied her clothes from the hangers, opened the drawers, and threw the clothes into the suitcases. The shorts and shirt came off and she pulled on jeans and a sweater. Nothing should be left behind. She dumped all her makeup into the train case.

Her mind had returned to a marvellous clarity. She lifted the slicker she had worn on the beach from its hook and slipped into it, then made two trips from the bedroom to the back door of the cottage to carry out her gear. The wind whipped the slicker. As she went to her car, rain beat against her face. When the motor was purring and the headlight beams flooded the back entrance, she climbed the steps again.

'Christie!' someone called from the door. The smoke from

Van's pipe hung in the wet air.

'Get into the car,' he said. 'I'll load your bags.' There was a lantern in his hand. He lifted it and looked into Christie's face. Wind had blown some of her hair around the hood of the yellow slicker. Her face was wet with rain. She had the dauntless look of a warrior entering battle.

'The crucial rule is *don't look back*,' he said. They stood together for a minute. Her eyes began to fill with tears.

'You'll cry later,' he told her as they trudged down the steps. He lifted the large suitcase into the back seat and helped her slide behind the wheel.

'I'm going back for the rest of your luggage.'

Christie sat behind the wheel in her wet slicker. Van slid the two smaller bags onto the back seat next to the suitcase and shut the door.

'Do you know where you're going?' he asked. The rain beat like the noise of a drum on the roof of the car.

'Back to Brandenburg. I have to begin something . . . of my *own*.'

Her voice sounded strong, with only a hint of tears.

'What?'

'I don't know yet. The roots are buried in the ground. But they're alive.'

He leaned through the window and kissed her cheek. Then he put something smooth and irregular into her hand.

'You forgot this,' he said, 'and I don't give away many treasures.' His voice became carefully casual. 'Don't go all the way to Brandenburg tonight. If you can find a place, stop somewhere.'

She held the driftwood between her hands for a few moments; then she laid it on the seat beside her. She smiled at him and released the brake. The car moved slowly around the circular driveway and disappeared in the dark embrace of the trees.

Chapter Seventeen

By the time Christie had left the gravel beach road and arrived at the Shore Drive, she was exhausted. The storm had not let up. She realized Mary's cottage must be about ten miles away, and it seemed a good idea to take Van's advice and spend the night there, avoiding the long trip to Brandenburg. Since it was a weekend, Mary might be there. If not, she would sleep in her car until morning.

Mary and her husband had been at the cottage since Friday. Tonight the storm had made her wakeful. She was astonished to hear, about 2 a.m., the sound of a car in the driveway. She got out of bed and switched on the backyard floodlight, to see Christie climbing out of the car with a small suitcase. Mary met her at the back door. Christie was drenched by the short run from the car to the house, and by the time she had dried off and wrapped herself in a robe, Mary had stoked up the remains of the fire and had hot cocoa ready.

They both curled up on the sofa and watched the flames take hold. Christie wrapped her arms around herself and shuddered.

'Thank God you're here. I was going to sleep in the car.'

Mary looked at Christie's face and saw the ravages of a strenuous evening. 'It's a helluva night for exploring the Shore Drive. Where did you come from?'

Christie cradled the hot cocoa under her chin, taking small sips and breathing the comforting fumes.

'I think I was about ten miles north on some godforsaken back road. I wasn't exploring. I was escaping.'

Mary watched her and waited. There was no use in

bombarding her with questions. Lance was volatile enough to have spawned any kind of crisis. She noticed how thin Christie's face was. Under her tan she looked drawn and slightly beaten. She moved closer to her and put her arm around her shoulders. Tears gathered in Christie's eyes.

'I thought Lance and I were having a love affair until tonight. Then it turned into a group grope – his old buddies, his old girlfriends. It was like waking up into a nightmare.'

Mary's eyes widened. She had conceived of only a quarrel, imagining that Lance had got somehow heavy-handed.

Christie spoke again.

'I froze, at first, when I saw what was happening. Some woman – a *hang-glider* or *skydiver*, or something – had brought dope – cocaine, I think, and pot. When I asked Lance to cut out of it he acted like a stranger. Told me to take off my clothes and join in. When I went to my room, his old girlfriend tried to get in bed with me.' Christie looked around for tissues, then blew her nose in a paper napkin.

Mary gave a long, low whistle and said, 'My God.' She thought for a while, then made a prediction: 'He'll come after you.'

'Not tonight.' Christie's tone was definite.

'He'll trail you to your apartment, then.'

Christie shook her head.

'I plan to go away for a while. I'll have the phone disconnected.'

'You can stay here, Christie, till you decide what to do.' Mary looked worried. 'Just so he doesn't track you down. He usually gets what he wants.'

Christie shook her head.

'I don't think so. He wants *good sports*. I'm not a good sport. I'm not a fun girl. I'm not even a fun drunk.' She sat watching the fire for a while, more tears rolling down her cheeks. 'Besides, he's already *had* me. He knew I was his. After a while that would have bored him. Tonight just speeded the downward spiral. I was never really his type. I'm always trying to figure out what things mean and how God works. God depresses him.'

431

'He was a great magician,' Mary commented.

'A great poet,' Christie added. She was remembering the Moon Castle, the love under the trees.

'But an *animal*,' Mary added. 'Wild and unhousebroken.'

There was a long silence. They stared into the fire.

'Have you heard from Victor?' Christie asked. She looked at Mary now, and thought her face looked strange.

'Let me heat up our cocoa,' Mary said. She walked over to the stove.

Christie felt like someone removed from the world, an astronaut who had been orbiting the moon and had returned. It was comforting just to be in her old bathrobe on Mary's sofa. No wild music. No one bursting into and out of rooms. Just the soft crackling of the fire and the distant roll of thunder.

Mary put the steaming cups on the coffee table. She reached over and put her hand on Christie's knee. Her voice was very gentle.

'Christie, I have to tell you some bad news.'

'Victor?'

Mary nodded.

'Victor ... is *dead*?'

Mary nodded again. Christie bit her lip. Tears filled her eyes.

'Where? *How*?'

'The way he lived. His own way. On his own schedule.'

'*How*?' Christie repeated.

'With Renée's knife,' Mary whispered. 'Hugh got to him before he died. He knew Hugh was with him.'

A strange look had come over Christie's face. She was almost smiling. 'Nothing bad ... could come to him ... from Renée,' she said.

'Christie, Vic was found unconscious on the River Bridge and brought to Broadcliff by police ambulance. As soon as he knew he was back in the hospital, he ... ended his life. He must have gone to the bridge with his mind already made up. He left letters for Stella and Father Franciscus and you.' Mary reached into a pocket of her robe. 'Franciscus gave me yours, thinking I might see you before he did.' She handed Christie an envelope with her name written on it in large, slightly wavering letters.

Christie tore open the envelope and began to read, studying each sentence as if she heard Victor's voice speaking for the last time.

Dear Christie,

I wanted my life to go on as long as I could operate on most of my cylinders. But I could see I was coming to the end of the holding pattern. I had to bottom out while I could think straight.

I want to thank you for helping me know I had given something good to Renée.

I would like to give you something important too. If I could show you yourself, you would see a woman who is beautiful and brave.

I hope you have something good and lasting with this guy you love. But if it doesn't work out, I know something far better will be waiting for you, up ahead.

I have a hunch that all that happens has a meaning and nothing is random and careless.

If I wind up in God's territory, I'll be keeping track of you, Christie.

Love,
Vic

Christie read the letter twice. Then she fell into Mary's arms, and they held each other until she had finished crying. Mary had already done her own weeping. She stroked Christie's hair and made the decision to tell her the rest of the story tomorrow. It had been a long night. The Virgil Prince accident could be dealt with tomorrow. Christie's sobs subsided gradually and became long sighs. She sat up and dried her eyes.

Mary filled her cup. 'Here, drink a little more cocoa. Then I'll tuck you in bed.'

Christie sipped the warm drink and watched the fire,

drawn into the comfort of its flames and her own exhaustion.

'Victor Vendetti was a *real* poet,' she said hoarsely.

Christie slept soundly the rest of the night, but awoke at dawn and knew it would be pointless to try to fall asleep again. She showered and dressed, then went barefoot onto the deck. Mary and her husband were sleeping.

The sky was streaked with grey and white clouds. The lake was the colour of tarnished silver. The world looked barren, as empty of comfort as a surrealist desert painting. Even the gulls were nowhere in sight. The only signs of life were two swans. Were they the ones she and Lance had fed? Thin mists hung over the surface of the water. The swans glided silently through it like spectres in a dream.

She pulled on her raincoat for protection against the dampness and climbed down the wooden stairs. A run would wake up her circulation.

She trotted slowly along the packed sand, outdistancing the swans, then stopping a few times to watch the changes in the sky as it grew light. As she approached the deep clefts in the dunes where they grew steeper in their climb towards the pines, she slowed to a walk. She recognized the promontory where she had fallen asleep before she met Lance, and averted her eyes from it. She searched the beach along the shoreline for signs of the Moon Castle. There were none. The beach was littered with debris from the storm – dead seaweed and wet driftwood. A few beer cans were scattered here and there among the charred remains of someone's fire. The sand was wet and heavy. The lake broke on the shore in listless ripples. There was no breeze.

She shivered and pulled her coat closer around her body. With an effort she forced herself to look at the top of the high dune. The pines were dark and motionless, guarding the roofs of Pacifica. The harsh voices of crows grated against each other somewhere in the depths of their branches. She wondered if Lance's wife lay sleeping alone in her room, the fur coverlet folded on a sofa, her trophies gleaming dimly in the leaden dawn.

434

She had mistaken the force of Lance's personality and his physical passion for love. She thought of Victor's extraordinary power and his ability to care for others in the midst of his body's decay, even as he walked towards death. His words in the letter to her had echoed in her head as she fell asleep last night:

'All that happens has a meaning and nothing is random and careless.'

She wondered what meaning she was carrying away from her time with Lance. When she had left him with his friends and driven away into the storm, she had felt as if all that was alive and strong and joyous in her had been killed. Now she sensed some unborn part of herself unfolding slowly from her centre. She had believed that the process of death was a gestation. Perhaps a kind of alchemy resulted from the death of love so that its residue contained a gift.

Lance's hedonism had affronted her and killed what was tender between them. His inability to share her perceptions had isolated her from him. She remembered suddenly the loathing in his face when he spat out the words 'The energy of death is communicable!' Well, perhaps so was the energy of life. That would be her legacy, her trophy, from this beach and the love she had found on it. For the first time she felt that she could shape her future.

Chapter Eighteen

The Bishop who had presided over the diocese when Father Franciscus came to Brandenburg had died, and a new bishop had taken his place. Several weeks after his installation he called Franciscus to meet with him. The new man was considerably younger than his predecessor. He told Franciscus he had called him in to discuss a new project the diocese had undertaken. An experimental religious community was being formed in Brandenburg.

'Experimental?' Franciscus leaned forward, startled by the announcement.

'Yes.' Bishop Goudy settled back in his chair. His eyes were alive with a quiet excitement expressing both energy and curiosity. He looked at Franciscus with unmistakable admiration.

'I have heard the property we're discussing referred to as Seminary Hill. If we can bring our project into being, it will embody the characteristics of a truly *seminal* community.' He paused and reached for the coffee container on his desk. 'Coffee?'

'Thank you,' Franciscus said. 'Please go on.'

The Bishop poured a cup for them both.

'Are you familiar with the term "holistic health centre"?'

'Yes. I've been reading about them.' Franciscus paused, then said quietly, 'My experience at the hospitals tends to force me to search for better solutions. There are quite a few springing up around the country.'

'Yes. There are. I'm glad you know about them. We want to start one here, Father. The Church has been concerned with the waste involved in the seminary facilities lying dormant. Before I came here I was involved in organizing a model centre in the east for holistic health care. I began to see that such a project would fill a need in any city. Here, there is an existing space ready to provide for it. It would solve the dilemma of what to do with the old seminary.'

Franciscus thought of another coincidental aspect. 'You know, of course, that the only activity remaining there is a small hospital for our nursing sisters who are incapacitated by age or who are chronically ill?'

'Yes.' The Bishop leaned towards Franciscus. 'In fact, it was the existence of that little hospital on the grounds that made me begin to think in terms of the holistic community. The staff of that hospital could be the nucleus for developing a hospice. They think in terms of comfort, of true human care. They do not depend on extensive mechanical devices.

436

Are you familiar with the hospice philosophy?'

'Yes.' Franciscus' mind had wandered back to the Broadcliff chapel, to Mrs Warsoski, to Martin Kiley and the angel who could not be conceived within an acute-care format. He wondered where Christie was now. The voice of the Bishop brought him back.

'A hospice would be part of the proposed community. We think of it as a *community*. It will have a church, a clinic, and a school where those who are already working with the sick can teach others.'

Stefan Franciscus was aware of a mounting excitement in himself, giving birth to a hope he almost feared to entertain.

'It is a tremendous vision; an answer to prayer,' he said. Then, lest his enthusiasm overwhelm the project, 'Visionary enterprises are often more difficult than they seem.' He looked down at his cup. 'We would need more than ever to be guided by the Holy Spirit.'

The Bishop's face was serious, but animated with his own confidence and hope. His words reassured Franciscus

'I have been involved in the formation of one such centre and have visited and studied others. There are many impediments; systems and agencies which must be dealt with. The most vital factor is a group of experienced workers. The concept is interdisciplinary. We need to find people in this city who have been hoping and dreaming for such a centre; who not only seek for a way to care for the suffering better, but for a way to prevent illness and to learn how to heal the sick.'

There was another silence.

'What can I do to help you?' Franciscus asked.

'We need a priest, for the church will be a pastorate. It will be connected to the school and to the hospital and to the clinic. The priest must be an ecumenicist. The community will cross the boundaries of religious particularism and dogma. I called you in because all I hear about your background tells me this project needs you. You come from a teaching model, not a medical one. You have had experience in hospitals and prisons. You have the record of an existentialist. You are not timid. We need a man who can fly by the seat of his pants.' The Bishop sat back and waited.

'When is the project scheduled to get under way?' Franciscus asked.

'We are beginning with the selection of a core group. But the building of the church has already begun. The classes, seminars, workshops will be held in the existing seminary building. When we have our core group we can begin to take in some students. We hope for a kind of interning arrangement with a local college.'

'When would you need me?'

'We would need you for the planning stage. We hope the church will be completed and the seminars organized by winter – perhaps Christmas or soon after the New Year.'

'And my assignments at the hospitals?'

'I have a young priest who can begin next week to learn the ropes with you. He has had chaplainship training in college. As he eases into the work, you can become more active in the planning phase of the centre. You would be with it on a full-time basis as soon as the church is completed.'

Franciscus leaned back in his chair and closed his eyes. He thought of his prayer 'Use me.' He had offered it up constantly as he went from patient to patient, not knowing the questions in the life of each one, not knowing the answers to the questions. Sometimes he had helped them find answers. Sometimes he could not. He had been able to bring them comfort, or peace, when he could not find answers. He had felt the prayer, since he had come to Brandenburg, almost on the intake of each breath. It had become an unconscious part of himself. Perhaps this was what it was to 'pray without ceasing.' He could not think other than that God had brought him to Brandenburg and Bishop Goudy.

Chapter Nineteen

Whenever he had a few minutes of extra time, in addition to his regular rounds, Richard Mulder stopped up to see Virgil Prince. It was now ten days since he had been brought into the Trauma Centre. His I.V.'s had been removed, also the chest tube. The Foley catheter remained.

Dottie came and sat with him several hours of every day and evening. Now that the acute stage of his injuries was over, her role had become more difficult and confusing. In the beginning, everyone's energies had been channelled towards the goal of his survival and the hope of a reversal of nerve damage. Now that his condition had stabilized, new dilemmas presented themselves. Dr Ransahoff had come up with a definite statement. Of course, he explained, it was always subject to unexpected reversal phenomena, but that possibility must be placed in the category of all rare and unexplained remissions. Prince was told that he would not likely regain the use of his legs, although physical therapy would begin soon, and that the neurologic damage extended to all functions below the groin.

As the days following his surgery passed, Mulder saw him ask fewer questions and become more and more silent. As he began to recover his strength, he erupted in angry rages, usually culminating in the eviction of some oversolicitous nurse. His anger did not often spill over on Dottie except for brief, quickly extinguished flashes. Now the angry incidents had receded and he had slipped into a state of mute removal from his environment. Dottie and Bracebridge brought him magazines, newspapers, and medical reports to read.

Bracebridge kept him up to date on his patients.

Most interesting of all to Mulder was the enigma of Brenda. He was not sure what tack she had taken. She had been coming on regular calls in the company of Bracebridge, presumably to join him in informing Prince about his patients. Mulder brooded gloomily over the futility of this charade. The exchange of information was received by Prince with an empty stare. It was apparent that his patient was bringing down the curtain on his past persona and activities. Dottie inhabited his limbo as a recognized and tolerated presence. Brenda and Bracebridge shared information and consulted with a ghost. When Mulder discussed the case with Dr Graham, he found himself struggling to define Prince's affect. He settled on the inadequate description that he was a man who had abdicated from himself. Many nights when Mulder should have been asleep, and on his rare days off, he wrestled with the problem of how to get Prince to take up residence in his body again, in spite of its diminishment. He also wondered why this had become so important to him.

He knew that Prince had now become a symbol to him. If the crippling of a man's legs and his reduction to impotence could wipe out his value as a person, cancel the weight of his knowledge, and destroy a faculty more precious than physical strength, his ability to create something within himself, then the system that had saved him was wicked.

Mulder remembered all the occasions when he had toiled with a Trauma team to wrest some victim from the clutch of death. Why did men battle to save a life? What was the essence in life that made it so precious? Could he rescue that essence from Prince's fortress of oblivion and somehow communicate it to him? Phrases of folk wisdom surfaced randomly into his consciousness. If a man would find his life, he must first lose it. A seed will not grow unless it falls into the ground and is buried. They all said the same thing – that Virgil Prince seemed to have fulfilled the prescription for finding his life. Yet he now sat staring unseeingly at an open book in his hand or at a report on a new experimental cancer drug. He gazed blankly out at the western view of

440

Brandenburg and the freeway interchange. His face was expressionless. His voice was toneless. He wasn't there.

He often wished that Christie were still at Broadcliff. It was ironic that an attack on Virgil Prince had occasioned her dismissal. She was especially good with patients who were angry or withdrawn. He believed it was because the emotion of pity was absent from her. Then he remembered that she had often asked Father Franciscus to see certain patients. He was seeing Joan Bentley now, even though she had lain for weeks in a coma. Was there a possibility Prince would respond to him? He immediately rejected the idea. There was no reason to believe Prince would be willing to talk with any clergyman.

Now that he was the Trauma resident, he seldom had time to talk to the staff on the Cancer Unit. He knew that Franciscus spent some time there each day, and if he was not there now, perhaps Mary would be able to tell him when he most often made his calls. If nothing more, he could at least discuss Prince's situation with him. Franciscus might be able to shed some light on matters with which he felt awkward. The thought of counselling filled him with a sense of helplessness. Psychology and religion were the subjects he knew least about. He checked in with the Surgery resident who was on call and told him where he could be reached. Then he took the elevator for Seven Main.

When he got to the Unit and started down the hall, he was overtaken by a mood the place always communicated to him. During his month's duty there he had fought his way through it. Now he was at one remove from the area and its problems. He stood in a shadowed corner by the drinking fountain and tried to name his feelings. There was an atmosphere of futility and secret despair. It seemed to have permeated the woodwork and the walls, to be trodden into the floor. He sensed an undercurrent of chaos and disintegration beneath the schedules, the protocols, the masses of records.

He looked around the hive of metal charts in the nursing station. Mary was not there. He began to walk down the hall

441

again, looking into the dark, crowded semiprivate rooms and finally into the three- and five-bed wards.

When he came to the West Wing and the private rooms, he saw a few nurses grouped around one of the doorways. It was Joan Bentley's room. A stretcher was being rolled out. The small body on it was covered with a sheet. Joan had lived through and beyond her son's wedding, but had not seen it.

Mulder leaned against the wall and watched the stretcher as it moved past him. Someone was taking the label on the door out of its slot. It said, 'JOAN BENTLEY,' and beneath that, 'VIRGIL PRINCE, M.D.' She had been in the room five months.

He walked through the door and found whom he was looking for. Mary and Father Franciscus were removing Joan's pictures from the bulletin board. Another nurse was taking things out of the drawers and putting them into a paper sack.

'Hi,' Mulder said. Neither of them had seen him come in. They both looked up at the same time. Mary's eyes were full of tears. They spilled over when she saw him. He moved towards her and put his arm around her. Behind her he saw Franciscus blowing his nose.

'You just missed her, Dick,' Mary said. Her voice was shaky and muffled against his shoulder.

'Were you with her?' Mulder asked Franciscus.

The priest nodded. Mary pulled a tissue out of a box on the nightstand and wiped her eyes. She and Franciscus stacked the photos into a sack.

Mulder asked, 'Can you take a minute to talk? I came up here to find one or the other of you. Guess I lucked out.'

Mary walked over to the window and opened it wide. An aide pulled the sheets off the bed, and two women from Housekeeping came through the door with equipment to scrub and disinfect the room.

'Let's go,' Mary said.

Franciscus turned to Mary. 'We need a cup of coffee. Can we get one in the conference room?'

442

'Sure,' Mary told him.

They left the room and went down the hallway together. Some of the staff were clustered in small groups as they approached the nursing station and main areaway. It always happened after a death: small clumps of people whispering together, then gradually dispersing towards the needs of the living.

The conference room was empty. They seated themselves around the small table. Mary found coffee mugs and mixed instant coffee. Nursing notices and the pages of a calendar made the soft, rustling sounds of dried leaves as they blew in the wind. There was a new touch of coolness mixed with the lazy warmth of sun. It was the first week of September. Mary turned to Mulder.

'You see people in the ICU, don't you?'

He took another sip of coffee. 'Yes,' he said. 'It's hectic, but I'd rather be there than here.'

'How is Dr Prince?' Mary asked.

'There have been all kinds of rumours,' Franciscus commented.

'Bracebridge comes up here on rounds with Brenda sometimes and sometimes he comes alone. There's even a rumour that Brenda's leaving. But they don't discuss Prince's condition with the field hands,' Mary told him.

Franciscus asked, 'Do they think he will have a full recovery?'

'As a matter of fact, it was because of Prince that I came up here.' Mulder looked at Franciscus with an expression of tentative hope. 'They are fairly sure of the prognosis now. It isn't good.'

He leaned back in his chair and thrust his hands into the pockets of his white jacket. He looked directly at Franciscus as he spoke.

'I won't go into all the technical detail about his injuries and surgery. He had a low spinal fracture involving nerve damage. Unless some unusual spontaneous repair takes place, he won't walk again. He will also be impotent. He has no feeling below the groin.'

Mulder paused. His glance moved from Franciscus to Mary.

Mary's eyes registered quick comprehension. Franciscus had leaned forward with his hands folded and his elbows on his knees. He seemed to be studying the floor. There was no sound but the fluttering of paper in the wind. Finally Franciscus looked up at Mulder.

'His wife?'

'Oh, she's terrific. Calm. With him every inch of the way. But ...' Mulder broke off again. He shifted his head and shoulders and moved uncomfortably in his chair. 'He accepts her presence, but that's all. He doesn't really respond to anyone or anything.'

Franciscus looked down at the knuckles of his clasped hands as he spoke. 'Dr Prince was a very powerful man.'

Mulder leaned towards him. 'You've heard of the term "catatonic"?'

'Yes.'

'Well, his attitude is reminiscent of catatonia, except that he answers when he's spoken to. Other than that he seems to have removed himself from his body and his surroundings.'

Franciscus thought for several moments before he spoke. 'I can see where it would be necessary for him to do that – for a time. But if his withdrawal goes on too long, becomes too profound –'

Mary broke in: 'Has Brenda been to see him? Has she talked with him? They were into it pretty heavy, you know. There were rumours of divorce.'

'She'd been to see him alone once that I know of.' Mulder stopped to reflect. 'It seems to me that his behaviour changed soon after that. Before he saw her he was angry a lot and asked a lot of questions. There was some of the old ego and power about him.'

Mulder walked over to the hot-water container and filled his cup again.

'Whatever the situation with Brenda is, Prince is in a crisis. He's been confronted with a sudden radical change – not a slow, gradual weakening, like cancer. One day he was a

444

whole man. The next day he had lost his identity.'

Mary spoke again. 'Has he got a minister? Seems to me I heard that the Princes were big church people.'

'His wife is.' Mulder put his cup on the table and fell back into his chair. 'But Prince issued an edict early on: "No pious, pitying preacher-pricks. ..." Excuse me, Father,' Mulder's face flushed, '"... are allowed in my room."'

Franciscus leaned back in his chair and smiled. 'Well, that allows him to have *some* control over his programme.' He added, 'He's not the first patient to make that rule.'

They sat silently for a while, each pursuing some clue that might be the key to Prince's crisis.

'Something, somebody has to reach him.' Mulder looked out the window at the freeway. 'I've seen Christie get through to people who were angry or locked inside themselves, but she's gone. Prince probably wouldn't talk to her anyway.'

Mary's face suddenly brightened. 'Hey, I saw Christie last week. I told Father Franciscus all about it. She arrived at our cottage in a downpour of rain one night ...' Mary hesitated and stopped. She didn't want to go into the circumstances that had precipitated the visit. 'She's going to a seminar on hospice in Chicago next week, and Kate's going with her. Did you know Kate has resigned from her job here?'

'No!'

Mulder felt a lift of spirit knowing that Christie had found a new direction. 'I don't know much except what's going on in the Trauma Unit,' he sighed. 'So Kate's gone too. Well, I don't blame her. This Unit chews 'em up and spits 'em out pretty regularly.' Mulder seemed to be musing to himself now. 'You know, I hated Prince; hated the way he manipulated patients and families, the way he even humiliated them. He was such a goddamned cocky bastard. Some of the patients were actually afraid of that so-called nurse of his.'

'I know,' Mary said.

'But I've had some conversations with his wife since he's been in the ICU. It was interesting to hear her view of him.' Mulder's face softened. 'There's no doubt he's a brilliant

445

doctor. She saw him as having a mystical streak; some real obsession with the "holiness in nature". He once wanted to be a marine biologist.'

'That's interesting.' Franciscus had been watching Mulder closely. He was learning as much about the young resident as he was about Virgil Prince.

'This Cancer Unit,' Mulder continued, 'it operates like the rest of the hospital, almost like an ICU – only they don't try to resuscitate them when they die. But you gradually get forced to lose yourself here, your *sensitivity*, unless you're some kind of saint. I see the successful doctors encase themselves in power, or get regularly drunk. It's not just on the Cancer Unit, either.' He paused again and stared out the window in the direction of the hills, wrestling with some clue to understanding, some hope of his own.

'Maybe the only way to survive in medicine is to go *beyond* death; to get some vision of meaning that takes you past this swamp, this goddamned zoo of suffering. If you don't you get to the point where the caring destroys you. Or you cancel yourself out consciously. You turn the patients into part of the mechanism.'

His shoulders slumped and a look of weariness came over his face. He looked at Franciscus with an expression that was strangely pained and contrite, as if the wounds of Virgil Prince had somehow taken residence in himself.

'He arrested, you know. Died. In the Emergency Room. His heart stopped. A tension pneumo. I was really on the ball. I jammed the chest tube in just in time. I saved his life – for *this*.'

The telephone on the wall jangled. Mary picked up the phone and was jolted back to the facts of the Unit schedule.

'Yes. Okay. I'll be right there.' She put the receiver on the hook. 'I've got to go, Dick. Let me know how it goes, will you?'

When the door closed behind her, Mulder folded his hands and leaned forward.

'Father, I came to see if you could help me, somehow. I don't think Prince would let you in the room, but I wish . . .'

He interrupted himself and shrugged his shoulders, a look of angry frustration tightening his face.

'He might be *wasted*,' he said. His lips tightened over his teeth. He spat out the word again: *'Wasted!'*

Mulder sat back in the chair now, a bit limp from the long soliloquy which had carried him into unaccustomed depths. He threw his open hands, palms up, on the conference table. 'He needs a *priest*!' he said.

'We can all be priests.' Franciscus' voice was so quiet as he spoke that Mulder did not respond immediately. He looked sharply at Franciscus, his eyes startled and questioning.

'We are all priests,' Franciscus said, 'and the sacrament that might prevent the waste of Virgil Prince is a sacrament that you may be the only person fitted to perform.'

Astonishment emptied Mulder's face. 'Me? A *sacrament*? I don't even know if I believe in God! What kind of sacrament could I ...' He stopped. It was an impossible thought.

'Virgil Prince doesn't need help from someone versed in ecclesiastical law. He doesn't need a psychiatrist or a social worker. Even a wife or a lover may not be able to give him the vision he needs.'

Mulder listened intently. A power beneath the priest's words stirred something in him.

'From what you have told me, Dr Prince is undergoing a kind of death. A death of all the strengths he has relied on. His wife has given you a vision of what he was at the beginning. You see him as still embodying a value – *values* – which could be wasted and thrown away.'

Mulder nodded.

'Speak to him, then. Not in terms of moral values, not in comparison with other "cripples". Tell him your vision of his worth. Tell him your *own* despair. If you weep or falter, give him the gift of your weakness.' Franciscus waited. He wondered where the words had come from. He had not formulated them. He sat and thought about what he had just said.

Franciscus looked at Mulder's hands. They were surgeon's hands: long and strong, with slender fingers. He imagined them plunging the chest tube into Prince's side. He sat stroking his chin. Then he looked up at Mulder and smiled. 'You might even give him back himself.'

Mulder sat motionless staring into Franciscus' eyes. 'Where did you get your training?' he asked the priest.

'I'm a Jesuit,' Franciscus answered.

'Did they tell you that all your training, even your ordination, would give you no special edge, since *all men are priests*?' Mulder's eyes glinted with mischief.

Franciscus did not answer immediately. Then his face softened and he said, 'A priest learns to discern priestly qualities in those around him. He doesn't always learn it in the seminary.' Franciscus rose to his feet and placed a hand on Mulder's shoulder. 'Good luck with your visit to Dr Prince, should you choose to undertake it.'

They walked together down the hall as far as the elevators. The Unit had returned to normal. The gaggles of whispering nurses had disappeared. The Housekeeping women were boarding the freight elevator with their scrub buckets. Joan Bentley's room was ready for its next occupant.

Richard Mulder shook hands with the priest and left for the ICU by the stairwell. As he descended the seven flights of stairs, he shed, one by one, the garments of his protection – his physician's power, his physician's vocabulary, and his physician's protocol. He stood at the door of Virgil Prince's private room feeling empty and new and very uncertain. Beyond death was, perhaps, nothing. But in case there was a knowing presence men called God, Dr Mulder prayed that it would use him.

Epilogue

Stefan Franciscus awoke on the morning of the last day in February to a white and silent world. A great snowfall had begun the afternoon of the previous day. It had been driven on high winds. Traffic had gradually disappeared from the streets by evening. The world seemed to huddle by its hearth and wait for the whirling obscurity and the punishing winds to wear themselves out.

St John's Church had been completed sooner than even the Bishop had projected, and this was the morning Franciscus had planned to make the official move to his new post.

He had packed up all his possessions – several black suits, an overcoat, a pile jacket, some shirts and slacks he wore on off-duty vacations, three pairs of shoes, and some sturdy snow boots. He also had a large metal box filled with a complete set of workman's tools, two twenty-five-pound weights, and two crates of books. When he had loaded it all into the car, he would drive up the long hill to the rectory.

He stood looking out the window and realized that the blizzard had been far worse than anyone had predicted. He switched on his small bedroom radio and heard only emergency announcements: 'No automobiles are allowed on the streets except emergency vehicles and snow ploughs.'

The streets outside were virtually empty. In the avenue that ran from St Thomas' Church to Seminary Hill, a narrow lane had been ploughed. A few brave souls were making their way along it on foot to get to nearby stores. He raised the window and listened to the silence. The noise of the freeway interchange – an eternal, grinding assault outside his bedroom – had been utterly stilled.

He knelt at the bedside with his Breviary and said the morning prayers. By the time he finished, he had made a decision. He would hike to the new church. To make the climb up the wooded bluff would be an adventure.

As soon as he had breakfasted, he took his coffee to his room and packed a briefcase with some papers he needed to transfer to his new office. He opened a flat cardboard box that lay on his bureau and carefully unwrapped the tissue paper that protected its contents. He lifted out a pale-grey piece of driftwood. He had received it from Christie. It had the shape of a cross; slightly skewed, very rough, but unmistakable. It had been not a gift, but a consignment. Now he stood and held it in his hands, running his fingers over its satiny grooves and holes. Its sculpture attested to violent weather and much time. He placed it back in its tissue-paper wrapping and closed the box. He slid it into the briefcase so that it would be cushioned by his personal documents and took out a recent letter:

Dear Fr Franciscus,

I will be spending the next few months travelling between seminars trying to learn some new methods of healing and how to prevent disease. I am spending a month in a religious community in the desert in New Mexico. The nun, who was my philosophy instructor at St Stephen's College is here. Then I will be visiting hospices. I am eager to hear about your new post. Mary has written me exciting things about it. Perhaps Kate and I will be applying to you for jobs!

Love,
Christie

He folded the letter slowly and carefully, smiling to himself. Then he placed it in his briefcase with his other papers.

He dressed for his winter hike. The pile jacket was warm

450

and weatherproof. He pulled on a wool hat with earflaps and a scarf. He tugged the high boots over his folded trouser legs. Then he picked up his briefcase and gloves and quit St Thomas' for the sacramental journey to St John's on foot.

The wind had died down, and the sun was shining. A few citizens were out with shovels, and he waved to them as he passed, sometimes stopping for brief conversations, as he made his way down the snowy street. He reached the foot of the bluff and began his climb to the summit. He walked slowly, traversing the hill at an angle, taking time to pause and savour the snow-draped weeds and trees, and the shrinking aspect of the city, as he ascended. The pines were heavy with glistening snow. Now and then a fluffy fall of it cascaded soundlessly from the branches.

Several times he crossed over the stream that led down to the river in Brandenburg before he arrived at the top of the bluff. It meandered through the clefts of the hillside, clear as crystal, murmuring quietly over stones and occasionally bursting into small rapids and waterfalls. One day soon he would explore the woods and trace it to its source – some hidden spring in a crevice of the hillside.

When he reached the top, he was breathing hard and perspiring. He had opened his muffler and removed the hat. The low winter sun shone directly against the hill. He stopped beneath a stand of pines at the edge of the bluff and marvelled at the white purity and silence of the city. The freeway was a series of empty white ribbons winding through it. The buildings, the churches and their steeples looked like the structures in a toy town. Broadcliff Hospital stood out dull and brown against the snow, its sprawling ramparts now minuscule in the distance on the other side of the river. Franciscus shielded his eyes against the brilliant sun and stared across at it. As a witness to the hospital's misery and conflicts, he had walked on holy ground. He had found Victor there.

He still saw Richard Mulder often. In fact, they had become friends. Mulder had not reported to him on Virgil Prince at length or in detail. He would say only that he talked with him regularly, that Prince was discussing many things with him, and that their conversations were extremely interesting. Mulder's eyes spoke what he would not yet dare to put into words. Franciscus saw his own hope for Virgil Prince's rebirth reflected in them.

The priest stood for a long time at the edge of the bluff, dazzled by the tranquil beauty of the snow. It contained both promise and treachery, order and destruction. Two cardinals startled him as they flew from the pine branches above his head. Their blood-red wings pierced the white serenity of the hillside in a glorious arc, then disappeared in a thicket near the stream.

Stefan Franciscus picked up his attaché case and brushed some fluffy crystals from it with his gloved hand. He turned back through the tall pines and approached the entrance to St John's. His heart affirmed whatever treasures and challenges his new life would bring.

STAR BOOKS BESTSELLERS

FICTION

WAR BRIDES	*Lois Battle*	£2.50 ☐
AGAINST ALL GODS	*Ashley Carter*	£1.95 ☐
THE STUD	*Jackie Collins*	£1.75 ☐
SLINKY JANE	*Catherine Cookson*	£1.35 ☐
THE OFFICERS' WIVES	*Thomas Fleming*	£2.75 ☐
THE CARDINAL SINS	*Andrew M. Greeley*	£1.95 ☐
WHISPERS	*Dean R. Koontz*	£1.95 ☐
LOVE BITES	*Molly Parkin*	£1.60 ☐
GHOSTS OF AFRICA	*William Stevenson*	£1.95 ☐

NON-FICTION

BLIND AMBITION	*John Dean*	£1.50 ☐
DEATH TRIALS	*Elwyn Jones*	£1.25 ☐
A WOMAN SPEAKS	*Anais Nin*	£1.60 ☐
I CAN HELP YOUR GAME	*Lee Trevino*	£1.60 ☐
TODAY'S THE DAY	*Jeremy Beadle*	£2.95 ☐

BIOGRAPHY

IT'S A FUNNY GAME	*Brian Johnston*	£1.95 ☐
WOODY ALLEN	*Gerald McKnight*	£1.75 ☐
PRINCESS GRACE	*Gwen Robyns*	£1.75 ☐
STEVE OVETT	*Simon Turnbull*	£1.80 ☐
EDDIE: MY LIFE, MY LOVES	*Eddie Fisher*	£2.50 ☐

STAR Books are obtainable from many booksellers and newsagents. If you have any difficulty tick the titles you want and fill in the form below.

Name_____

Address_____

_____

Send to: Star Books Cash Sales, P.O. Box 11, Falmouth, Cornwall. TR10 9EN.

Please send a cheque or postal order to the value of the cover price plus:
UK: 45p for the first book, 20p for the second book and 14p for each additional book ordered to the maximum charge of £1.63.

BFPO and EIRE: 45p for the first book, 20p for the second book, 14p per copy for the next 7 books, thereafter 8p per book.

OVERSEAS: 75p for the first book and 21p per copy for each additional book.

While every effort is made to keep prices low, it is sometimes necessary to increase prices at short notice. Star Books reserve the right to show new retail prices on covers which may differ from those advertised in the text or elsewhere.

STAR BOOKS BESTSELLERS

THRILLERS

OUTRAGE	*Henry Denker*	£1.95 ☐
FLIGHT 902 IS DOWN	*H Fisherman &*	£1.95 ☐
	B. Schiff	
TRAITOR'S EXIT	*John Gardner*	£1.60 ☐
ATOM BOMB ANGEL	*Peter James*	£1.95 ☐
HAMMERED GOLD	*W.O. Johnson*	£1.95 ☐
DEBT OF HONOUR	*Adam Kennedy*	£1.95 ☐
THE FIRST DEADLY SIN	*Laurence Sanders*	£2.60 ☐
KING OF MONEY	*Jeremy Scott*	£1.95 ☐
DOG SOLDIERS	*Robert Stone*	£1.95 ☐

CHILLERS

SLUGS	*Shaun Hutson*	£1.60 ☐
THE SENTINEL	*Jeffrey Konvitz*	£1.65 ☐
OUIJA	*Andrew Laurance*	£1.50 ☐
HALLOWEEN III	*Jack Martin*	£1.80 ☐
PLAGUE	*Graham Masterton*	£1.80 ☐
MANITOU	*Graham Masterton*	£1.50 ☐
SATAN'S LOVE CHILD	*Brian McNaughton*	£1.35 ☐
DEAD AND BURIED	*Chelsea Quinn Yarbo*	£1.75 ☐

STAR Books are obtainable from many booksellers and newsagents. If you have any difficulty tick the titles you want and fill in the form below.

Name_____

Address_____

_____

Send to: Star Books Cash Sales, P.O. Box 11, Falmouth, Cornwall. TR10 9EN.

Please send a cheque or postal order to the value of the cover price plus:
UK: 45p for the first book, 20p for the second book and 14p for each additional book ordered to the maximum charge of £1.63.

BFPO and EIRE: 45p for the first book, 20p for the second book, 14p per copy for the next 7 books, thereafter 8p per book.

OVERSEAS: 75p for the first book and 21p per copy for each additional book.

While every effort is made to keep prices low, it is sometimes necessary to increase prices at short notice. Star Books reserve the right to show new retail prices on covers which may differ from those advertised in the text or elsewhere.